Fuel and Energy

ENERGY SCIENCE AND ENGINEERING:
RESOURCES, TECHNOLOGY, MANAGEMENT
An International Series

EDITOR

JESSE DENTON

Belton, Texas

LARRY L. ANDERSON and DAVID A. TILLMAN (eds.), Fuels from Waste, 1977

A. J. ELLIS and W. A. J. MAHON, Chemistry and Geothermal Systems, 1977

FRANCIS G. SHINSKEY, Energy Conservation through Control, 1977

N. BERKOWITZ, An Introduction to Coal Technology, 1979

J. F. KREIDER, Medium and High Temperature Solar Processes, 1979

B. SØRENSEN, Renewable Energy, 1979

J. H. HARKER and J. R. BACKHURST, Fuel and Energy, 1981

Fuel and Energy

J. H. HARKER and J. R. BACKHURST

Department of Chemical Engineering
University of Newcastle upon Tyne

1981

ACADEMIC PRESS

A Subsidiary of Harcourt Brace Jovanovich, Publishers

London   New York   Toronto   Sydney   San Francisco

ACADEMIC PRESS INC. (LONDON) LTD
24/28 Oval Road,
London NW1 7DX

United States Edition published by
ACADEMIC PRESS INC.
111 Fifth Avenue,
New York, New York 10003

British Library Cataloguing in Publication Data

Harker, J. H.
  Fuel and energy.
  I. Power resources   II. Backhurst, J. R.
  I. Title
  333.7   HD9502.A2   LCCCN 80-42194

Cased edn. ISBN 0-12-325250-4
Paperback edn. ISBN 0-12-325252-0

Text set in 10/12 pt Linotron 202 Times, printed and bound
in Great Britain at The Pitman Press, Bath

Preface

The massive increases in oil prices in the early 1970s, and their continued increase, have had far reaching and lasting effects. It is clear that the days of cheap fossil fuels are over, at a time when energy has attained a dominating role in man's industrial and social activities. In the UK alone, the industrial and domestic spheres are vitally concerned with questions of energy, how it may be conserved and consumption reduced. Most commercial organizations have an energy manager, if not a group, devoted to minimizing energy demands at every stage. Such activities have been complemented by a wide variety of new courses in energy and energy-related topics at both undergraduate and postgraduate levels, coupled with the publication of numerous books and journals devoted mainly to energy policies, resources and strategies.

This book aims to show that while the topic of energy and particularly the study of fuels is not new, there has been a considerable change in emphasis in recent years and the field of fuel science has broadened into what might be termed energy studies. The term embraces all forms of energy, the production and conversion of energy, and its efficient utilization. Our treatment builds on the well established discipline of fuel science and is intended to present an up to date account of developments in this field set in the overall energy scene. A discussion of energy sources and resources is included, though the major part of the book is devoted to the production, properties and utilization of primary and secondary fuels with particular emphasis on the calculations involved, especially in the combustion process. A discussion of nuclear energy and renewable energy sources is included and the book concludes with a section on economics including some consideration of the costs involved in energy conversion processes. SI units have been used throughout and, as is essential in an introductory text, many references to more detailed treatments in the literature are included.

The book is intended for students at the undergraduate level and for engineers seeking an introduction to fuel science and others taking the newer courses in energy studies. Postgraduates should also find the book useful as well as practising engineers in industry, particularly those who are involved in energy conservation and who require an introduction to the energy scene coupled with basic facts on fuel properties and calculations.

"Fuel and Energy" is based on and draws heavily from "Fuel Science" by Harker and Allen, published some ten years ago as part of a series of chemical engineering monographs. Although the series did not come to fruition, "Fuel Science" achieved a modest success and I am grateful to my present publishers for promoting it in its new and considerably expanded guise. I am indebted to David Allen for allowing me to draw on the three chapters he contributed to "Fuel Science" and also to John Backhurst who has contributed about one quarter of the present text as coauthor. No book of this type can be written in isolation and I am pleased to acknowledge the help I have received over the years from colleagues and students and particularly from established texts on the topic.

J. H. HARKER
Newcastle upon Tyne

Contents

Chapter 10. ENERGY ECONOMICS

Energy

1

I. INTRODUCTION

A. Forms of Energy

The word "energy" has many meanings. Some of these are nebulous—
"nervous energy" for example, whilst others are quite precise such as
"kinetic energy", the energy of motion and "potential energy", the energy
of position, both of which are terms used widely in science and engineering. No matter how basic man's existence, two sources of energy are
essential. Firstly food, which contains a chemical form of potential energy,
converted by the body into kinetic energy and secondly, shelter from the
elements, which in non-temperate climates really means heat or thermal
energy. As civilization has developed, demands for energies other than
chemical and thermal have increased especially where tasks must be
undertaken involving forces normally beyond man's modest abilities. This
is particularly true of mechanical energy which is obtained by conversion
from some other form of energy since energy like mass is neither created
nor destroyed. The usual energy source is of course chemical energy in a
fuel. The combustion of fuels thus releasing energy as heat, which can then
be converted to mechanical energy, is always accompanied by an exhaust
stream, which is usually polluting and undesirable. This, coupled with the
need to transmit energy over long distances, has led to the development and
utilization of electrical energy, which is probably the most convenient form
of energy in modern civilizations.

Thus, four important forms of energy are basic to man's well-being—
chemical, thermal, mechanical and electrical energy—and it is with these,
and particularly the conversion between these forms of energy, that this
book is primarily concerned.

1

It has already been seen how chemical energy in the form of food is converted within the body to thermal and particularly mechanical or kinetic energy. Thus food may be considered as a fuel, a general term for those materials with a structure such that they contain chemical energy which can be converted into a useful form, usually thermal energy. This conversion process is termed combustion and in this sense the conversion of food within the body is a slow combustion process. Using the general definition of a fuel, almost anything which combines with oxygen in an exothermic reaction may be included, although it is necessary to be rather more specific since the heat must be released at an acceptable and preferably controllable rate. In the main, most fuels contain carbon and usually hydrogen, which are converted to carbon dioxide and water, and the normal definition of a fuel refers to fossil fuels, that is those fuels which occur naturally in the Earth's crust. Thus, the main fossil fuels are coal, crude petroleum and natural gas and all derived or secondary fuels emanate from these.

So far the discussion has been limited to fuels which release energy, usually thermal, by means of a chemical reaction involving a rearrangement of the outer electrons of the atom only, leaving the nucleus unaffected. There are, however, several fuels in which the nucleus can be disturbed by bombardment with high energy subatomic particles and such fuels are termed nuclear fuels; the energy conversion taking place by a nuclear reaction. Because the protons and neutrons are packed together by forces many thousands of times greater than ordinary chemical forces, the energy released is correspondingly greater. It has been estimated for example, that the energy released by the fission of all the nucleii in one kilogramme of the 235 mass number isotope of uranium is equivalent to the chemical energy released by the combustion of 500 000 Mg of coal.

In essence, then, there are four major forms of energy, chemical, thermal, mechanical and electrical of which thermal and electrical are probably the most convenient and these are produced by conversion from chemical energy which is contained in chemical and nuclear fuels. Chemical fuels may be subdivided into primary fuels, those which are derived from the Earth's crust by physical processes only, and secondary fuels, which involve a chemical reaction at some stage of their manufacture.

Much the largest proportion of all energy on and in the earth has been and is derived from the sun. This solar energy takes two forms: the daily input which manifests itself in solar radiation, the winds and waves and hydropower; and the energy which has come from the sun since the formation of the earth which is stored in the earth's crust primarily as fossil and nuclear fuels together with geothermal energy and vegetation. This may be thought of as capital energy. Primitive man drew only slightly

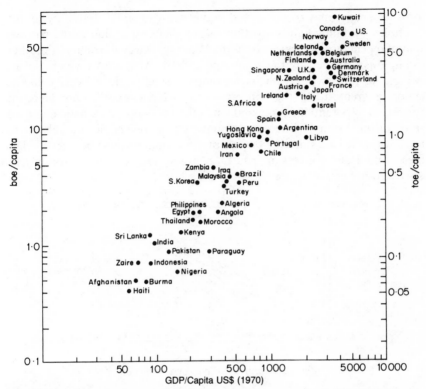

Fig. 1. *Primary energy per capita versus GDP per capita* (Beijdorff 1979).
Ordinates: boe, *barrels of oil equivalent;* toe, *tonnes of oil
equivalent.*

on this capital wealth, the burning of wood and so on, though as the
general demands of civilization developed, man's energy requirements
escalated such that the capital wealth has rapidly diminished and indeed is
today in danger of depletion. To some extent, this demand for energy as a
function of increased development is illustrated in Fig. 1 in which the
power requirements per head of population are plotted against the gross
national product, which is itself a measure of the development of a nation.
Comparing a developed nation, the United States for example, with a
developing nation, such as India, the demand for energy is some sixty times
greater.

B. Energy Conversion

The conversion of chemical and nuclear energy into thermal, mechanical
and electrical forms is of prime importance to modern man. The fact that

forms of energy may be converted in this way can be illustrated by simple examples. Rubbing hands together makes them warm due to the conversion of mechanical energy into thermal energy by way of friction. Another example is provided by the simple pendulum. At the lowest point of its swing, the bob moves with its maximum velocity and hence its kinetic energy is greatest. As the bob moves to its highest point, this energy is converted to potential energy and when the bob stops, its kinetic energy is zero. In this example, the energy conversion is reversible, though this is not always the case since the laws of thermodynamics must be obeyed. The more important conversion routes between the four forms of energy discussed in Section A are shown in Fig. 2.

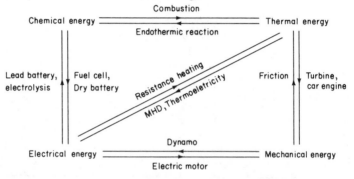

Fig. 2. *Examples of energy conversion.*

Probably the most familiar conversion process is combustion, in which the chemical energy of a fuel is released as heat (and to some extent as light) in a flame; a process which is of major industrial significance. The thermal energy so released can be transferred to water, thus producing steam as in boiler plant. A nuclear reactor achieves the same end result, since the reactor may be considered as simply replacing the combustion plant. The energy in the steam generated in this way may now be used to drive a steam turbine, thus effecting conversion to mechanical energy. This in turn may be converted to electrical energy by coupling the turbine to a generating set. This sequence of conversions, chemical–thermal–mechanical–electrical, by way of combustion and a turbo-generator is of course combined in a modern power station fuelled by coal, oil, gas or nuclear fuel. As discussed in the next section, the efficiency of this operation is limited and ways have been sought by which thermal energy may be converted directly to electrical energy. Thermoelectrics is one obvious method, in which a loop formed of two dissimilar metals is arranged so that an electrical current flows in the circuit by maintaining one junction at a low temperature and heating the other—the principle of the thermocouple.

Magnetohydrodynamics (MHD) provides another direct conversion route between thermal and electrical energies. Faraday's second law states that if a conductor moves in a magnetic field, a current will flow in the conductor in a direction at right angles to both the direction of its motion and the magnetic field. It is not essential that the conductor should be a solid and indeed Lord Kelvin showed that tidal water (salty, and therefore conducting) flowing in a river estuary in the Earth's magnetic field can act as a simple generator. In the modern concept of an MHD generator, the conducting fluid is a high-temperature (ca 3000 K) gas seeded with salts with low ionization potentials to enhance its electrical conductivity. Such methods have the advantage of eliminating moving parts, that is the mechanical energy step.

Chemical energy may be converted directly to electrical energy by means of a fuel cell. In its simplest form, a fuel cell consists of two electrodes separated by an electrolyte arranged such that the fuel, say natural gas, and the oxidant can be supplied to the respective electrodes avoiding direct reaction, and the waste products removed. In this system the principle is essentially that of reversed electrolysis, which is the splitting of water into hydrogen and oxygen by the passage of electrical energy. Indeed all the routes discussed so far can be reversed to some extent or other. In a lead accumulator, for example, electrical energy is converted to chemical energy during charging and the process reversed when a current is drawn from the cell.

A simple example of the conversion from electrical to thermal energy is resistance heating, as in an electric fire, and similarly an electric motor reverses the conversion from mechanical to electrical energy. Mechanical energy is converted to thermal energy by way of friction and indeed most forms of energy usually end up as low-grade heat. An endothermic reaction is the reverse of combustion, which is an exothermic reaction. Figure 2 is not complete in that two important forms of energy have been omitted: nuclear energy and light. The former is converted to electrical energy by the conventional route or, in a possible future plant, by MHD power generation. Light may be converted to electrical energy using solar cells and also to thermal energy in a solar panel. In a sense light is also converted to chemical energy by photosynthesis, and is then stored in vegetation. Ultimately this will be converted to fossil fuels thus completing the cycle.

C. Efficiency of Energy Conversion

Whilst the routes by which energy may be converted as described in the previous section are all feasible, in many cases the efficiency of conversion is low and the conversion processes are of limited commercial interest, especially on a large scale. The other factor is, of course, capital cost. These two considerations, cost and efficiency, limit the choice of conversion route and, for the large-scale generation of electrical power, the prime choice of system is a boiler followed by a turbo-generator. Typical conversion efficiencies are shown in Table 1 and it is seen that for a power station the boiler has an efficiency of 88%; the remainder being losses in the flue gases and some radiation to the surroundings. The steam turbine has an efficiency of around 45%, the losses here being the enormous amount of low grade heat in the condensers.

The generator is of high efficiency and yet the overall efficiency for the complete conversion from chemical to electrical energy is around 35%, which although apparently wasteful is still the cheapest way of producing electricity on the large scale, regardless of whether the fuel is coal, oil, gas or indeed a nuclear fuel. There seems much to be said for omitting the mechanical energy stage, that is avoiding moving parts, and using a direct thermal–electrical conversion route such as MHD. In theory this is an excellent scheme since the waste gases from the MHD duct may be fed to a conventional boiler plus turbo-generating set. In this way the overall efficiency of generation would be "topped-up" above the 35% level to possibly 60–65%. The problem, however, is finding suitable construction materials and so far the net output of an MHD generator, for any length of time, is around 10 kW. There are similar problems with thermoelectric devices, as not only is the conversion efficiency low at around 10%, but also the n-type and p-type semiconductors which are proving to be the best materials are very expensive. The principle is finding application, however, in specialized locations, albeit on a small scale. The absence of moving parts, simplicity of construction and lack of maintenance makes their use in space vehicles especially attractive and, for example, in the US satellite Transit 4A, a generator weighing only 2·1 kg produced 2·7 W of power for the transmission of signals for more than 5 years. A mercury battery to achieve the same task would weigh some 1350 kg, illustrating that high initial cost was more than offset by low weight in this particular application. Similar problems are found in fuel cells—the direct conversion route—in which the electrode materials, electrolytes and catalysts are very costly, although a high conversion efficiency is theoretically possible. With the development of new materials, fuel cells may prove to be economical in office blocks and flats, for electrical propulsion and in remote locations such as lighthouses.

It has been seen that, although a conversion route is feasible, the efficiency of conversion and the costs are the overriding factors as far as commercial exploitation is concerned and as is so often the case, a

TABLE 1. *Typical efficiencies (%) in energy conversion*

TO:	Chemical	Thermal	Electrical	Mechanical
FROM				
Chemical		power station boiler (88) domestic oil boiler (65) space rocket (50) steam turbine (45) thermal power plant (41) diesel engine (38) gas turbine (35) car engine (25) steam engine (8)	dry battery (90) car battery (74) fuel cell (70)	
Nuclear		nuclear power plant (30) nuclear battery (5)		
Thermal		—	nuclear battery (5) MHD (10) thermoelectrics (10) thermoionics (15)	steam turbine (45) thermal power plant (41) diesel engine (38) gas turbine (35) nuclear power plant (30) car engine (25) steam engine (8)
Mechanical			electrical generator (98) pumped storage (75) thermal power plant (41) nuclear power plant (30)	—
Electrical	car battery (74)		—	large electric motor (93) pumped storage (75) small electric motor (65)
Light			solar cell (10)	

compromise solution has to be adopted. With the increasing development of new materials and techniques, alternative methods of energy conversion are likely to become commercially viable in the not too-distant future.

II. ENERGY SOURCES AND RESOURCES

A. Sources

The source of almost all the world's energy, including coal, oil, natural gas, wood, food, waves and wind, is solar power in the form of radiation from the sun. At the earth's surface, solar energy shows itself in a number of different ways, the most obvious being direct radiation. In principle, this may be utilized by man, since it can be focused whilst diffuse radiation, that is radiation scattered by the clouds, requires a different technology for

TABLE 2. *Energy sources, resources and demands*

	MJ	MJ/year	TW†
Sources			
photosynthesis		$1 \cdot 6 \times 10^{16}$	500
solar radiation to earth		$5 \cdot 4 \times 10^{18}$	$1 \cdot 8 \times 10^5$
solar		$1 \cdot 1 \times 10^{29}$	$3 \cdot 5 \times 10^{15}$
Resources			
geothermal energy	$4 \quad \times 10^{14}$		
oil and gas	$2 \cdot 5 \times 10^{16}$		
coal	$2 \cdot 0 \times 10^{17}$		
fission (ores)	$1 \cdot 5 \times 10^{17}$		
fusion (deuterium)	$3 \cdot 0 \times 10^{29}$		
Demands			
man		$5 \quad \times 10^3$	$1 \cdot 6 \times 10^{-10}$
large power station		$3 \quad \times 10^{10}$	$9 \cdot 5 \times 10^{-1}$
UK energy consumption		$7 \quad \times 10^{12}$	$0 \cdot 22$
World energy consumption		$1 \cdot 6 \times 10^{14}$	5

† 1 TW = 10^{12} W.

harnessing it. The evaporation of water by the sun and the resulting gain in potential energy is the source of power for hydroelectricity, and solar heating of the earth's surface gives rise to winds which in turn generate waves. Associated with solar heating are the temperature gradients and currents within oceans, which can provide yet another source of power. Green plants use solar energy in converting carbon dioxide and water into carbohydrates providing food for animals, including man, and also a wide range of useful materials such as wood which may be used as a fuel. Green plants are also the original source of fossil fuels. Although these are still being formed, it is at a rate which is very much less than the rate of consumption.

The most important capital source of energy is nuclear energy contained in uranium, deuterium and other reserves, which although exhaustible, are potentially a very large source of energy indeed. In addition, tidal energy which is due mainly to the gravitational energy between the earth and the moon may be regarded as an exhaustible supply,

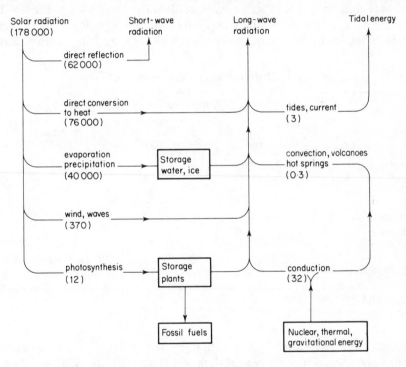

Fig. 3. *Global energy in the Earth's climatic system: units,* 1 TW = 10^{12} W. (World Energy Conference 1978)

since any energy extracted should in theory slow down the rotation of the earth. Geothermal energy, which may be the result of the natural nuclear decay of radioactive materials in the earth's core, is an exhaustible supply and again non-solar.

Of the total solar output of 3.5×10^{15} TW, some 1.8×10^5 TW falls on to the earth's surface, as shown in Table 2. Figure 3 shows that some 30% of this is reflected as short-wave radiation, whilst a further 45% is converted to heat. The remaining 4×10^4 TW manifests itself in the evaporation of water, in wind and waves and in photosynthesis. In theory, about 25% of the solar radiation reaching the earth is usable by plants, though in practice even the most efficient crop, sugar cane, uses only some 1·4% of the available solar radiation during the year and the conversion efficiency for a forest is about 0·5%. By far the greatest impact of solar radiation at the earth's surface is in the evaporation of water from seas, lakes and rivers. In returning to the earth during precipitation, some water falls on higher ground, thus retaining some potential energy which is partially converted into kinetic energy as the water flows back to the sea. It is this kinetic energy which may be used to drive mechanical devices such as turbines in hydroelectric power schemes. By studying stream flow

TABLE 3. *Hydropower and tidal power resources* †

	Hydropower		Tidal Power
	Potential (GW) ‡	Developed (GW)	Potential (GW)
North America	313	59	27
South America	577	5	6
West Europe	158	47	13
Africa	780	2	–
Middle East	21	–	–
SE Asia	455	2	–
Far East	42	19	–
Australia	45	2	–
USSR, China	466	16	16

† King Hubbert (1962, 1969).
‡ (1 GW $= 10^9$ W).

records in a given area, some estimate can be made of the potential hydropower capacity and typical data are given in Table 3. It should be noted that the total estimated world potential, approximately 3×10^6 MW, is only a fraction of one per cent of the solar power used in evaporation of the water.

By comparison with water power, the potential energy from the wind is very small indeed and a figure of 370 TW has been estimated as that available across the globe. Although much of this is in inaccessible regions, the available power is still greater than man's energy requirements of 5 TW, if only it could be tapped. In a windy region, such as the UK, with an average wind speed of 10 mph (4·5 m s^{-1}), the theoretical power availability is some 35 W m^{-2}, assuming an efficiency of 60%. Because of the long attenuation distance and decay time, the countries of Western

Europe are well placed to take advantage of wave power and it has been estimated that 80 kW could be recovered from each metre of wave front yielding 0·1 TW for the total coastline of the UK. The technical problems are enormous, however, and realistic efficiencies have still to be achieved.

The total power available from tidal sources is estimated to have a potential of 3 TW, with details given in Table 3. Again because of unsuitable sites and the fact that likely efficiency of a tidal scheme is around 25%, the true potential of tidal power may be around 0·015 TW, which is about 1% of the total available hydropower. The total flux of geothermal energy, mainly by conduction to the earth's surface, is about 32 TW though the low temperatures involved at any reasonably accessible depth preclude large-scale energy conversion. Hot springs and geysers account for about 1% of the total flow and allowing a 25% conversion efficiency to electricity, this would provide some 0·06 TW for 50 years.

Some data are given in Table 2 for various energy demands and a tentative estimate for the world energy consumption of 5 TW is included. With the solar radiation of $1·7 \times 10^5$ TW and the other natural energy flows considered in this section, the concept of an energy crisis seems somewhat strange, though the problems of tapping the natural sources, which are dealt with in later chapters, still remain a major challenge to man's ingenuity.

B. Resources

The most important product from the photosynthesis of bygone ages, apart from the development of man himself, is of course the fossil fuel bank on which the world is now drawing heavily. Geological evidence suggests that much of the coal mined at the present time is the remains of the lush vegetation of the Carboniferous period some 300 million years ago. It is certain that the present rate of accumulation is very much less than the rate of consumption, so that coal must be regarded as an exhaustible source of energy, though a responsible approach to energy supplies at the present time, might ensure that coal is not in fact required in the future.

The exact quantity of coal in the world which is held in reserve is difficult to predict because of the definition of what is mineable. This of course depends on the state of technology at any time. Data based on a United Nations survey (1972) are presented in Table 4 and these, coupled with figures from a US Geological Survey, suggest an energy store of around 2×10^{23} J. It is of interest to note that the major coal-consuming nations are for the most part the major producers. Peat, because of its lower calorific value, 11·5 MJ kg^{-1} compared with 23–32·5 MJ kg^{-1} for coal, is of lesser importance as a fuel and yet there are large amounts in the

TABLE 4. *Reserves of fossil fuels*†

	Coal (hard + lignite) ($Mg \times 10^9$)	Oil‡ ($m^3 \times 10^9$)	Gas ($m^3 \times 10^{12}$)	Peat ($Mg \times 10^9$)
Algeria	–	1·1	3·6	–
Argentina	–	0·4	–	–
Australia	111	0·2	0·9	–
Brazil	11	–	–	–
Canada	85	1·0	1·6	27·3
China	1011	3·2	0·7	–
Colombia	13	–	–	–
Cuba	–	–	–	0·9
Czechoslovakia	22	–	–	–
Finland	–	–	–	28·5
Germany (East)	30	–	–	11·4
Germany (West)	70	–	–	–
India	106	0·5	–	–
Indonesia	–	1·7	0·7	2·7
Japan	19	–	–	0·6
Libya	–	4·1	0·7	–
Malaysia	–	0·4	0·4	–
Middle East	–	36·0	14·1	–
Netherlands	–	–	1·8	–
Nigeria	–	3·1	1·3	–
Norway	–	0·9	0·5	2·1
Poland	61	–	–	6·9
South Africa	72	–	–	–
Sweden	–	–	–	10·2
USSR	5527	12·4	26	182
UK	16	2·7	0·8	10·5 (inc Eire)
USA	1506	5·0	6·2	15
Venezuela	–	2·4	1·2	–

† United Nations (1972), Olenin (1963), Anon. (1976)
‡ (Some 1980 data on the reserves of crude petroleum are presented in Table 17)

USSR and it is used on quite a substantial scale in Eire. Recent estimates of world peat resources vary from $2-3 \cdot 5 \times 10^{11}$ Mg which represents a store of around 7×10^{22} J. This compares favourably with coal although much of it is inaccessible. It has been suggested that the annual accumulation of peat is about 200 Mg km^{-2} and on this basis, not only is it a large source of fuel, but also a renewable one. In spite of this, the present world consumption, 9×10^7 Mg yr^{-1}, is greater than the rate of accumulation of usable material.

In the case of gas and oil, care must be taken to differentiate between the total amount of known and proved reserves, where the potential has been accurately assessed from the point of view of commercial exploitation (Mayer 1978). Typical data on this basis are shown in Table 4 and 17. It has been estimated that the world oil reserves are roughly 10^{22} J with about the same amount of energy in the reserves of gas. Thus it is evident that these values are much less than the coal reserves, around 10% in fact, and it is of importance to transfer some of the burden of world energy demands from oil to other sources such as coal, nuclear power and the so-called natural power sources (Maalauf 1979). Examination of Table 4 shows a factor of major importance, in that oil is absent in many of the world's industrial nations with a vast concentration in the Middle East. As a result, oil is a major item in world trade and quite unlike coal in this respect. When the member countries of OPEC raised their oil prices sharply in 1973, the world suffered the economic effects for several years, not because of a shortage of oil but from the political association of most of the producers. There are two possible solutions to the situation, firstly the discovery of new sources of oil in countries with different political policies and secondly, a diversification of the sources from which the world gets its energy, a long-term but more lasting approach. Some idea of the variation in the estimates of gas reserves is indicated in Table 5. These are proved

TABLE 5. *Estimates of world proved reserves of gas*†

Source	Year	Reserves (EJ)‡
Resources Survey, World Energy Conference	1974	1930
US Bureau of Mines	1974	2451
World Oil	1975	2362
	1976	2441
Inst. of Gas Technology	1975	2480
	1976	2468
Oil and Gas Journal	1976	2532
	1977	2743

† World Energy Conference (1978).
‡ 1 EJ = 10^{18} J.

reserves, whilst undiscovered recoverable reserves are estimated at 8150 EJ (World Energy Conference 1978).

The estimates of the reserves of nuclear energy depend very much on the technology used to extract it. In 1973, an OECD estimate based on a price of less than 20 \$ kg^{-1} of U_3O_8 was 10^6 Mg ore which appears generous although the predicted demand without the use of breeder reactors is around 2×10^6 Mg by the year 1990 which poses serious problems as does the low discovery rate of $6 \cdot 5 \times 10^4$ Mg yr^{-1}. The situation changes dramatically, however, with the development of breeder reactors in which the energy release is about 8×10^{13} J kg^{-1}; equivalent to a total reserve of 10^{23} J which is comparable with the coal reserves. This value is probably an underestimate, since with such high energy yields even expensive sources of uranium are worth exploiting, that is those in excess of 20 \$ kg^{-1} (1973). The energy from breeder reactors is dwarfed by the possibilities of fusion, for which there are two likely reactions; tritium–deuterium and deuterium–deuterium. In the former, the available resources are limited by lithium supplies to about 2×10^{23} J—again comparable with coal, though if the D–D reaction can be made to work, it has been estimated that enough energy would be available to maintain the world's present energy demands for 6×10^6 yr.

TABLE 6. *Estimated world uranium resources*†

Region	Resources (Mg)‡	
	Reasonably assured	Possible additional
North America	825 000	1 709 000
Western Europe	389 300	95 400
Australia, New Zealand and Japan	303 700	49 000
Latin America	64 800	66 200
Middle East and North Africa	32 100	69 600
Southern Africa	544 000	162 900
East Asia	3 000	400
Southern Asia	29 800	23 700
Total	2 191 700	2 176 200

† World Energy Conference (1978).
‡ Based on a recovery cost of up to US \$ 130/kg U (1977).

III. PRESENT AND FUTURE ENERGY DEMANDS

It has been seen in the previous section that fuel supplies are limited and for the most part exhaustible and that the technologies for handling long-term energy sources require extensive development. Forecasts vary as to the future position and some recent data are presented in Table 7. It is certain however that oil reserves will decrease rapidly towards the end of the present century, given the present rate of consumption and there will be a natural diversification to other energy sources as a result of ever increasing oil prices (Hill 1978, Beaujean and Charpentier 1979). Because of the greater reserves, coal is likely to be re-established as the dominant fossil fuel and nuclear energy will obviously play a greater role, though it is vital that breeder reactors become commonplace if this is to be a long-term

TABLE 7. *Potential world primary energy production* (EJ)†

Resource	1972	1985	2000	2020
Coal	66	115	170	269
Oil	115	216	195	106
Gas	46	77	143	125
Nuclear	2	23	88	314
Solar/geothermal, photosynthesis	26	33	56	100
Other	0	0	4	40
Total	269	488	690	1000

† World Energy Conference (1978).

benefit. The same reasoning applies to thermonuclear fusion if this can be made to work. Even if these alternative energy sources are exploited, the supplies of fossil fuels are still limited and it is important that they should be conserved, by reducing waste and the substitution of other sources of energy over an extended period, for use in their proper place—as a feedstock for the chemical industries. The amount of energy likely to be recovered from solar sources is modest, as shown in Table 8.

It has been suggested in Table 2 that the present world energy consumption is around 5 TW which compares favourably with a value of 4·4 TW for world production of thermal power from coal and oil (King Hubbert 1969). A similar result may be obtained by splitting the world

TABLE 8. *Forecast contribution from solar energy sources*†

Source	Application	Global resource (TW)	Theoretical recovery‡ (TW)	Contribution by 2020 (TW)
Solar		178 000	50–100	
	Thermal Energy			0·5–2·0
	Electrical Energy			0·1–0·3
Wind		350	?	
	Electrical Energy			0·01
	Mechanical Energy			0·20
Waves		3	0·1–1·0	
	Electrical Energy			0·01
Tides		3	0·06	
	Electrical Energy			0·01

† World Energy Conference (1978).
‡ Assumes appropriate technology can be developed economically.

population of 3.5×10^9 into 1×10^9 in developed nations consuming 5 kW per capita and 2.5×10^9 living in developing nations consuming 0.5 kW per capita—this gives a result of 6.3 TW (Open University 1974). If the same calculation is now made using estimated population figures for the year 2000, the result is 9.3 TW, though allowing a 6% compound growth rate, the energy demand becomes 46.5 TW. It is seen then that forecasting in this way is extremely difficult, though some guidance may be gained from the pattern of energy usage in the past. The changing pattern of fuel use in the UK is shown in Fig. 4 and it is important to note that these are

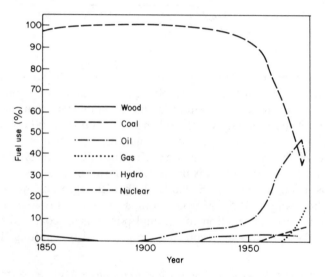

Fig. 4. *Pattern of energy usage in the UK.* (McMullan *et al.* 1976)

percentage data and not absolute values. The complete domination of coal is apparent together with the reluctance to change over to oil-fired plant for much of the twentieth century. In fact, oil did not become the dominant fuel until the early 1970s when it was apparent that supplies were limited. The other feature is the small role played by other energy sources; for example in 1974 only some 12% of the electricity generated in the UK was from nuclear power. Hydroelectric power makes an even smaller contribution at approximately 2%. In the United States (see Fig. 5), the traditional fuel was wood and coal only took over in the later part of the nineteenth century with oil dominating around 1950, mainly because of the very large reserves, though at present the United States has become a large importer of oil and gas.

Thus Western civilization is highly dependent on oil and gas which is running out, as highlighted by the energy crisis of 1973–74. Many solutions have been proposed, some long-term and some short-term. Firstly, there is the possibility of returning to a simpler agrarian economy, though this is no solution to the immediate problem. A more realistic proposal is conservation of energy, though here the important question is the pay-back time in *energy terms*. How long does it take to recoup the energy expended in producing and installing insulation, for example? On the domestic scale there is probably little which can be done other than to insulate, reduce temperatures and to install heat pumps in the hope that oil does not give

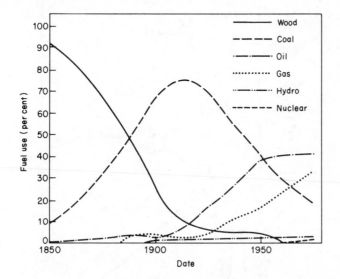

Fig. 5. *Pattern of energy usage in the US.* (McMullan *et al.* 1976)

out too soon. On the industrial scale, however, there is considerable scope for improvement, in that vast quantities of low-grade heat may be recovered in preheating operations, and a major rethink in industrial and commercial architecture, especially if the use of glass is minimized, would pay huge dividends.

The reserves of various energy sources have been considered in the previous section. What is more important is the predicted lifetime of a given reserve, which can be estimated if the pattern of exploitation is known. Sadly only the past pattern is known and yet fairly intelligent guesses can be made as shown in Fig. 6. It is clear that oil is only a small contributor to the world's energy supply in the long term and perhaps even more interesting is the contribution of nuclear power if breeder reactors are not introduced. By contrast, solar power has an enormous potential providing the problems of high capital cost and difficulties of implementation can be overcome. If the fusion reactor can be made to work, and, as with breeder reactors, safety must be paramount in this, any energy crisis will vanish forever.

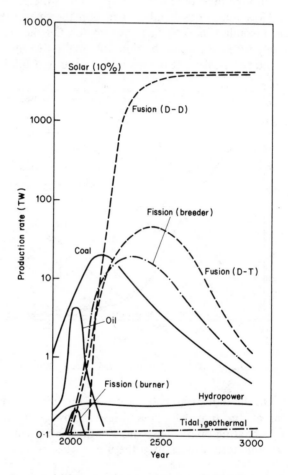

Fig. 6. *Projected lifetimes of energy sources.* (McMullan *et al.* 1976)

The immediate conclusion is that there is no energy crisis at all, but rather a short-term problem of Middle Eastern oil supplies and a medium-term problem of diminishing oil reserves. Similar problems will eventually apply to coal, though vast supplies of other energy sources do exist: only the technology is lacking.

IV. FURTHER READING

Alves, R. (1978). "Living with Energy". Academic Press, London and New York.

American Petroleum Institute (1952). "Petroleum—Facts and Figures". 10th Edition. New York.

Annual Bulletin of General Energy Statistics for Europe, 1975. UN Economic Commission for Europe (1977) Vol. VIII, Geneva.

Beaujean, J. M., Charpentier, J. P. and Nakicenovic, N. (1977). Global and International Energy Models—a survey. Annual Review of Energy **2**, 153.

Bell, P. C. (1971). "Industrial Fuels". Macmillan, London.

Bloodworth, I. J., Bossanyi, E., Bowers, D. S., Crouch, E. A. C., Eden, R. J., Hope, C. W., Humphrey, W. S., Mitchell, J. W., Pallin, D. J. and Stanislaw, J. A. (1978). World Energy demand to 2020. "World Energy Resources 1985–2020". IPC Science and Technology Press, Guildford.

CEPCEO (1977). "Energy in Europe—the vital role of coal". 10th World Energy Conference, 1977. 6 Vols. Istanbul.

Fells, I. (1978). "Energy for the Future". Arthur Rank Lecture, Luton. University of Newcastle upon Tyne.

Hafela, W. and Sassin, W. (1977). The global energy system. Annual Review of Energy **2**, 11–32.

McMullan, J. T., Morgan, R. and Murray, R. B. (1976). "Energy Resources and Supply". Wiley, Interscience, London.

Moody, J. D. "An estimate of world energy reserves" (March 1977). World Petroleum Congress, Tokyo 1975. Exxon Corp.

NCB "Facts and Figures" (1974). National Coal Board, London.

OECD (1966). Energy Policy, Paris.

Office of Technology Assessment, US Congress, Washington DC. "Enhanced oil recovery potential in the United States" (January 1978).

Royal Institute of Chemistry (1976). "Conservation of Resources", Glasgow, Chemical Society, London.

Russell, C. R. (1967). "Elements of Energy Conversion". Pergamon Press, Oxford.

Shephard, M. L. (1976). "Introduction to Energy Technology". Ann Arbor Science Publishers, USA.

Survey of Energy Resources (1974). World Energy Conference.

Tomalin, J. (1968). "The Energy Men". Cox and Wyman, London.

Transport and Road Research Laboratory (1976). "Future Transport Fuels". Department of the Environment.

Ubbelohode, A. R. (1963). "Man and Energy". Penguin Books, London.
UNITAR (1976). "Future supply of nature-made Petroleum Gas". Perga-
    mon Press, Oxford.
Updated Statistical Tables (1976). World Energy Conference.
Vivian, J. (1978). "Wood Heat". Rodale Press, Berkhamstead.

Primary Fuels: Solid Fuels

2

I. INTRODUCTION

In Chapter 1, it was shown how the greater part of the energy on the Earth eminates from the sun and how a store of this energy has been accumulated in the form of fossil fuels, particularly coal, crude petroleum and natural gas. Until such time as economically viable systems are developed for the direct utilization of solar energy, man must continue to draw on this, albeit limited, store for his energy needs. It is convenient at this stage to classify non-nuclear fuels into two groups—*primary fuels*, which occur naturally and which undergo no chemical processing before utilization and *secondary fuels*, which involve some chemical treatment in that their composition or structure is modified during a processing stage. On this basis, primary fuels include coal, wood and peat, crude petroleum, the products of distilling crude petroleum, natural gas and so on, whilst coke, coal gas, the products of cracking and reforming petroleum products and synthetic natural gas would be classified as secondary fuels.

This chapter is concerned with solid primary fuels and in particular coal, since this is such an important fuel compared with wood and peat. Coal is a primary fuel, since, although physical operations are involved in its production—cleaning, drying, screening, and washing—there is no change in its composition or structure before it is burned to liberate heat. After a brief discussion of the formation and structure of coal, other properties are considered within a framework of the results of the ultimate and proximate analyses of the material.

21

II. THE FORMATION OF COAL

Coal is a stratified rock which was formed many millions of years ago from the remains of decaying trees and vegetation. As such it is unique amongst rocks because it is organic in composition; it contains the elements of carbon, hydrogen and oxygen with small amounts of nitrogen and sulphur, and only traces of inorganic material, which are not chemically combined with the organic material forming most of the coal.

Coals are widely distributed, both geologically and geographically. Geologically, some coals are known to be more than 250 million years old while the youngest are at least twenty million years old. Geographically, the older coals are found in many parts of the world, but younger coals are less plentiful, particularly in Europe and on the sub-continent of North America. In the United Kingdom, the coal mined is primarily an older carboniferous coal, found in locations such as North and South Wales, Central Scotland, Northumberland, Durham, Yorkshire, Nottinghamshire and Derbyshire.

It is generally accepted that coal has been formed from decaying vegetation and mineral matter, compressed beneath many layers of fallen trees, leaves and soils. The two theories which have been proposed for the origin of coal seams are the *"in situ"* theory and the *"drift"* theory. The *"in situ"* theory proposes that the coal seam occupies roughly the same position as that in which plants and their remains originally died and accumulated, while the "drift" theory suggests that material drifted from the area where it grew to a location such as an estuary or lake, in which it was deposited. The former theory gives the more satisfactory explanation for the formation of the stratified, very uniform coal deposits found in the Northern Hemisphere. In the Southern Hemisphere, however, coal is frequently found in deep basin-like structures which are more likely to have been formed by a drift of material.

On dry ground, fallen trees and plants are attacked by oxygen from the surrounding air. Cellulose, which is their principal constituent, is slowly converted to carbon dioxide and water, and the tree rots away leaving very little trace. If the trees and vegetation are water-logged, however, air cannot penetrate to the cellulose and decay takes place anaerobically (i.e. in the absence of air) by the action of various bacteria. In this case, decay takes place slowly and is gradually halted as the products of decomposition accumulate and bacteria can no longer survive. During the period of bacterial decay, the trees and vegetation are covered by fresh debris of vegetation, soil and rocks deposited by movements of the earth's crust. Because bacterial degradation of cellulose is a slow process, the products of decomposition have been buried to a considerable depth by the time that bacterial action ceases. To form the coal mined today, the products would then have been subjected to a high pressure, stemming not only from the mass of the hundreds of metres of material above them, but also from movements of the earth's crust. It is likely also that these products would be heated to a greater or lesser extent by molten igneous rock below the seam. Variations in the conditions of temperature and pressure to which the seam was exposed have led to variations in the transformation of the decaying wood. These differences may be summarized as follows:

(i) Conditions which were not truly anaerobic led to the formation of peat.

(ii) Low alkalinity (and hence low absorption of CO_2) in the surrounding clay led to the formation of lignites.

(iii) High alkalinity in the surrounding clay led to the formation of bituminous coals.

Absorption of the carbon dioxide produced allowed decay to proceed further as there was no accumulation of the decomposition products.

As decomposition proceeded, hydrogen and oxygen were gradually excluded from the residual solid so that the various stages in the decomposition from cellulose to (ultimately) graphite show a reduction in the H and O content of the fuel.

TABLE 9. *Approximate compositions of various coals*

Coal	%C	Parts of			Calorific value (kJ kg^{-1})
		C	H	O	
Cellulose (pure)	44·5	100	13·9	111	–
Wood	50·0	100	12·0	88	19 770
Peat	59·9	100	10·0	57	18 663
Lignite	61.8	100	7·8	54	20930–25590
Brown coal	69·5	100	7·9	36	27 200
Bituminous coal	78·7	100	6·0	21	32 100
Anthracite	91·0	100	4·7	5·2	32 560
Graphite (pure)	100·0	100	–	–	32 910

In Table 9 the coals are "ranked" according to their carbon content. The rank of a coal is a measure of the change it has undergone in the transition from wood to graphite. A low rank indicates a small change, e.g. in peat, and a high rank indicates a large change, e.g. in anthracite.

Under the action of heat and pressure, some chemical action took place to expel water and oxides of carbon from the coal. The volatile matter content therefore varies with rank; the lower the rank, the higher the volatile matter content of the coal. Because oxygen is expelled during the limited chemical reaction, the calorific value of coal increases with rank, as the presence of oxygen in any fuel tends to reduce the calorific value. This is because it is assumed that the oxygen is combined with hydrogen as water; the heat of this reaction has already been evolved and is therefore not available during combustion of the coal. To summarize, the calorific value increases, the carbon content increases, and the coking power rises to a maximum and then decreases, as the rank increases. This is illustrated in Fig. 7 (MacRae 1966) and forms the basis of coal classification which is further discussed in Section V of the present chapter.†

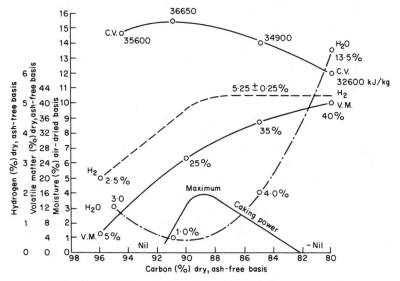

Fig. 7. *Variation of properties with rank for British coals.*

The study of the formation of coal is an ongoing topic of research and a survey has been presented by CSIRO (1971). Porcher (1973) discusses processes during formation and their importance in relation to the final characteristics of the coal substance. A recent paper by Beesling (1977) deals with coke reactivity as a function of rank.

III. THE STRUCTURE AND PETROGRAPHY OF COAL

A macroscopic study of a seam of coal indicates that coal is not homogeneous, and three constituents are immediately obvious: bright

---

† MacRae has also presented a useful summary of the mechanism of coal formation and this is shown in Table 10.

TABLE 10. *Schematic diagram of coal genesis*

WOODY MATERIAL

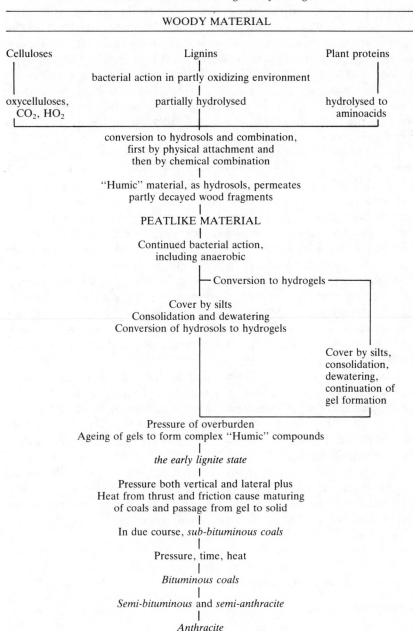

| Celluloses | Lignins | Plant proteins |

bacterial action in partly oxidizing environment

oxycelluloses,
CO_2, HO_2 | partially hydrolysed | hydrolysed to
aminoacids

conversion to hydrosols and combination,
first by physical attachment and
then by chemical combination

"Humic" material, as hydrosols, permeates
partly decayed wood fragments

PEATLIKE MATERIAL

Continued bacterial action,
including anaerobic

Conversion to hydrogels

Cover by silts
Consolidation and dewatering
Conversion of hydrosols to hydrogels

Cover by silts,
consolidation,
dewatering,
continuation of
gel formation

Pressure of overburden
Ageing of gels to form complex "Humic" compounds

the early lignite state

Pressure both vertical and lateral plus
Heat from thrust and friction cause maturing
of coals and passage from gel to solid

In due course, *sub-bituminous coals*

Pressure, time, heat

Bituminous coals

Semi-bituminous and *semi-anthracite*

Anthracite

(MacRae 1966)

coal, dull or hard coal and mineral charcoal (Ghosh 1971). Bright coal accounts for 60–90% of the coal in British seams. It has a high lustre, and breaks into fragments, which have essentially the same shape as the original sample. Dull coal is black and lustreless, but is harder and stronger than bright coal and hence coals with a high proportion of dull coal are easier to transport. Between 0% and 40% of a seam is dull coal and as this has a lower tendency to coke than a bright coal, it is more suitable for steam raising. Mineral charcoal contributes up to 3% of a seam and is found on the bedding planes. It is a dull, fibrous substance which easily crumbles to a powder.

Marie Stopes (1919, 1935) carried out a thorough examination of bituminous coal and showed that most pieces consist of four readily distinguishable bands known as vitrain, durain, clarain and fusain. Vitrain, the purest constituent of coal is jet black with a glossy lustre, and each band seems to have been formed from a separate fragment of wood or bark which frequently retains its original structure. Durain has a dull earthy lustre and is hard with a granular irregular fracture. This material contains 10% ash and appears to have been formed from vegetation which was easily transported by water and deposited in calmer areas of a swamp. Clarain consists of alternate strips of vitrain and durain though it breaks irregularly and is less friable than the former. Fusain is essentially another name for mineral charcoal. This may be either the product of aerobic decay which took place during a temporary emergence of the decaying vegetation into the air or natural charcoal from forest fires.

A general survey of the composition of the coal substance has been presented by Horton (1955) and Seyler (1950) and the latter isolated further groups of coal constituents, such as vitrinite and fusinite, in some earlier work (Seyler 1937). These have been further examined by Schumann (1970) and McCartney (1971), who used automatic micro-scope scanning techniques.

The structure of coal is virtually a science in itself and certainly beyond the scope of this chapter. It will be seen however, that even casual visual examination of the coal sample can reveal significant information on characteristics which may be encountered in combustion and gasification of the material.

IV. SAMPLING AND ANALYSIS OF SOLID FUELS

A. Sampling

Before a fuel can be analysed or, indeed, before any of its properties can be determined, a small sample of the material is required which is representative of the bulk material in every respect. There is little difficulty when dealing with liquids and gases, though in sampling the latter, changes in temperature and pressure must be taken into account. Coal, which varies both in size and composition, is quite a different proposition. Size may vary from large lumps to dust and the material may contain shale, slate, rocks and so on, in addition to the coal. It must also be noted that the bulk is unevenly mixed and one random sample is in no way representative of the bulk material.

The original method of dealing with this problem is known as "quartering". A large amount of coal is thoroughly mixed and heaped into a cone, which is then flattened and divided into four portions or "quartered". The opposite quarters are then mixed and the process repeated many times to obtain the sample. This sampling technique involves a great deal of manual labour, but is valid if no other methods are available.

More modern techniques which have been specified by the British Standards Institution (1960) involve taking a number of small samples or increments at points uniformly distributed across the coal bulk, as, for example, in a wagon. The final sample is the sum of the increments and it is obvious that the greater the number of increments, the greater the accuracy. There are empirical relationships available which indicate the size and number of increments required as a function of the experimental analysis. The higher the degree of heterogeneity, the greater is the number of samples required. This also applies to a coal with a high ash content, where the specification demands that, 99 times out of 100, the determined ash content should be within 0·5% of the mean. The size of each increment must be such that the inclusion of a piece of shale for example does not appreciably affect the ash content of that increment and in general large coal requires larger increments.

The whole question of sampling is somewhat complex and different procedures based on the above principles have been developed depending on the tests to be carried out on the sample. A general review of sampling techniques and the analysis of coal has been presented by Haltmann (1970) and the British Carbonisation Research Association (1978) and a more recent trend is the development of automated sampling techniques described for example by Nailen (1970) and Kvasnitskaya (1970). For sampling large quantities of material, a sampling chute is often used and the design of these has been discussed by Huntington (1971).

B. Analysis of Coal

Coal is analysed in two ways depending on the data required and these are known as the ultimate and proximate analyses.

1. *Ultimate analysis*

Ultimate analysis is the straightforward chemical analysis of material. It involves the determination of the more important chemical elements in coal, which are usually carbon, hydrogen, nitrogen and sulphur, and occasionally phosphorus and chlorine. Oxygen is not determined directly, but calculated as the sum of the elements plus moisture and ash subtracted from 100. This quantity is termed "oxygen plus errors". The results of an ultimate analysis are important for several reasons. The concentrations of carbon, hydrogen and oxygen are particularly relevant in the classification of coal and in combustion calculations, and the amounts of sulphur and phosphorus have a significant bearing on the metallurgy of iron and steel. It is important to know the concentration of arsenic when the fuel is used in food and brewing processes, and chlorine and elements such as vanadium are vital in considering corrosion and the problems of boiler deposits.

In carrying out an ultimate analysis, the moisture and ash are determined as outlined in Chapter 6. To evaluate the amounts of carbon and hydrogen present, the coal is completely combusted in oxygen and the concentrations calculated from the amounts of carbon dioxide and water formed. The Eschka method is used to determine the sulphur present. In this test, the coal is heated with sodium carbonate and magnesium oxide to convert the sulphur to sulphites and suphides of sodium and magnesium. The residue is washed into a beaker, oxidized with bromine water and the sulphur precipitated as barium sulphate. The weight of sulphur is then equal to 13·73% of the barium sulphate obtained. In the Kjeldahl method, the carbon in the coal is oxidized with concentrated sulphuric acid, and the nitrogen forms ammonium sulphate. This is distilled off with a quantity of a standard acid, and the amount of ammonia and hence the percentage of nitrogen is obtained by back titration.

An example of the calculation of calorific value of a solid fuel from the results of the ultimate analysis is included in Chapter 9.

2. *Proximate analysis*

Proximate analysis involves the determination of the moisture, ash, volatile matter, coke and fixed carbon, all as a percentage of the original weight of the coal sample. The details of the analysis are discussed in Chapter 6, which provides a simplified procedure based on the British Standard Specification (1956). The term proximate is used as the analysis varies with the procedure adopted; it should not, however, be thought of as implying "approximate", as a high degree of accuracy is required at all times. The results vary, particularly with the temperature of heating in determining the volatile matter, the duration of heating, the type of crucible used and the atmosphere under which the drying takes place. The term "fixed carbon" is hypothetical and does not imply the existence of uncombined carbon in the coal substance, nor does it bear any resemblance to the total carbon as determined in an ultimate analysis. Fixed carbon is not a precise constituent of coal. This quantity is not determined experimentally, but is calculated as the sum of the percentages of moisture, volatile matter and ash subtracted from 100.

The results of both the proximate and ultimate analyses may be expressed as either "as sampled" or on a dry, ash-free asis. The former includes all the items based on the coal as received. The latter is more useful in many ways, especially in classification, as it eliminates the variables ash and moisture. Typical results expressed on both bases are shown in Table 11.

TABLE 11. *Analysis of a Durham coal*

	Basis:	As fired		Dry, ash-free†	
Carbon		80·35		87·34	
Hydrogen		5·00		5·44	
Oxygen		4·31		4·69	100% ultimate
Nitrogen	100%	1·48		1·61	
Sulphur	ultimate	0·86		0·92	
Moisture		2·20		0	
Ash		5·80	100%	0	
			proximate		
Volatile matter		26·9		29·4	100% proximate
Fixed carbon		65·1		70·6	

† dry, ash-free = 100 (as fired)/(100−% moisture−% ash).

C. Significance of Test Data

1. *Ultimate analysis*

In this section the significance of the various elements which are determined in an ultimate analysis is considered, with particular reference to gasification and combustion processes.

(a) *Carbon.* As discussed earlier in this chapter, the amount of carbon depends on the type of coal and it increases with rank in passing from lignites to anthracites. The amount of carbon, therefore, provides an important basis for classification. As will be seen in Chapter 9, a knowledge of carbon content is vital in combustion calculations, especially in evaluating air requirements and actual air used.

(b) *Oxygen.* Oxygen is also important in the classification of coals, as the amount is high in lignites and low in anthracites. It is important to appreciate that the presence of oxygen in a coal reduces the available hydrogen. It may be assumed that the oxygen is combined with hydrogen in the coal substance and hence the heat of this combination has already been evolved and is not available during combustion. The greater the percentage oxygen in a coal, the lower is the tendency to form a high-grade coke.

(c) *Nitrogen.* The concentration of nitrogen in coal varies from 1% to 2·25% and this is the chief source of ammonium compounds, cyanides, etc., which are important by-products in gas manufacture by carbonization processes.

(d) *Sulphur.* Sulphur in coal varies from 0·5% to 2·5%, a typical value being 1·7%. It occurs in essentially three forms: pyrites, FeS_2; organic compounds in which the sulphur is combined with carbon in the coal substance; and gypsum, $CaSO_4$. The presence of pyrites in coal can have disastrous effects in combustion processes, as the resultant clinker, which fuses at a relatively low temperature, forms a eutectic with the firebars resulting in severe corrosion.

When the coal is carbonized, 65–70% of the sulphur remains in the coke, 20% passes into the gas as hydrogen sulphide and the rest appears in the tar and aqueous liquor. Coke thus contaminated with sulphur cannot be used for metallurgical processes; in this case it is necessary to produce a high-grade coke starting with a washed coal containing less than 0·8% sulphur. The coke thus formed contains less than 0·6% sulphur. Sulphur in coal gas must be reduced to 0·5 g m^{-3} and hence scrubbers and purifiers are required.

In combustion processes, sulphur forms its dioxide and some trioxide, which may produce a film of corrosive sulphuric acid on cooler parts of the plant. All fuels containing hydrogen form water on combustion and where the flue gas is cooled below the dew point (in, say, the air preheater or the economizer), a film of water which absorbs sulphurous gases is formed. It should be noted that the dew point of the acid film may be several degrees higher than that for water vapour and great care must be exercised in avoiding this condensation. The presence of sulphur oxides in the atmosphere has been shown to be a major hazard to health and a contributing factor in the formation of smog. It is important to realize that where a coal with a high sulphur concentration is used, it is necessary either to process the coal in a washery or to scrub the flue gas before venting to the atmosphere. The general aspects of sulphur in coal have been discussed recently by Attar and Corcoram (1977) and Gluskoter (1977).

(e) *Phosphorus.* The amount of phosphorus in coal is relatively low (about 0·1%) and yet this can have an important bearing on metallurgical processing. Blast furnace cokes should not exceed 0·01% phosphorus wherever possible.

2. *Proximate analysis*

(a) Moisture is present in coal in three forms. Surface moisture is acquired during washing and spraying of coal during storage and cleaning. Inherent moisture is absorbed and adsorbed in capilliaries in the coal substance, and combined moisture is held in loose combination, as in hydrates. On exposure to the atmosphere, the surface moisture and some of the inherent moisture evaporate until the residual moisture is in equilibrium with the surroundings. In this state the coal is said to be "air dry" and the concentration of moisture depends on the relative humidity of the air and the maturity of the coal. The lower the rank of a coal, the higher the percentage moisture which is retained after drying under standard conditions. The highly oxygenated coals, i.e. those of low rank, have the highest combined and inherent moisture. Washed coals may contain up to 20% moisture when drained.

Moisture diminishes the gross calorific value of a fuel, though in large boiler plant, up to 15% water is added to the coal feed to keep fine material in the combustion zone of the furnace.

(b) Ash is defined as the incombustible material which remains when a coal is burned. Ash may be classified as either inherent or accidental depending on the source from which it is derived. The former is present in the original vegetable material from which the coal was formed and is inseparable from the coal substance. It consists of the oxides of potassium, sodium, magnesium, calcium, silicon, etc., and makes up 0·7–1·2% of the coal. Accidental or extrinsic ash is dirt and material picked up from adjacent earthy or stony bands in the coal seam. This consists of various materials such as shales, clay, pyrites and ankerites. During washing and cleaning the coal, some, but not all, of the extrinsic ash can be removed, though flotation processes have to be employed to remove inherent ash. As noted previously, small coal usually has the highest percentage of ash. Ash is detrimental in combustion processes for the following reasons:

(i) It lowers the calorific value of the coal.

(ii) It must be removed and disposed of after combustion.

(iii) Firebars tend to be covered in ash, thus increasing resistance to the flow of air and the plant has to be shut down for cleaning at frequent intervals.

(iv) In many cases, ash forms a clinker which fuses with the firebars, resulting in severe corrosion.

Typical compositions of coal ash are shown in Table 12. It is important to note that the ash left when a coal is burned differs from the original ash present in the coal both in quantity and composition. For the sake of

TABLE 12. *Composition of coal ash*

	1	2	3
SiO_2	57·8	41·2	36·9
Al_2O_3	38·2	33·4	25·8
Fe_2O_3	5·7	17·2	25·0
CaO	0·4	3·7	5·7
MgO	0·8	1·9	3·2
Alkali oxides	3·1	2·6	3·4
Colour	white	buff	red
Fusion point	1775 K	1660 K	1375 K

clarity, the original ash in coal before combustion is usually termed mineral matter. In most British coals,

$$\% \text{ mineral matter} = 1\cdot15 \times \% \text{ ash.}$$

The principle changes which mineral matter undergoes when coal is burned are:

(i) dehydration of hydrates; for example gypsum,
$CaSO_4 \cdot 2H_2O \rightarrow CaSO_4 + 2H_2O$ (loss 2%).

(ii) decomposition of carbonates and sulphides, calcium carbonate, $CaCO_3 \rightarrow CaO + CO_2$ (loss 44%);
pyrites, $FeS_2 + \frac{3}{4}O_2 \rightarrow \frac{1}{2}Fe_2O_3 + 2S$ (loss 33%).

(iii) volatilization of alkali chlorides—usually negligible.

(iv) other reactions in which sulphur is fixed as the trioxide in combination with calcia and high-temperature combinations of oxides, silicates and free silica, for example.

In addition to the relation already given for the mineral matter as a function of the ash formed on incineration, more elaborate formulae are available. These include a simplified form of the King–Crosby relation:

$$\%MM = 1\cdot10A + 0\cdot53S + 0\cdot74CO_2 - 0\cdot32$$

and the Parr (US) formula:

$$\%MM = 1\cdot08A + 0\cdot55S$$

where A is the % ash on incineration, S is the total sulphur in the coal and CO_2 is the total carbonate (as CO_2 in the coal).

(c) Volatile matter is defined as the percentage loss in weight when finely powdered coal is heated in its own atmosphere at 1200 K for 2400 s. In carrying out this test, it is important to prevent oxidation of the sample during both heating and cooling and to subtract the percentage moisture which is determined in a separate experiment, from the result obtained. Volatile matter contains essentially three components:

(i) Gases. These are all combustible and include hydrogen, carbon monoxide, methane, ethane and hydrogen sulphide.

(ii) Tar. This is a complex mixture of hydrocarbons and other organics and includes benzene, toluene, phenols, cresols, naphthalene, anthracine and free carbon.

(iii) Ammonia liquor. This contains nitrogen and sulphur compounds with cyanides in an aqueous condensate, formed not from free or inherent moisture but by decomposition of hydrates for example.

Volatile matter is the result of decomposition rather than occlusion and it is usually expressed as a fraction of the dry ash-free coal, with allowances being made for inorganic constituents such as chlorine formed during the heating.

The role of volatile matter in gas production is discussed in detail in Chapter 5, and the effect of the carbonization temperature on the coke and tar produced is summarized in Table 13.

TABLE 13. *Effect of temperature on carbonization*

Temperature	Coke	Tar
900 K	Soft, brittle and very reactive—sold as "coalite" or smokeless fuel	More tar is produced at lower temperatures.
1200–1300 K	Product of gas works— used in water gas plant and domestic applications	A typical yield is 9 cm³/kg coal carbonized. At 1300 K, the yield falls to
1300–1500 K	Coke oven process—very hard product—used in blast furnaces	5 cm³/kg and cracking occurs producing free carbon and reducing the amount of oil produced on distilling the tar.

In combustion processes, volatile matter is the cause of smoke, which is essentially aerosols of tar and fine carbon particles. A typical amount of air required for burning coal is 10 kg/kg^1 coal ($\approx$ 10 m^3). Approximately 50% of this is required to carry off the smoke and is supplied to the furnace as secondary air. In large power stations, coals are blended to produce a fuel of constant volatile matter, which is as low as possible.

(d) Coke. The manufacture and properties of coke are discussed in detail in Chapter 5. The important feature is that the production and composition of a coke depend very much on the application for which it is used, usually either metallurgical or heating purposes. Typical compositions are shown in Table 14. Containing mainly carbon, coke finds extensive use as a reducing agent in many chemical processes.

TABLE 14. *Composition of coke*

	Gas coke	Metallurgical coke
C	85·54	93·15
H	0·52	0·72
O	0·90	0·80
N	1·28	1·00
Ash	11·76	4·33

The mechanism by which coke is formed from coal is of interest in that an understanding of the processes involved permits a degree of control of the final coke product during carbonization. When coal is treated with pyridene, 20–30% of the coal, known as the α fraction is soluble and a residue known as the β fraction remains. The α fraction is a tar-like material, which fuses at a low temperature to produce rich hydrocarbon gases which burn with a smoky flame. A hard black residue of carbon remains after the heating operation. The β fraction does not melt, but gives off carbon oxides and water vapour at 700 K and a considerable amount of hydrogen at 750 K, leaving an incoherent carbonaceous deposit. The mechanism of coke formation is therefore associated with the formation of a plastic layer during carbonization due to the fusion of the α type constituents in coal. Gasification then taking place in the plastic mass develops the pore structure which is rendered permanent at the completion of the plastic stage by the carbon residue of the α phase.

V. THE CLASSIFICATION OF COAL

A. Introduction

No coal is homogeneous and, as seen earlier in this chapter, it consists basically of a heterogeneous coal substance with mineral matter and water as impurities. Classification is therefore a matter of some difficulty and at the best an imprecise procedure. An ideal classification would be one which could be made with a few straightforward tests and which would indicate the uses to which the coal was most suited. In a simple way, this is possible by determining, say, the carbon content and hence an indication of the rank of the coal. This gives only a very broad classification and no information on calorific value, coking properties and so on. More detailed methods of classification are available, which are based in the main on either the ultimate or the proximate analysis with the results expressed on a dry ash-free basis.

B. Methods of Classification

In 1928, Parr evolved a simple method of classifying American coals in which the calorific value of the sulphur-free coal was plotted against the volatile matter. The results are shown in Fig. 8 with the various bands in

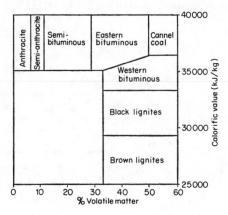

Fig. 8. *Parr classification.*

which the data could be grouped. The calorific value of the sulphur-free coal is calculated as

$$CV = \frac{CV \text{ of dry coal} - 5000S}{1 - (1 \cdot 08A - 0 \cdot 55S)}$$

and the volatile matter as

$$VM = 100 \frac{FC \text{ of dry coal}}{1 - (1 \cdot 08A - 0 \cdot 55S)}$$

where A is the ash content, S the sulphur and FC the fixed carbon in the coal as sampled. This form of classification is based on the proximate analysis and the calorific value only and whilst it provides for a preliminary grouping of a sample, there is no attempt to correlate the ultimate composition and information on coking properties, for example. A similar treatment has been proposed by Ralston (1915), though this suffers from the same limitations.

The first important attempt at classifying British coals was made by Regnault (1837) and his scheme, which is shown in Table 15, was modified by Gruner (1874). This classification is based on the ultimate analysis on a dry-ash free basis of, in particular, carbon, hydrogen and oxygen, and this is correlated against the behaviour of the coal on carbonization. The scheme has two disadvantages in that several of the classes of coal overlap, and no indication of the range of calorific values is included. Nevertheless, the chart provides a fairly broad classification of the important British coals and incorporates a great deal of useful information.

A more comprehensive classification is that compiled by Seyler (1900) which is shown as a simplified form of his coal chart in Fig. 9. The basis is a

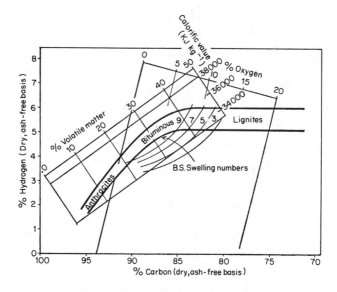

Fig. 9. *Simplified Seyler's coal chart.*

plot of percentage carbon against hydrogen, both on a sulphur-free basis, as in Parr's work. Most British coals fall within a fairly narrow band as shown. The results for a plot of volatile matter and calorific value fall within a similar band and hence this curve may be superimposed on the previous graph. Other data, such as oxygen content and the maximum inherent moisture may also be included on the chart and it is possible to

TABLE 15. *Regnault–Gruner classification*

Coal type	Coking and burning characteristics			Composition			VM (%) at 1200 K	Moisture (%)	Chief uses
	Coking	Coke	Flame	C	H	O+N+S			
Lignites	non	–	long, smoky	60–75	5	20–35	45	20	domestic, steam gas producers
Bituminous	non	–	long	75–80	5	15–20	40–45	10–20	domestic, gas producers, gas making
	coking	porous	long	80–85	5·6	10–15	32–40	5–10	domestic, gas producers, gas making
	hard coking	dense	–	84–89	5–5·6	5·5–11	25–32	5	metallurgical coke
	hard coking	very dense	short	88–90	4·5–5·5	5·5–6·5	18–26	5	metallurgical coke
Semi-Bituminous	very weakly	–	short, smokeless	90–92	4–4·5	4–4·5	10–20	2–3	steam raising
Semi-Anthracites	non	–	short, smokeless	92–94	3–4	3–4·5	8–15	2	steam raising
Anthracites	non	–	very little flame	92–94	3–4	3–4·5	8	–	domestic and central heating. Small gas producers

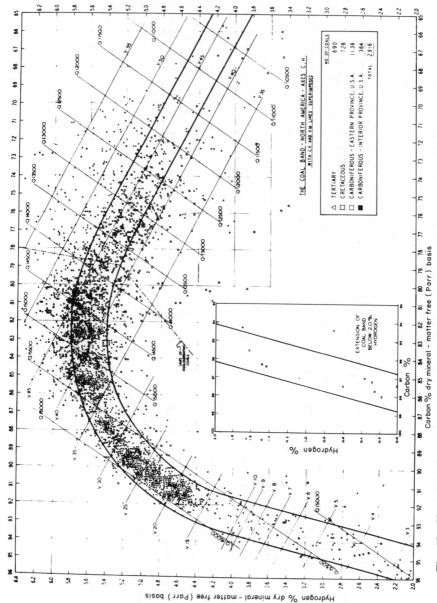

Fig. 10. *Chart for US coals. Calorific values are in BTU/lb:* (1 BTU/lb = 2·326 kJ kg⁻¹.) (Mott 1948)

indicate coking properties by plotting coals with the same British Standard swelling number. This is obtained according to a standard specification in which a given mass of coal is coked in a crucible and the resulting swollen coke compared with a set of standard profiles. This chart, therefore, incorporates a great deal of information and, given any two pieces of data about a sample, the chart should in theory give a reasonably comprehensive ultimate and proximate analysis and an indication of the calorific value and coking properties. Unfortunately the heterogenous nature of coal does not provide such an exact correlation beteen composition and properties and in using the chart, several corrections are required, and the information obtained must only be used as a rough guide. A more recent classification of coals on a similar basis has been presented by Drakeley (1923) and an equivalent treatment for US coals, published by Mott (1948) is shown in Fig. 10.

In the UK, the NCB classification is perhaps the most comprehensive in use today. This is based on the percentage volatile matter at 1200 K on a dry, ash-free basis and the character of the residue obtained by carbonizing coal at 900 K in a Gray–King test as discussed in Chapter 6. The main features of the classification are shown in Table 16 and it should be noted that in actual practice many of the codings are broken down into further subgroupings. For example, between 100 and 300, there is further subdivision on the basis of the volatile matter evolved (6·1–9·1% VM is coded 102). Between 400 and 900, further subdivision is based on the Gray–King coke type.

The subdivision of classes 200 and 300 is on the basis of coking power and denoted by 1–6 as the third digit of the code. A summary of the main uses of the various coal types is as follows:

400,	production of metallurgical cokes in ovens,
401,	coking coals for coke ovens,
500, 600,	steam raising, carbonization, blending with strongly, coking coals for use in coke ovens,
700, 800, 900	steam raising.

An international system of classification is based, like that used in the UK, on the volatile matter yield, and group coals into seven main classes. These are then subdivided according to the British Standard or continental swelling number (Chapter 6) and calorific value where a coal contains greater than 33% volatile matter. In addition, this somewhat complicated system includes the Gray-King coke type in the code.

New methods of classification are under continuous development and as far as the UK is concerned, that produced by the EEC is probably of increasing significance.

TABLE 16. *NCB classification*

Type of coal	Designation	Volatile matter (%)	Gray–King residue at 900 K†	Coking	Code No.
Anthracite	Anthracite	4·5–9·5	A	non	100a, b
Low volatile	Dry steam	9·6–14·0	A–B	non	201a, b
	Coking steam	14·1–15·5	C–G	weakly	202
		15·6–17·5	C_1–G_4	medium	203
		17·6–20·0	G_5–G_8	strongly	204
	Scottish steam	9·6–20·0	A–D	non	206
Medium	Coking coal	20·1–30·0	G_6+	very strongly	301
volatile	Scottish	20·1–30·0	A-G_5	very weakly	300
Highly volatile		30·1–37+	G_9+	very strongly	400
		30·1–37+	G_5–G_8	strongly	500
		30·1–37+	G_1–G_4	medium	600
	Gas coals	30·1–37+	E–G	weakly	700
		30·1–37+	C–D	very weakly	800
		30·1–37+	A–B	non	900

† Description of solid residue from Gray–King Test:
  A   pulverent
  B   breaks into powder on handling
  C   coherent, but friable on rubbing
  D   shrunken, moderately hard
  E   shrunken, hard
  F   slightly shrunken, hard
  G   hard, occupies same volume as original coal, "standard coke"
  G_1 slightly swollen, hard
  G_2 moderately swollen, hard
  G_3 highly swollen, hard, fills tube
  G_4+ very highly swollen

VI. THE STORAGE OF COAL

Where there are significant daily and seasonal variations in power demands the storage of coal is important and the precautions to be taken are now considered. The prime hazard is that of spontaneous combustion of the coal, and it is worth noting that oxidation at the surface of coal takes place at all temperatures, is exothermic and is promoted by a rise in temperature (Marinov 1977). In addition, spontaneous combustion is more likely to occur where there is a high percentage of combined moisture and a large amount of fine coal present. For this reason, it is advantageous to store screened coal. There is no evidence to suggest that sulphur plays any part in spontaneous combustion.

The height of a coal dump should not exceed 5 m in order to permit adequate ventilation and in any event ventilation pipes should be provided, with large coal forming the sides of the dump. Thermocouples are usually inserted in the dump to monitor any temperature fluctuations.

Chamberlain (1970) discusses the detection of spontaneous combustion and Dunningham (1927) gives a good account of practical experiences during coal storage. There is an abundance of published material on the mechanism of spontaneous combustion and the general concepts have been discussed by Carr (1970), who deals with particle behaviour during storage, and by Baldwin *et al.* (1972).

The mechanism of spontaneous combustion is thought to be associated with the formation of very unstable products known as peroxides. The normal reaction for the oxidation of ethane may be written:

$$C_2H_6 + 7/2\,O_2 \rightarrow 2CO_2 + 3H_2O$$

It is possible, however, to form peroxide materials in the following chain of events:

$$C_2H_6 + O_2 \rightarrow CH_3O.OCH_3 \qquad\qquad \text{ethane peroxide}$$
$$\downarrow$$
$$H_2O + CH_3CHO \qquad\qquad \text{acetaldehyde}$$
$$\downarrow \qquad (+\tfrac{3}{2}O_2)$$
$$CO_2 + H_2O + HCHO \qquad\qquad \text{formaldehyde}$$
$$\downarrow \qquad (+O_2)$$
$$H_2O + CO_2$$

Figure 11 illustrates the relative concentration of peroxide on the surface of a bituminous coal as a function of temperature. Peroxides are very important in many other combustion processes; for example tetrethyl

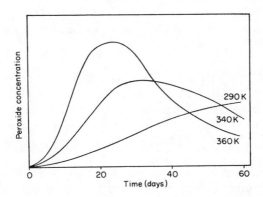

Fig. 11. *Concentration of peroxide on the surface of bituminous coals as a function of dump temperature.*

lead, an additive in petrol, reduces knocking in petrol engines by reacting with peroxides formed. A great deal of work is still required before the precise mechanisms are fully understood.

The Wheeler test provides a convenient method of determining the temperature at which coal spontaneously ignites. This value is known as the auto-ignition point. Referring to Fig. 12, the coal sample is surrounded by a sand-bath with air blown at a fixed rate through the coal. The

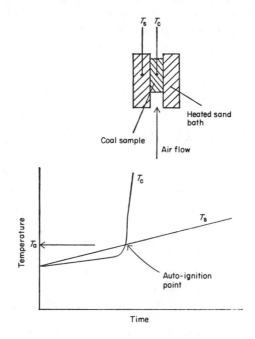

Fig. 12. *Determination of the auto-ignition temperature.*

temperatures of both the coal and sand are noted as the sand is heated and the temperature at the point of intersection of the temperature–time plots is defined as the auto-ignition point. For low-rank coals this has a value of 430 K ranging to 575 K for anthracite. The test may also be carried out on materials such as rubber and linoleum, which exhibit similar auto-ignition properties.

One practice which is still not widely exploited is the storage of coal under water. Porter (1917) has studied the deterioration in properties under such conditions, particularly that of calorific value, and claims that this is much reduced compared with storage in air.

VII. FURTHER READING

Bangham, D. H. (1950). "Progress in Coal Science". Butterworth, London.

Department of Energy (1978). "Coal Technology". HMSO, London.

Griswold, J. (1946). "Fuels, Combustion and Furnaces". McGraw-Hill, New York.

Henderson, P. L. (1953). Brown Coal—its Mining and Utilization. Cambridge University Press, Cambridge.

Humus, G. W. (1958). "The Elements of Fuel Technology". Leonard Hill, London.

Lowry, H. H. (1945). "Chemistry of Coal Utilization". Wiley, New York.

MacRae, J. C. (1966). "An Introduction to the Study of Fuel". Elsevier, Amsterdam.

Ministry of Power (1958). "The Efficient Use of Fuel". HMSO, London.

Pope, P. C. (1949). "Coal—Production, Distribution and Utilization". Industrial Newspapers, London.

Spiers, H. M. (1962). "Technical Data on Fuel". World Power Conference, London.

Starkman, E. S. (1971). "Combustion Generated Air Pollution". Plenum Press, London.

Thring, M. W. (1957). "Air Pollution". Butterworth, London.

Wilson, P. J. and Wells, J. H. (1950). "Coal, Coke and Coal Chemicals". McGraw-Hill, New York.

Primary Fuels: Liquid and Gaseous Fuels 3

I. INTRODUCTION

The main primary fuel occurring naturally as a liquid is crude petroleum and this is usually associated with natural gas. Crude petroleum is not used directly as a fuel, but is separated into its various components or fractions by physical processes, the most important of these being distillation. As no chemical processing is involved in this operation, it is convenient to classify distillation products as primary fuels and hence this chapter is concerned with the properties of crude petroleum and the production of fuels from this raw material by physical processes only. The formation of secondary products by chemical processing is discussed in Chapter 4 and the general properties of petroleum products are dealt with in Chapter 6.

Crude petroleum is found in many parts of the world and the output from various countries is shown in Table 17. At one time America produced half the world's total output of crude petroleum, though this proportion fell owing to the development of other oil-producing areas, the most important being the Middle East. As the beginnings of the modern oil industry were founded in America, much of the nomenclature used in Britain is significantly different and it is worth defining some of the more common terms at this stage. The world "petroleum" refers to crude petroleum from the well and includes oil products in general. Gasoline is defined as the fraction obtained by distilling crude petroleum, which boils below 475 K. This is known as petrol or motor spirit in the UK, and the fraction boiling between 475 and 495 K is termed naphtha. Kerosene is the illuminating fraction usually known as paraffin in the UK, and paraffin wax is a mixture of solid hydrocarbons. Liquid paraffin, a highly refined

TABLE 17. *Production and consumption of crude petroleum*

Country	Reserves (10⁶ Mg)	Production Rate (10⁶ Mg/ year)	Production Span† (year)	Consumption Rate (10⁶ Mg/ year)	Consumption Span† (year)
North America	5 500	554	10	975	6
Latin America	5 800	240	24	202	29
Western Europe	3 300 (UK = 2300)	84	39	715	5
Middle East	50 300	1062	47	83	606
Africa	7 700	277	28	60	128
Asia-Pacific	2 700	137	20	443	6
Communist Bloc	12 800	702	18	598	21
Total world	88 100	3056	29	3076	29

† Span is the period of time oil can be consumed or produced at the present rate. (Pearce 1980)

lubricating oil, which is transparent, colourless and tasteless, is called medicinal oil in the USA. Asphaltic bitumen is the dark, semi-solid residue obtained from distilling petroleum, and is usually sold as bitumen in Britain. The term asphalt should be reserved for natural products such as Trinidad lake asphalt and artificial mixtures of asphaltic bitumen with minerals.

II. CRUDE PETROLEUM

A. Origin

The formation of petroleum is much less clearly understood than that of coal. Since petroleum is a mixture of fluids, both liquid and gaseous, it is not necessarily found in or near the place where it originated. It may have diffused some considerable distance (up to 20 km) from the source rocks.

Many theories have been advanced for the origin of petroleum but none has so far been proved. A good survey of these has been presented by Philippi (1969) and Kartsov (1972), whilst new theories of formation are discussed by Rudakov (1970).

It has been suggested that petroleum was formed from animal, vegetable or mineral origins by anaerobic decay of marine plant and animal life. The most favoured theory proposes that, in a very calm, shallow sea, dead plants and animals fell to the bottom to be covered by a layer of silt. Under such conditions, the dead organic matter which was settling continuously decayed under near anaerobic conditions. As with coal, the steady accumulation of mud above the organic matter led to an increase in temperature and a rise in pressure—conditions which have been shown to favour the formation of liquid and gaseous hydrocarbons and hydrogen sulphide (H_2S).

The oil and its associated natural gas produced within the rock structure surrounding the sea (the source rock) would be forced, by the high pressures to which they were exposed, into any channels or porous rock around the pocket containing them. Under such conditions, the oil could migrate in many directions up to a distance of several kilometres from the

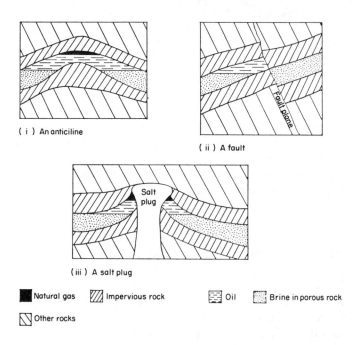

(i) An anticiline

(ii) A fault

(iii) A salt plug

▮ Natural gas   ▨ Impervious rock   ▦ Oil   ▦ Brine in porous rock

◻ Other rocks

Fig. 13. *Rock structures containing oil.*

source rock, depending on the rock structure through which it passed (Chapman 1972).

Any oil or natural gas which found its way to the surface would be evaporated and lost, leaving the high boiling point fraction (heavy fraction) as a natural deposit of pitch. The oil and gas moving in other directions would have continued to migrate until they reached a formation of rocks which was impervious to oil or gas. Here the oil and gas would have accumulated to fill up the enclosed porous rock. Such oil reservoirs occur in the form of an anticline, a fault or a salt plug (Fig. 13).

Certain features are common to all types of oil reservoir. The reservoir is bounded above by a layer of impervious rock known as the cap and below by a second layer of impervious rock. The region between these layers is filled with porous rock such as limestone or sandstone which contains the oil and/or natural gas within its pores. The structures differ primarily in the shape of reservoir and the way in which the oil is contained at the sides of the reservoir. The oil is tapped by drilling through the cap rock. In the initial stages, the oil may emerge from the bore hole under hydrostatic or gas pressure but in later stages it will have to be pumped from the reservoir.

B. Composition

Crude petroleum differs from the class of materials to which coal belongs in three important respects. Unlike coal, it is usually liquid at room temperature, and it is completely soluble in organic solvents such as benzene and carbon disulphide. On combustion it leaves very much less ash than coal.

Crudes vary widely in composition and appearance, depending on their source. For example Arabian oils smell of hydrogen sulphide, whilst oils from other parts of the world contain only small amounts of sulphur. Many crudes are dark in colour and contain solid waxes. A discussion of the composition of Australian crudes has been presented by Matthews (1970). The major components in crude petroleum may be grouped under four headings.

1. *Hydrocarbons*

These form the greater part of most crudes and are present in a wide range of molecular weights, varying from dissolved gases to solid waxes. The main group of hydrocarbons in crudes is the paraffins (Egloff 1931) and compounds in the series above $C_{16}H_{34}$ are present as solids. The molecules of these paraffins have a straight-chain structure, such as *n*-octane:

$$
\begin{array}{ccccccccc}
 & H & H & H & H & H & H & H & H & \\
 & | & | & | & | & | & | & | & | & \\
H- & C- & C- & C- & C- & C- & C- & C- & C & -H \\
 & | & | & | & | & | & | & | & | & \\
 & H & H & H & H & H & H & H & H &
\end{array}
$$

Isomers (with the same molecular mass but a different structure) are also present. An example is iso-octane, which is used as a high standard fuel in knock-rating tests on motor spirit:

$$
\begin{array}{ccccc}
& \text{H} & & & \text{H} \\
& | & & & | \\
\text{H--C--H} & & \text{H--C--H} \\
\text{H} & | & \text{H} & | \\
\text{H--C} & \text{---C---} & \text{C} & \text{---C--H} \\
\text{H} & | & \text{H} & | \\
\text{H--C--H} & & \text{H--C--H} \\
& | & & & | \\
& \text{H} & & & \text{H}
\end{array}
$$

In addition to the paraffins, crude petroleum contains cyclic compounds such as the naphthenes and aromatic compounds, including dicyclic compounds such as naphthalene and pyridine. Other important hydrocarbons are the olefins, e.g. popylene or propene, $CH_2CH.CH_3$, which also exist as both the normal straight chain structures and as isomers. Many of the olefins readily polymerize; that is, many molecules join together to form one very long molecule or polymer. This is a disadvantage in such chemical processes as cracking (Chapter 4), for example. In this process, long chain hydrocarbons are snapped to form more useful, shorter molecules ($C_{16}H_{34}{\rightarrow}2C_8H_{18}$) during which polymerization of olefines may form undesirable gums. However, polymerization is an extremely useful process in the petrochemical industry where it is the basic reaction in the production of plastics and synthetic rubbers. One example is the production of a synthetic rubber from the diolefin, isoprene ($CH_2C.CH_3CH.CH_2$).

There are thus four basic series of hydrocarbons in crude petroleum; paraffins, olefines, aromatics (i.e. containing a benzene ring) and cyclic compounds such as cyclopentane:

$$
\begin{array}{ccc}
& CH_2 & \\
& \diagup \quad \diagdown & \\
CH_2 & & CH_2 \\
| & & | \\
CH_2 & \text{------} & CH_2
\end{array}
$$

It is important to note that a very large number of isomers are possible, especially amongst the higher members of a series. In addition, small quantities of mixed hydrocarbons are present. Toluene, $C_6H_5.CH_3$ is a mixed hydrocarbon in that it contains a benzene ring, which is the basic aromatic structure, with a CH_3 branch—the shortest possible aliphatic side chain. Mixed hydrocarbons of every conceivable type occur in crude petroleum and very many of these have been isolated. One fairly complex example is tetrahydronaphthalene:

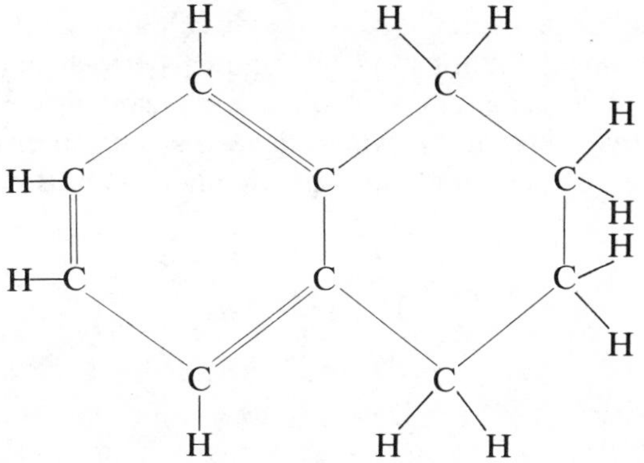

2. Oxygen compounds

Besides hydrocarbons, organic compounds containing oxygen are present in small amounts. One important group is the naphthenic acids, which are carboxylic acids containing a naphthene ring:

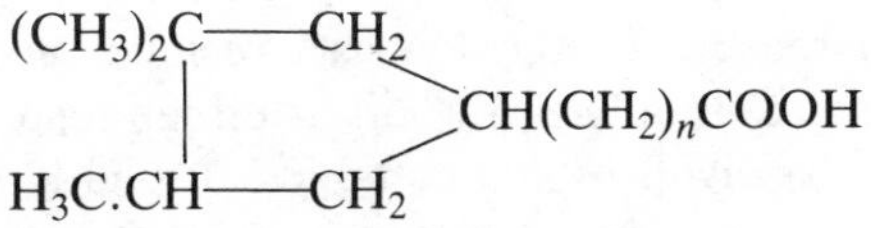

Many Russian oils are rich in naphthenic acids (Vustavkina 1930). These may present problems in distillation processes as, in addition to corrosion problems, they promote the formation of an emulsion of water in oil in the presence of alkalis and are usually removed as salts by adding soda lime. Certain petroleum products contain phenols which are formed from naphthenic acids during cracking and these are also removed with alkali. Oxygen compounds are sometimes formed in petroleum products due to contact with atmospheric oxygen. For example, the ageing of lubricating oil is due to this reaction, the main products being peroxides.

3. *Sulphur compounds*

The amount of sulphur in a crude oil varies from a trace to several per cent depending on the source. For example, Middle East crudes are richer in sulphur than Indonesian samples. Refining operations may concentrate the sulphur in a certain product to concentrations approaching 10% and for most applications, especially fuel oils, this must be removed. In a large refinery, the sulphur recovered is converted to sulphuric acid, which is then used in the refining of lubricating oils and in petrochemical synthesis. Among the sulphur compounds in oil are mercaptans or thiols (e.g., CH_3CH_2SH, ethyl mercaptan), which have a strong unpleasant odour, thio-ethers and ring compounds such as thiophene (US Bureau of Mines 1972):

Although certain Californian oils are rich in nitrogen, there are usually only small amounts of this element present in most oils often as derivatives of pyridine and quinoline (Schulze 1930).

4. *Inorganic compounds*

One feature of crude oils is the small amounts of inorganic compounds present—the main reason for the low ash residue on combustion. The inorganic elements are usually in the oil as either suspended particles of mineral matter or dissolved organometallic salts. Oils from Mexico and Venezuela are rich in vanadium, which on burning as fuel oils is usually lost in the flue gas, though some attempt is made to recover this valuable material in large installations. Small amounts of water, often containing inorganic salts, may be present in the crude, frequently as a suspension or an emulsion if natural emulsifiers are present. These emulsions may be quite stable and somewhat elaborate techniques are necessary for breaking them and removing the water.

This brief survey of the more important components of crude petroleum illustrates the vast range of products which can be obtained from the physical processing of crude oil. These include petroleum gases, kerosene, gasoline, fuel oils, diesel oils, lubricating oils, wax and asphalt.

Certain chemical processes are involved in later refining operations in order to produce a product to what is usually a very close specification. As discussed in Chapter 4, chemical processes are also used to provide high-grade fuels from material for which the demand is not as great. Crude oil also provides the source of raw materials for the rapidly growing petrochemicals industry and products such as detergents, paints, plastics, drugs, rubbers and synthetic fibres are produced by many complex operations from the lighter components obtained from the primary distillation of crude petroleum. As well as these organic materials, petroleum materials form the starting point for many inorganic compounds, produced from synthesis gases manufactured by gasification of oil as, discussed in Chapter 5.

C. Oil Wells

1. *Construction*

The first stage in the construction of a well is the drilling operation, which almost always involves rotary drilling. A derrick or drilling mast, consisting of a pyramidal framework, is used to support the hoisting gear for raising and lowering the drilling equipment and to support the drilling string which is the collective term for the rotating drillrods, each some 30 m long. Derricks are expensive structures and the modern trend, certainly for land-based operations, is towards collapsible, lattice-steel masts which can be used for holes up to 3000 m in depth. The lengths of steel pipe transmitting torque and vertical pressure to the drilling bit are also known as "rods" and these convey the drilling fluid to the bit. Two classes of bit are used: firstly, one which crushes the opposing rock to create a cylindrical hole; and secondly, a bit which cuts out an annulus producing a core for detailed examination on the surface. A paper on bit design has been presented by Gains (1970) and more recently by Garner (1977). Normal rates of bit rotation are in the range 1–5 Hz. Drilling fluid or mud which is often a suspension of fine clay, is used to cool the bit and to flush out debris, to support the wall of the hole and, most importantly, to seal porous rock thus preventing leakage of gas, oil or water. Commonly, the first 100 m or so of the hole, which is 450–500 mm in diameter is cased with steel pipe and the hole proper may be 200–300 mm in diameter. The top of the hole is fitted with valves to control the flow of mud and later the petroleum gases. Oil wells range in depth from 2000 to 10000 m and techniques have been developed for drilling the sea bed promoted by the ever increasing demands for oil. In shallow water, barges or fixed platforms can be used, though mobile platforms which are virtually self-contained movable steel islands are used for deep-water applications. Typical of many papers on such techniques is that presented by Rijen (1970) who discusses work in Quatar. When a well has been proved, the complete hole is cased with steel tubing cemented in position (Suman 1977). This not only strengthens the walls but ensures the exclusion of fluids other than oil and gas from the product. Perforations are then made through the casing into the producing stratum and usually the oil flows by natural flow up the tubing to the control valves and outlet pipe system.

2. Operation

The passage of oil depends on the viscosity of the fluid and the permeability of the porous stratum, but most importantly on the driving pressure. This can be due either to gas, as in 'a gas-cap reservoir, or to water, as in a water-drive reservoir. Where the initial pressure is inadequate, or when the flow of oil decreases due to the fall in gas or water pressure, some form of secondary recovery must be practised, especially as perhaps only 30% of the oil present can be recovered by natural flow. The injection of water, known as water-flooding, is one method. Alternatively, gas or liquified petroleum gases such as butane may be used. In the latter case, some solution of gas in the crude takes place which increases its mobility by a reduction in viscosity. At the surface, where the pressure may still be 50 MN m^{-2}, gas often comes out of solution in the oil and helps to lift the oil by expansion. This is often augmented by passing gas down between the tubing and casing to promote the "air-lift" effect. Reservoir engineering is a relatively new science and forms the basis of several post-graduate courses. Simulation of reservoirs is of great importance and surveys of such work have been presented by Thackuk and Wallenbarger (1970) and Johnson (1978).

The production from each well passes to a central gathering station where gas is separated and water and solids are removed by either settling or centrifuging. The gas separation is purely mechanical at this stage and involves directing the mixture against baffles in cylindrical vessels. The separated crude oil and gas are now ready for further processing.

III. PHYSICAL PROCESSING OF CRUDE PETROLEUM

A. Introduction

After dirt and water have been removed from crude petroleum and the bulk of the associated natural gas separated, the processing into finished products may be considered under three headings. These are physical processing or separation, chemical processing or conversion, and refining operations.

This section is concerned with only the first of these operations and in particular the basic unit operations such as distillation, absorption and filtration, which are employed in separation processes. Chemical processing and refining operations or treatments in which impurities are removed are considered in Chapter 4. Not every product passes through all three stages. For example, petroleum gases are liberated in the primary distillation of crude petroleum and these can be sold without any further chemical or refining treatment. If the market demand for the various products (kerosene, gasoline and so on)—obtained from the distillation of crude was in the same ratio as the amounts of each product obtained, then the chemical processing or conversion required would be greatly reduced. Conversion processes are necessary, however, to produce the kind and quantity of materials demanded by fluctuating market requirements.

B. Distillation

The primary separation process which is used in almost every stage of petroleum processing is fractional distillation. This involves the separation of a mixture of liquids into its components or fractions, each with a limited range of molecular mass, by virtue of their different boiling points. When, for example, a mixture of water and acetone is heated and the vapour formed then condensed by cooling, the condensate collected is initially pure acetone. As the concentration of acetone in the heated vessel decreases, the mean boiling point of the mixture and hence the temperature rises and the condensate contains increasingly greater amounts of water. The condensate collected can then be divided into two portions or fractions: one containing almost pure acetone and the other a dilute acetone–water mixture, and in this way pure acetone has been collected from the initial mixture. As described, this distillation would stop when all the liquid had been distilled over from the heated vessel and, being non-continuous, the process is termed batch operation. The distillation of crude petroleum, whilst based on these elementary concepts, is complicated by two factors—the need to operate on a continuous basis and the complexity of the liquid mixture feed, which may contain many thousands of compounds. In the primary distillation of crude petroleum, the aim is not to separate pure components, but to divide the feed into say 8–10 fractions each with a limited range of boiling point (usually 50 deg K). These fractions are then separated into their various components by subsequent distillation operations.

The main unit in which distillation is carried out is the fractionating column, which is shown diagrammatically in Fig. 14. Feed material is first pumped through banks of heat exchangers in which heat is recovered from product steams leaving the plant, and then through a tubular oil-fired furnace to the column. When dealing with crude oil, the temperature of the feed, which is partially vaporized on entering the column, is about 600 K. The column usually contains a large number of trays each fitted with bubble caps as shown in Fig. 15. The temperature on each tray decreases up the column and hence the liquid on each tray, which is boiling over a

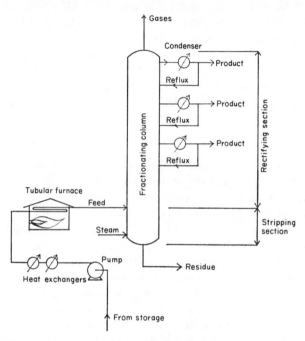

Fig. 14. *Fractional distillation scheme.*

fixed temperature range, has a different composition. As hot vapours pass up the column, the heavier components with higher boiling points condense out and return as liquid to a lower tray. The latent heat released vaporizes lighter components which rise as vapour up the column. Each tray therefore serves to continuously condense and partially re-evaporate the liquid, and the column may be thought of as a series of small distillation units. At steady state, each tray contains liquid within a limited range of temperature, and hence composition, which may be drawn off as a side stream. It passes through a water condenser to extract heat and the condensate is removed as product for further treatment, whilst some liquid is returned to the column as reflux. Above the feed tray, the feed is being continuously separated into the various fractions and this section of the column is known as the rectifying section. Below the feed tray, liquid containing heavier components runs down the column and steam is blown through this residue to strip out any light components and carry them into the rectifying section. The lower part of the column is known as the stripping section. The residue leaving the column is cooled and further distilled under vacuum, which enables the operation to be carried out at lower temperatures, and avoids decomposition of the material.

The bubble cap tray is a relatively cheap and efficient way of ensuring good contact between vapour and liquid. The vapour passes up a riser

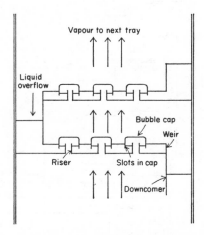

Fig. 15. *Schematic diagram of a bubble-cap column.*

through the liquid and escapes via slots in the bubble caps. The liquid condensing plus reflux spills over a weir at the edge of the tray and falls down the downcomer to the next tray. The tray is designed so that there is a sufficient head of liquid in the downcomer to overcome the resistance to flow of liquid across the tray. There are other types of tray in use, such as perforated trays and valve trays, and the choice of equipment is basically one of economics, depending on capital and running costs, efficiency, maintenance and so on (Backhurst and Harker 1973).

A general flow scheme for the primary distillation of crude petroleum is given in Fig. 16. Before entering the main fractionating column, the feed is preheated, usually in a tubular furnace, to $400 \, \text{K}$ at $350 \, \text{kN m}^{-2}$, and subjected to a flash distillation. In this column the pressure is reduced as the feed enters and the higher volatile components, mainly hydrocarbon gases, flash off, leaving a residue which is pumped to the main primary distillation column. The top product or overheads from the flash distillation may be partially condensed, and this volatile liquid is either sold as primary flash distillate or subjected to secondary distillation treatment in which further separation into its components is achieved. An important treatment prior to distillation is that of subjecting the crude to "viscosity breaking", in which the crude is heated under pressure and the long-chain heavy hydrocarbon molecules are broken or cracked to form hydrocarbons

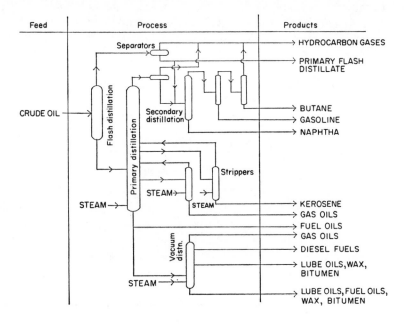

Fig. 16. *Primary distillation of crude petroleum.*

of intermediate molecular size in the gas oil range. The two effects of this process are to increase the yield of gas oil, for which there is a high market demand and greatly to reduce the viscosity of the crude. In many cases this treatment is necessary in order that the crude may be pumped. With light crudes, viscosity breaking is only applied to the residue from the primary distillation column.

The overheads from the primary distillation contain hydrocarbon gases, kerosene and gasoline, which are condensed out. The light gases—methane and ethane—are used as a feedstock for the production of petrochemicals and as a fuel, and the heavier gases—butane and propane—are liquefied by compression and sold as liquefied petroleum gases

(LPG). The liquid phase known as light distillate is refractionated in smaller columns to achieve further separation. Side streams taken from the primary fractionator are stream-stripped in further columns to produce a fraction or cut in the kerosene–gas oil range, and the residue may be sold as a fuel oil or distilled under vacuum, to avoid decomposition at high temperatures, to produce additional gas oil, lubricating oils, waxes and bitumen.

This summary of the primary distillation must of necessity be only an outline and reference should be made to more detailed discussions given in Section VI of this chapter. A general survey of the processing of crude petroleum over the past forty years and indeed to the year 2010 has been presented by Uhl (1970) and a discussion of the cost of future refineries is given by Grigsby (1973). Recent trends in refinery operation, particularly computer control of distillation plant are discussed by Farrar (1970), and energy conservation in distillation operations by Mix (1978).

C. Solvent Extraction

A further important unit operation used in petroleum refining not only for separating components, but also for removing impurities from product streams, is solvent extraction. To take a simple example, consider an oil in which common salt is dissolved. If this is thoroughly mixed with water, the salt, being more soluble in water is transferred into this phase, which may be then separated from the oil by allowing the mixture to separate out into two phases. This process is shown in Fig. 17. The important features are

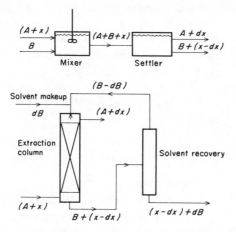

Fig. 17. *Principles of solvent extraction.*

that the raffinate, in this case the oil, and the solvent (water in this case) should be immiscible and that the salt should be more soluble in the solvent than the raffinate. The solution of salt and water is known as the extract. In the petroleum industry, the material extracted is usually a liquid, such as a mixture of hydrocarbons for example, where one hydrocarbon is more soluble in a particular solvent than the rest. The process may be carried out in a simple piece of equipment, consisting of a mixer in which intimate contact between the raffinate and the solvent is obtained, and a separator, in which the two phases settle out. It is more efficient, however, to employ counter-current operation and this is usually carried out in a column containing perforated or sieve plates. Mixing occurs at each plate followed by separation between the plates and in this way many stages are achieved in the single piece of equipment, if a mixer–settler combination is considered as one stage. Packed columns are also used, containing specially designed packings such as ceramic rings and saddles; in this case mixing and separation take place continuously and such a column contains many stages. As shown in Fig. 17, the extract is treated in a distillation process to liberate fresh solvent for re-use in the extraction column.

One specific application of this operation is the Edeleanu process (Cottrell 1933), in which unwanted aromatic hydrocarbons are removed from kerosene, the solvent being liquid sulphur dioxide. The sulphur dioxide is recovered by evaporation and then compressed to the liquid state for re-use, and the last traces are removed from the kerosene raffinate by a sodium hydroxide wash. By this process the aromatic content in kerosene can be reduced from 20% to 2% and the extract contains 70–80% aromatics.

A further application is found in the separation of lubricating oils from the residue of the vacuum distillation, for which a liquid propane solvent is used. In an operation similar to the Edeleanu process, aromatics are removed from high-grade lubricating oils using solvent extraction techniques with furfural as the solvent (Bryant 1935).

Although the use of solvent extraction is not as widespread as distillation operations, it is an extremely useful technique, especially in the purification of product streams.

D. Absorption

When a mixture of ammonia and air is sprayed with water, the highly soluble ammonia is absorbed into the water and in this way the air is purified or stripped of ammonia. Such an absorption operation is used widely in separating and purifying petroleum products. As discussed later in this chapter, the process is used to extract high-boiling hydrocarbons from natural gas and it is also used to effect a primary separation of the gases produced in cracking operations. For the separation of propane and butane from methane and ethane the solvent is usually a gasoline fraction. The equipment consists of a tower which contains perforated plates, or more usually a random packing of rings or even crushed coke, providing a high contact area between the gas rising up the column and the absorbant which is sprayed onto the top of the packing. The absorbant is stripped of the absorbed gas in a distillation tower with steam and passed to the top of the column as recycle (Fig. 18). The system as described is simplest from of operation and more complicated processes involve high temperatures and pressures, selective absorption, and absorption accompanied by chemical

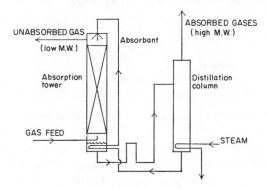

Fig. 18. *Absorption process.*

reaction. Absorption is used in many processes, not only as a major step in the manufacture of a given product, but also in removing solvents and intermediate components used or formed in a previous operation.

E. Crystallization and Filtration

These unit operations are not used extensively in petroleum refining, though one important application is in the manufacture of paraffin wax. This product is separated from the lubricating oil distillate and the residue obtained from the vacuum column by a combined process of crystallization and filtration. The distillate is mixed with a solvent, usually a ketone, and cooled in chillers in which wax crystals are formed and allowed to grow (Lund 1952). The chillers consist of a series of long tubes through which the wax–solvent slurry is drawn by means of a slowly rotating screw. The edge of the screw is fitted with spring scrapers which remove the wax from the tube walls. The tubes are surrounded by a jacket through which either brine or liquid propane is pumped as a coolant. The choice of coolant depends on the temperature to which the wax is to be cooled and careful control of this parameter, and the amount and position of introduction of the solvent stream, greatly influence the type and form of wax produced. Waxes formed from the vacuum residue have very fine crystals and when dispersed in a little oil can be sold as a jelly known as microcrystalline wax. The wax slurry from the chillers is usually filtered on a continuous vacuum unit (Fig. 19) or centrifuged. The vacuum filter consists of a rotating drum partially immersed in slurry. A vacuum is pulled on the inside of the drum and a layer of material is formed on the cloth around the circumference.

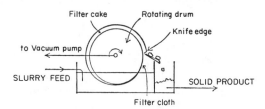

Fig. 19. *Principles of continuous filtration.*

Filtrate is withdrawn from the cake as it rotates, until the point is reached at which the cake is removed by a knife blade. The wax collected in this way is melted and cast into blocks for transporting to the consumer and the filtrate is separated and the solvent is re-used.

Another application of filtration is in the use of decolorizing clays which are used for improving the colour of a product or for removing traces of previous refining agents (Davis 1928). For example, in order to remove sulphur from an oil, the product is washed with concentrated sulphuric acid. This is removed by an alkaline wash after which the oil is mixed with a clay to remove the last tracers of acid and to improve the colour. The spent clay is separated from the oil by filtration using a batch plate and frame unit, or in more modern plant by a rotary vacuum unit (Davidson 1943).

IV. NATURAL GAS

A. Introduction

The important primary fuel associated with crude petroleum is natural gas. This is produced in large volumes from oil wells, where it has collected in pockets above the crude oil, and also gas wells, which may be quite remote from the oil-bearing strata. In this case, the gas has migrated through porous rocks away from the oil. The range of composition of a natural gas is shown in Table 18, though the analysis varies widely depending on the locality (Moore 1977). For example, gas from Pennsylvania has a high ethane concentration and consequently a low amount of methane. Lacq gas from France contains 17% hydrogen sulphide whilst Gröningen gas is rich (15%) in nitrogen. Certain natural gases contain the rare gases such as argon and helium, which are sometimes extracted on a commercial scale. In addition to gases from gas fields and those obtained from above crude oil, certain crudes contain large concentrations of dissolved gases, which are separated at the well-head. The two basic types of natural gas which

TABLE 18. *Composition of natural gas (by volume)*

Methane	CH_4	70–90%
Ethane	C_2H_6	
Propane	C_3H_8	0–20%
Butane	C_4H_{10}	
Hydrogen	H_2	nil
Carbon dioxide	CO_2	0–8%
Oxygen	O_2	0–0·2%
Nitrogen	N_2	0–5%
Hydrogen sulphide	H_2S	0–5%
Rare gases	A, He, Ne, Xe	trace

may be noted are therefore "dry" gas from a gas well, which is primarily methane with no oil or higher hydrocarbons, and "wet" gas, which has been separated from oil at the well-head. It contains valuable additional compounds such as pentanes and hexanes, and also natural gasoline. When these additional compounds have been separated from the wet gas, the product is essential dry gas (Goor 1978).

There are many descriptions of gas plants in the literature; two examples are Ewing (1970) and Barton (1970). Streich (1970) describes the removal of nitrogen and this is further discussed by Jacks and McMillan (1977). Liquefied natural gas plants are described by Chiu (1978).

B. Separation of Natural Gasoline from Wet Gas

The three methods of separating natural gasoline from wet gas and thus providing a dry gas for use as a fuel and chemical feedstock are compression, absorption and adsorption.

1. *Compression*

Referring to Fig. 20, the wet gas is firstly compressed to 2400 kN m^{-2} and then cooled to 300 K, when the higher hydrocarbons separate out. The gas is then further cooled to 270–275 K, by interchange with the product stream and the remaining gasoline is removed. The now dry gas leaves the plant by way of an expansion engine and the cold gas is used to cool the interstage stream. This process is used where the dry gas is required under pressure, for example where it is to be transported through a pipeline.

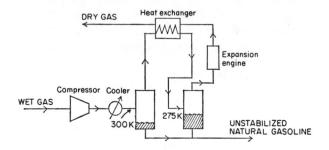

Fig. 20. *Separation of natural gasoline from wet gas.*

2. Absorption

This method provides a further example of the operation described in Section III. D. In this case, the wet gas is passed up an absorption tower under slightly elevated pressure and the natural gasoline is absorbed by a light gas oil flowing counter-currently. The solvent is then heated and passed to a stripping column, in which the natural gasoline is removed with steam. This process is most profitable where there is a low concentration of natural gasoline in the wet gas.

3. Adsorption

The wet gas is passed through a vessel containing particles of activated charcoal. The natural gasoline is adsorbed onto the surface of the charcoal and operation is continued until the charcoal is saturated, when the feed is switched to another vessel. The adsorbed hydrocarbons are removed from the charcoal by steam, which is then allowed to condense and the organic phase is separated out. The carbon is dried with a hot gas and the wet gas stream is readmitted. This process is limited to feeds containing low concentrations of sulphur, as the carbon is easily poisoned by, for example, hydrogen sulphide. The efficiency of the process is high, however, and a good yield of natural gasoline is recovered.

The natural gasoline obtained by these methods cannot be blended with motor gasoline as it contains dissolved gases such as propane, which render the material unstable and susceptible to "vapour lock". This phenomenon involves the release of gas in fuel lines, especially where the pressure is low, thus causing an interruption in the supply of fuel to the engine. It is a feature prevalent in aircraft at high altitudes, where of course no break in the fuel supply can be tolerated. Propane is therefore removed from natural gasoline by distillation under pressure and in this way the fuel is stabilized (Burdick 1931).

Newer techniques for the processing of natural gas include cryogenic operations, discussed by Garwin (1970).

C. The Uses of Natural Gas

Natural gas may be used directly as a fuel in both industrial and domestic applications. Special burners are necessary, though it may be burned in appliances designed for operation with coal gas if the gas is modified. This may involve blending the gas with a low-grade fuel or reforming the natural gas as discussed in Chapter 5 to produce a coal gas. Where natural gas is used directly as a fuel, as in the UK gas grid, it is necessary to add an odourant to enable leaks to be apparent and detectable. In addition to the manufacture of coal gas, natural gas is reformed into synthesis gases and is therefore an important feedstock in chemical processing. One important use in this respect is the production of hydrogen—the starting-point for ammonia and hence fertilizer production. Carbon black is also produced from natural gas by burning the gas under fuel-rich conditions to produce a smoky flame from which the soot is collected.

As discussed in Section II.C.2, when an oil well has ceased to produce crude, the flow of oil may be started again by repressurizing the oil field with natural gas. This is an example of using the dry gas obtained by the compression process. Natural gas produced in an oil field may be transported over considerable distances by pipeline. The pressure is usually 2000–4000 kN m^{-2} and pumping stations are required every 200–350 km.

V. LIQUEFIED PETROLEUM GASES

Liquified Petroleum Gases (LPG) may be considered as a primary fuel since it is mainly produced from crude oil or natural gas by physical processing only. In the United States, LPG, which is a mixture of propane and butane, is obtained by fractionating natural gas (Temple 1970), though in the UK it is a product of the primary flash distillation, the primary distillation, cracking and reforming operations. In the latter cases, small amounts of propene and butene are also present.

Both propane and butane have low vapour pressures (750 kN m^{-2} and 165 kN m^{-2} respectively at 290 K) and are easily liquefied. LPG is sold under various trade names as a liquid under pressure either in bulk or in steel bottles. On evaporation, one volume of propane produces 270 volumes of gas and hence a large amount of heat energy may be stored in a small volume. In Europe, a standard LPG cylinder holds 0·026 m^3 liquid, which is equivalent to 10 kg propane. The calorific value of propane is 46 000 kJ kg^{-1} and hence a standard cylinder of propane contains 485 000 kJ of stored heat energy. The equivalent figure for butane is 604 000 kJ— these high values making LPG especially suitable for portable applications and for providing gas in remote locations.

Table 19 shows that both propane and butane have combustion properties differing widely from coal gas and natural gas. The volumetric

TABLE 19. *Properties of propane and butane*

	Explosion limits		Stoichiometric air requirements
	Low	High	
Propane	2%	11%	23 : 1
Butane	1·7%	9%	30 : 1
Coal gas	4%	70%	6 : 1
Natural gas	5%	14%	10 : 1

concentrations in air providing combustible mixtures are much narrower than with coal gas and in this respect LPG is less hazardous. It is important, however, to be aware of the greater relative density of these gases compared with air and the need to provide adequate ventilation, especially at ground level, where the gas from a leak would tend to accumulate. It is seen that the amounts of air required for burning both propane and butane are much greater than for natural gas and hence special burners are required for burning these gases, An important point to note is the low boiling point of butane, 273 K. Because of this, it is imperative to use the gas above freezing conditions if incomplete vaporization of the liquid on leaving the cylinder is to be avoided.

LPG is used as both a domestic and industrial fuel—not only for heating and cooking, but also in refrigeration and for lighting in remote locations. Propane is used as an urban gas in the US though its main use is in industry, where it is used in the heat treatment of metals, portable heaters, small internal combustion engines and as an oxy-propane flame in welding and cutting operations. LPG is widely used as an important feedstock in chemical synthesis and also for reforming into synthetic natural gas.

VI. FURTHER READING

Aldus, L. (1955). "Liquid–Liquid Extraction". Elsevier, New York.

American Petroleum Institute (1952). "Petroleum Facts and Figures". 10th Edn. A.P.I., New York.

Backhurst, J. R. and Harker, J. H. (1973). "Process Plant Design". Heinemann, London.

Beychok, M. R. (1967). "Aqueous Wastes from Petroleum and Petrochemical Plants". Wiley, New York.

British Petroleum (1972). "Gas Making and Natural Gas". London.

Brooks, B. T. and Dunstan, A. E. (1955). "Science and Petroleum". Vol. 5, Part 3, Refinery Products. Oxford University Press, London.

Coulson, J. M., Richardson, J. F., Backhurst, J. R. and Harker, J. H. (1978). "Chemical Engineering", Vol. 2. Pergamon Press, Oxford.

Evans, E. B. (1959). "Modern Petroleum Technology". The Institute of Petroleum, London.

Gay, J. H. and Handwerk, G. E. (1975). "Petroleum Refining". Dekker, New York.

Goodger, E. M. (1975). "Hydrocarbon Fuels". Macmillan, London.

Have, J. H. van der and Verver, C. G. (1957). "Petroleum and its Products". Pitman, London.

Hobson, G. D. and Pohl, W. (1975). "Modern Petroleum Technology". Applied Science Publishers, London.

Institute of Petroleum (1946). "Modern Petroleum Technology". London.

Institute of Petroleum (1978). "Methods of Analysis and Testing". Heyden, London.

Kobe, K. A., McKetta, J. J. (1961). Advances in Petroleum Chemistry and Refining", Vol. IV. Wiley, Interscience, New York.

Longhurst, H. (1959). "Adventure in Oil". Sidgwick and Jackson, London.

Longman, J. (1972). "Petroleum and Organic Chemicals". Chemical Technology Publishing Co. Inc., USA.

MacRae, J. C. (1966). "An Introduction to the Study of Fuel". Elsevier, Amsterdam.

Nelson, W. L. (1970). "Petroleum Refinery Engineering". 4th Edn. McGraw-Hill, New York.

Nelson, W. L. (1976). "Petroleum Refinery Engineering". McGraw-Hill, Tokyo.

Popovich, M. (1959). "Fuels and Lubricants". Wiley, New York.

Sell, G. F. (1963). "The Petroleum Industry". Oxford University Press.

Shell Refining Co Ltd. (1966). "The Petroleum Handbook", 5th Edn. Shell, London.

Sherwood, T. L. and Pigford, R. L. (1975). "Mass Transfer", 2nd Edn. McGraw-Hill, New York.

Tiratsoo, E. N. (1967). "Natural Gas". Scientific Press Ltd., London.

Van der Have, J. H. and Verver, C. G. (1967). "Petroleum and its Products". Pitman, London.

Watkins, R. N. (1973). "Petroleum Refinery Distillation". Gulf Publications Co., Houston.

Williams, D. A. and Jones, G. (1963). "Liquid Fuels". Pergamon Press, London.

Secondary Fuels: Conversion Processes

4

I. INTRODUCTION

In Chapter 2, a classification was made between primary fuels obtained from crude petroleum by physical operations, and those products, generally termed secondary fuels, which involve chemical processing at some stage of their manufacture. Chemical treatment of secondary fuels is necessary for two important reasons. Firstly, the amounts of the various fractions separated in the distillation of crude petroleum do not correspond with market demands. A good example of this is motor spirit, where the demand has grown enormously during this century. The yield produced by the distillation of crude petroleum alone could not hope to cope with the present requirements without the increased production of "unwanted" heavier components, which would render operation uneconomic. Secondly, it is essential for the economic operation of a large, complex refinery, that the amount of the crude oil (and therefore energy) which is wasted, that is unused on the plant or unsold, must be kept to an absolute minimum and every attempt is made to produce the greatest quantity of the more valuable components demanded by the consumer. Apart from petrochemical activities, the present oil industry is based to a large extent on the chemical processing of the distillation products of crude petroleum, and a discussion of such conversion processes forms the greater part of the present chapter.

There are essentially two main types of chemical process which are carried out, "reforming" and "cracking", in addition to processes employed in the treatment of the various process streams to form finished products. In simple terms, reforming alters the form or structure of a

67

chemical, whilst cracking involves a change in molecular weight. In some operations, both processes can take place at the same time. One good example of a reforming operation is the conversion of a petroleum fraction, naphtha, into fuel and synthesis gases in the presence of steam and a catalyst. This type of process is discussed in Chapter 5.

Both cracking and further reforming can be carried out by heat or in the presence of a catalyst—thermal processing and catalytic processing respectively—and these headings form a convenient classification for discussing the various operations involved.

The products of physical processing such as the distillation of crude petroleum and chemical processing, even when split into suitable fractions must undergo further refining or treatment before they can be marketed. For example, gases need to be desulphurized and hydrogen sulphide must be removed from distillates before transport to intermediate storage in order to avoid corrosion problems. With gasoline fractions, the sulphur content must be reduced to a specified maximum and both kerosine and gas oil require desulphurization by acid-treatment, solvent extraction or hydrogenation operations. Such refining processes are discussed in the latter part of the chapter. A general outline of basic refining operations such as distillation, cracking and reforming is shown in Fig. 21.

II. CRACKING PROCESSES

A. General Principles

Cracking can best be considered as distillation under pressure; it involves the snapping or rupturing of the long chain hydrocarbon molecules into smaller fragments, thereby producing a range of components of lower molecular weight (Hurd and Spence 1929). The operation is thus ideally suited to the production of low-boiling point materials demanded by the consumer from heavy (i.e. high molecular mass) products such as waxy distillates, for which there is a limited demand. In simple terms, cracking is achieved by heating a heavy fraction to a temperature well above its boiling point (up to 800 K) and subjecting it to pressures of up to 4000 kN m^{-2}. Such treatment produces a mixture of low boiling point liquids, petroleum gases and free carbon. Not all the products are straight-chain saturated components (i.e. containing only single bonds within the structure); some reforming also takes place. Indeed, such is the demand for unsaturated (double bond) hydrocarbons, such as ethylene and propylene, that to produce these chemicals special cracking processes have been developed on which the petrochemicals industry is based. In producing a motor spirit, a high concentration of unsaturated hydrocarbons is less desirable, though

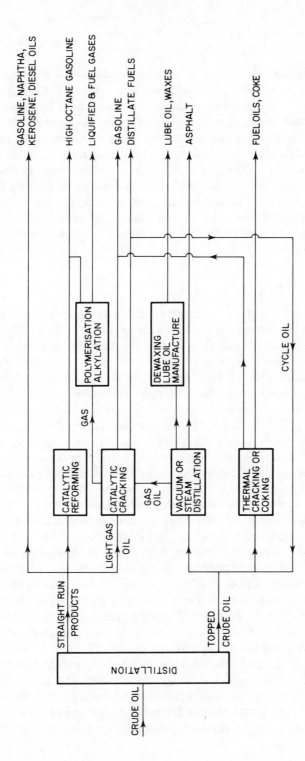

Fig. 21. *Basic refining operations.*

when hexadecane, $C_{16}H_{34}$, a straight chain paraffin, is cracked, for example, the products would include n-octane, C_8H_{18}, and the unsaturated di-isobutylene, C_8H_{16}, with possibly the branched paraffin, 2,2,4-trimethylpentane, an isomer of octane. This example oversimplifies the reactions involved and it is important to realize that although the mean molecular mass is greatly reduced, the product stream from a cracking process is a complex mixture of many components and requires additional distillation, separation and further conversion stages before the finished products are obtained. In relation to gasoline, cracking not only breaks down large molecules, but converts paraffinic hydrocarbons of low octane number (Chapter 6) into olefins which in most cases have a higher octane rating (Nelson 1947).

B. Thermal Cracking

The earliest cracking processes involved heat and high pressures only and are termed thermal cracking processes (Silliman 1871, Bell 1930). These have now been largely superseded by catalytic processes, which have many advantages, not least of which is that of a more economic mode of operation, because they allow the cracking operation to proceed effectively at lower temperatures and pressures. One important feature of thermal crackers, is the production of coke as a by-product and it is likely that, certainly in the UK, the demand for this product will increase in the future. For this reason alone, thermal cracking is still an important operation. A thermal cracking unit suitable for handling liquid feedstocks is shown in Fig. 22. This appears somewhat complex, though in fact a great deal of the equipment is duplicated (although operated under different conditions), so that a wide range of feeds may be handled (Lambrix 1969). The feed is passed to a fractionating column, where lighter components are separated, the bulk of the material passing through a pipe furnace (B) and into the reaction chamber where the cracking takes place at high pressure. In the flash chamber, the cracked products flash off and are sent to a fractionator, whilst the residue is either withdrawn or passed via a further column to form coke. A greater part of the free carbon produced by cracking is contained in the residue material. The light fractions and gases separated in the column are sent to the final distillation column, after which they are separated into gasoline and petroleum gases (Chapter 3), whilst the heavier components are heated in a pipe furnace (A) to a higher temperature than before and recycled through the reaction vessel. This stage is necessary as shorter chain, and therefore more volatile, components are more difficult to crack and a higher temperature is required. In addition to this type of plant, similar units have been used for cracking in the vapour phase, though in all cases the yield and quality of gasoline produced depends on the process and the nature of the feedstock. A wide range of feeds may be processed and typical products yields are:

gasoline 38–54%
gas oil 0–23%
fuel oil 34–38%

The gases produced, propylene and butylene, are used for the manufacture of "polymer gasoline". As noted previously, thermal cracking processes have become uneconomic in relation to catalytic and reforming

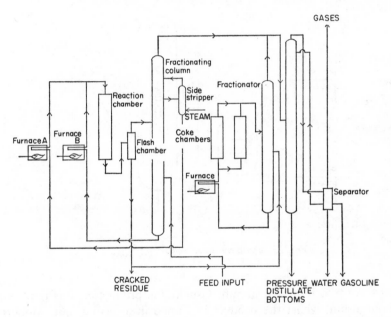

Fig. 22. *Thermal cracking process.*

processes due to the increased demand for higher octane gasolines, though they are still used to a small extent for reducing the viscosity of fuel oils—a process known as "viscosity breaking" in which heavy oil molecules are broken down to smaller ones of lower viscosity.

Mention has already been made of the use of thermal crackers in the manufacture of petroleum coke, a process in which a gas oil distillate, suitable for catalytic cracking, is also formed from a residual oil feed. If a heavy crude oil is used as the feed in addition to the coke, a synthetic crude oil is produced which may be processed in the usual way. The yield of gasoline is 5–15%, gas oil 75–80% and providing the feed has a low sulphur content, the coke is suitable for the production of electrodes (Nelson 1952, Stockman 1940). A simplified flow diagram of the process is shown in Fig. 23. The feed is heated and passed to a distillation column in which the lighter materials are removed and the unvaporized bottom product is heated in a second pipe-still from which the vapour–liquid mixture passes to one of a series of coke drums in which the product is formed (Jakob 1971). Uncoked oil from the drums is returned to the column and is mainly

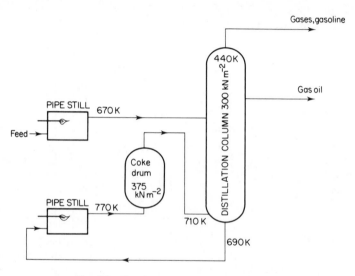

Fig. 23. *Production of petroleum coke.*

gas oil recovered in a side stream. Usually the product coke is removed from one drum, whilst the product is formed in a second unit. Modern processes employ a coke drum usually in the form of a rotating kiln or fluidized bed from which coke is removed continuously (Mekler 1953, Anon 1956).

C. Catalytic Cracking

As explained previously, thermal processes for the production of motor gasoline have now been largely superseded by catalytic processes which have many important advantages. The gasoline produced has a higher concentration of aromatic compounds (benzene for example) and it can therefore be used for blending with high-grade gasolines to give a product with a high octane number (see Chapter 6). In general, gasoline produced by catalytic cracking has an octane number 10–15 higher than the thermally cracked product and yields vary between 40% and 65%. The percentage of unsaturated components (i.e., containing a double bond in the molecular structure) such as diolefins in the product is much less and hence the gasoline is more stable and requires less after-treatment. Although the amount of methane and other gases produced is greatly reduced compared with thermal processes, a greater olefin production is attained in the range C_3+ for which there is a high demand, especially as starting materials in the synthesis of petrochemicals. Most catalytic processes can tolerate feeds with high sulphur contents and, although the capital and operating costs are higher, these are more than offset by the advantages accrued by way of product quality. The presence of a catalyst, which is either a clay or a synthetic compound based on silica and alumina, allows cracking to take place under less severe conditions of temperature and pressure and greatly reduces the yield of petroleum coke for which, up to now, there has been a limited demand. In the presence of a catalyst, the cracking takes place with the feed stream usually in the vapour phase and hence it is essential to have good contact between the gas and the solid catalyst. For this reason the catalyst is usually in the form of pellets or even a powder, thus presenting a large surface area to the gas per unit volume of reactor. Catalytic cracking units may be grouped according to the way in which the catalyst is handled and the two main types are fixed bed and fluidized bed units (Hansford 1947).

In the fixed bed type, the bed of catalyst pellets is supported on a grid and the hot feed passes under pressure through the material, as a vapour. The cracking operations take place on the surface of the catalyst and the effluent vapours are passed to a fractionating column for separation into their component fractions. After a time, the cracking performance falls off; firstly, because of the adsorption of oil vapours on the catalyst; and secondly, because of the build up of carbon on the catalyst particles. The reaction chamber is therefore subjected to a blast of steam which strips off the valuable oil products adsorbed on the catalyst. When this stage is completed, a blast of preheated air is passed through the bed. This burns off the carbon and regenerates the catalyst. The cracking of the feed may then be resumed. The process is endothermic so that the bed cools down as cracking proceeds. The temperature level is partly restored by the exothermic regeneration stage, though in the Houdry process (the original catalytic process), a bed temperature of 750 K was maintained by molten salt circulating in pipes passing through the bed. This particular process employs three catalyst beds which are run in sequence, that is while cracking is taking place in one chamber, the second bed is being stripped of adsorbed oil vapours and the catalyst in the third chamber is undergoing regeneration. This type of cyclic operation is uneconomic for two reasons: first, only a small part of the equipment (i.e. the cracking section) is actually productive at any one time and secondly, the control of such a unit is highly complicated. To overcome these difficulties the modern fluidized bed "cat-cracker" has been developed. This is shown in Fig. 24.

When gas is passed upward through a bed of fine particles, the bed expands with increased gas velocity until a stage is reached at which the particles are just suspended in the gas stream. The bed is then said to be fluidized. Under these conditions, the bed has an effective density between

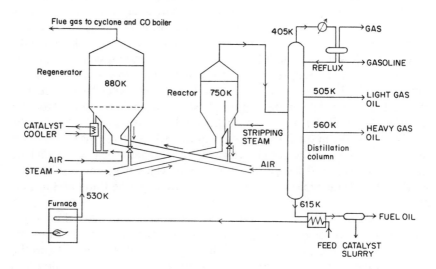

Fig. 24. *Catalytic cracking unit.*

that of the gas and the solid particles and it behaves as a liquid. It can be pumped along pipes from one reaction vessel to another. An important feature of fluidized beds in relation to cracking processes is that a high degree of mixing within the bed is achieved and hence good contact is promoted between the solid and gas phases. In addition, the turbulence within the bed promotes high rates of heat transfer with uniform temperatures, and the control of the latter parameter in the bed is thus simplified. In the cat-cracker, the catalyst is extremely fine (50 μm compared with 5 mm in a fixed bed process) and is supported by the feedstock vapours. The feed, which is usually a waxy fraction boiling in the range 360–450 K, or a heavy distillate, is preheated by the bottom product of the fractionating column and passed to a pipe furnace where vaporization takes place. It is then carried by a steam blast into the reaction vessel with hot catalyst from the regenerator. In this way some reactions take place before the material enters the reactor, allowing fractions with high boiling points to be processed, a feature not available in fixed bed processes. After cracking is completed, usually at 720–810 K, the various fractions are then separated in a conventional distillation column to yield gases, gasoline, gas oils and residual oils. The latter may be treated in a second stage cracker. Catalyst carried over into the column is removed as a slurry and some prior removal of catalyst may also be effected in a cyclone. As in the fixed bed process, the catalyst in the reactor becomes coated with oil and carbon and the former is stripped off by a steam bleed to the reactor. The spent carbon-coated catalyst is then allowed to spill over a weir and blown with a preheated air blast into the regenerator where the carbon is burnt off. This is a highly exothermic operation and the temperature is maintained at 810–880 K by a cooler. Some of the heat released in the regenerator is recovered by a waste heat boiler and the rest is used to preheat the catalyst before it mixes with incoming feed material and returns to the reactor. Flue gas leaving the regenerator is rich in carbon monoxide and, after removal of catalyst in a cyclone, this is burnt in a boiler to generate steam for the process. This is a good example of energy conservation within a system, without which the process would be uneconomic.

Catalytic cracking units are built on a large scale such that the top of the regenerator may be 120 m above ground level and the vessel may be as large as 10 m in diameter. Throughputs of 5000 Mg day^{-1} are not uncommon and with a catalyst/feed ratio of 5:1 to 8:1 by mass, the catalyst recirculation rate may be as high as 300–350 kg s^{-1}. Compared with fixed bed processes, the fluidized bed cat-cracker has low labour requirements and, as with fixed beds, the yield and quality of the products depend on the nature of the feedstock and the processing conditions (Nelson 1952a, Pohlenz 1970).

Fluidized cat-cracking was developed in order to reduce carbon formation; at the time the coke was an unwanted by-product. Nowadays the demand for pure carbon is increasing, not only for electrodes and as a filler for tyres, but as a useful material in the construction of chemical plant. In addition, the demand for unsaturated hydrocarbons, in particular ethylene and propylene, which are important starting materials in synthesis of a vast range of materials, has far exceeded the production as by-products from cracking processes designed to produce gasoline. Consequently, cracking processes have now been developed which provide ethylene and propylene as the main products. The investment in catalytic cracking units is very high and the economics of the operation are such that reforming processes are becoming increasingly more attractive by comparison.

III. REFORMING PROCESSES

A. Reforming

As discussed in Section I, not only can the molecular mass of a feed be reduced as in a cracking operation, but the entire structure of compounds may be modified to give new materials. This is known as a reforming process. Typical examples include the conversion of straight chain paraffins to isomers (i.e. with the same molecular mass) which have a branched structure or the production of aromatic compounds, which contain a benzene ring in their structure. Indeed, as far as gasoline obtained from the primary distillation of crude petroleum is concerned, the quality of this fraction can be greatly improved by an increased concentration of aromatics and iso-paraffins. The presence of these types of molecules greatly improves the efficiency of performance of a gasoline in an internal combustion engine. As with cracking, reforming of gasoline can be achieved by purely thermal processes and also in the presence of a catalyst.

B. Thermal Reforming

In thermal reforming, light petroleum fractions, termed naphtha, are heated under pressure such that the straight-chain paraffin components are converted into olefins and aromatics. By this means a gasoline with an octane rating of 70–75 is produced from naphtha or a heavy gasoline with an octane rating of around 40. A flow diagram of the process is shown in Fig. 25.

The feed is heated in tubes to about 800–900 K and a pressure of around 7000 kN m^{-2}, at which the reforming reactions take place. These produce not only aromatic paraffins and iso-paraffins, but some cracking also takes place, thus lowering the molecular weight of the straight-chain paraffins. When the required degree of reaction has been attained, the vapours are removed from the reaction zone and rapidly cooled or quenched by a spray of oil which effectively "freezes" the stream and stops any further reaction taking place. The vapours are then passed to a distillation column where any dissolved gases are stripped from the now high-quality gasoline. This removal of residual gas effectively stabilizes the gasoline, reducing the tendency for "vapour lock" to occur (see Chapter 3).

Improvements in engine design in recent years have resulted in an increased demand for fuels of higher octane ratings than those produced in thermal reforming and as a result the process has been largely replaced by catalytic reforming processes, although for many years thermal reforming was the only process for upgrading the octane rating of heavy naphtha.

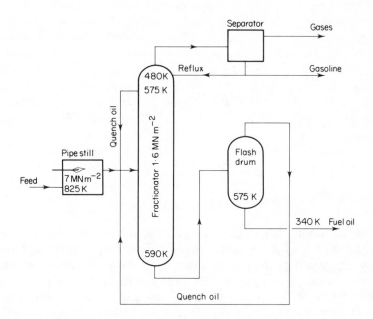

Fig. 25. *Thermal reforming.*

C. Catalytic Reforming

1. *Reactions involved*

Modern requirements for gasolines with octane ratings of around 100 have limited the amount of material produced by distillation of crude petroleum which can be blended into such fuels and at the same time the demand cannot be met by thermal cracking and reforming processes. Attention has therefore turned to catalytic reforming processes which are used very widely and are being continually improved. The feed is normally a straight run naphtha boiling in the range 350–475 K, though appreciable amounts of cracked naphtha may also be processed, providing excessive sulphur is removed.

Because of the high pressures and temperatures involved, some cracking does take place, though there are two types of reaction which predominate: dehydrogenation and isomerization. An example of the former is the conversion of cyclohexane to benzene:

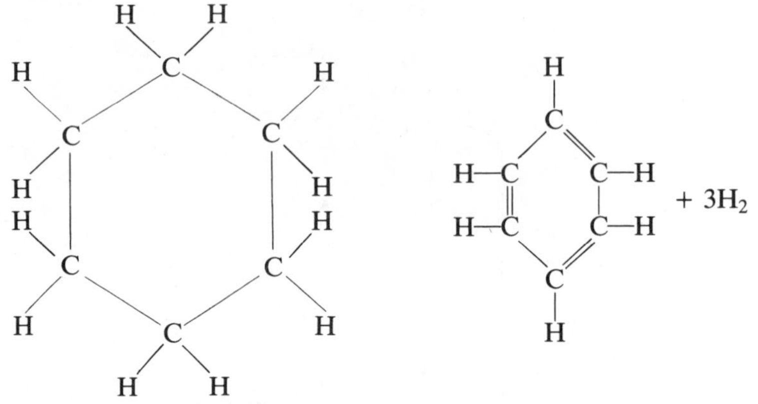

The evolution of hydrogen is significant in that the whole process is carried out in a hydrogen atmosphere. This serves a threefold purpose. Firstly, hydrogen promotes the cracking of large molecules to smaller species; secondly, it conveniently hydrogenates any unsaturated compounds during the cracking operation; and thirdly, the hydrogen can be used for removing sulphur from the feed as H_2S—this is important where poisoning of the catalyst must be avoided at all costs (see Section V). For example:

$$C_4H_9SH + H_2 = C_4H_{10} + H_2S$$

butyl   butane

mercaptan

The final product then requires no further processing other than stabilization.

The other important type of reaction which takes place is that of isomerization, which is a change of structure without a change in molecular weight. For example, the straight-chain paraffin hexane,

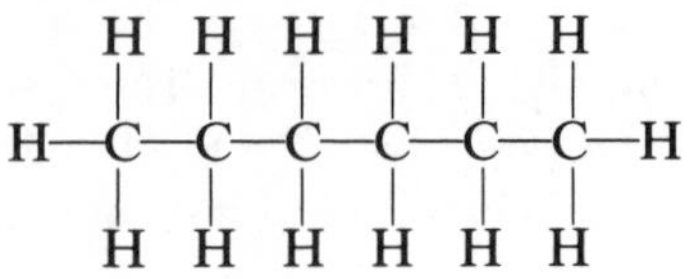

might be converted to its isomer isohexane or 2-methylpentane:

```
                    H
                    |
              H—C—H
              H  |   H  H  H
              |  |   |  |  |
          H—C—C—C—C—C—H
              |  |   |  |  |
              H  H  H  H  H
```

Incidentally, isohexane can be converted by a process of dehydro-cyclization to methyl cyclopentane, a naphthene:

```
          H         H  H
          |         |  |
      H—C———————C—C—H
          |            |
          |            H
          |            |
      H—C         C—H
         /  \      /  \
        H    C    H
            / \
           H   H
```

which can undergo isomerization to cyclohexane. As already shown, this compound can be reformed into benzene by a process of dehydrogenation.

By the various stages of isomerization, dehydrocyclization, isomerization and dehydrogenation, a straight-chain paraffin is reformed into an aromatic hydrocarbon compound, which, as discussed previously, has an important bearing on the quality and performance of gasoline. In addition, reforming processes provide in this way a valuable source of the aromatic materials which are increasingly required by the chemical industry, primarily for synthesis reactions.

There are essentially two types of process, depending on whether or not the catalyst is regenerated. With non-regenerative operation the catalyst is usually platinum supported on an inorganic carrier in fixed beds.

2. Platforming

Platinum-catalysed reforming or "platforming" is a good example of fixed bed operation in which the catalyst is not regenerated although the platinum content is, of course, recovered from the spent material (Haensel 1950, 1953). A flow diagram is shown in Fig. 26.

The feed, usually a fraction from primary distillation, is first heated and passed to a fractionating column, in which components with low boiling points (less than 400 K) are removed with any dissolved oxygen and water. Material boiling at temperatures in excess of 470 K is removed as residue and the remaining fraction is drawn off as feed for the reforming process. As explained, hydrogen is evolved during the reforming reactions and this is now recycled and mixed with the feed. The mixture is then heated to about 750 K in a furnace and compressed to 4 MN m^{-2} before passing to the reaction section. This consists of three vessels each containing a fixed bed of the catalyst, which is platinum on an alumina base in the form of pellets. As in cracking operations, the reforming reactions are

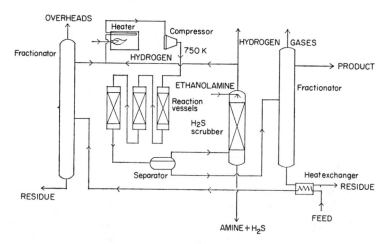

Fig. 26. *Simplified flowsheet of the platforming process.*

endothermic and the vapours are reheated to the reaction temperature between each reactor. On leaving the reaction stage, the stream is separated into liquid and gas phases; the latter is mainly hydrogen and also contains hydrogen sulphide formed from the sulphur compounds in the feed. This is removed from the hydrogen by washing the gases in a scrubber with diethanolamine which absorbs the hydrogen sulphide. The purified hydrogen is in part returned to be mixed with incoming feed and the surplus is used in other operations. The amine is regenerated by boiling, and recycled; the hydrogen sulphide liberated is usually converted to sulphur and sulphuric acid to be used in other reactions and purification processes. The condensate from the separation stage is passed to a fractionating column in which the product is stabilized, i.e. dissolved gases are stripped off and high-boiling components are removed as a residue. A portion of these may be recycled through the process. The catalyst in the platforming process is not automatically regenerated and, after a time, its activity decreases and the material is replaced. This is usually carried out on one reactor at a time so that the rest of the plant can remain in operation.

3. *Regenerative operation*

Where the catalyst is regenerated within the plant, molybdenum, cobalt–molybdate or chromium-based catalysts are used in a process not dissimilar in principle to fluidized bed catalytic cracking (Jaggard 1956). A diagram of such a process is shown in Fig. 27.

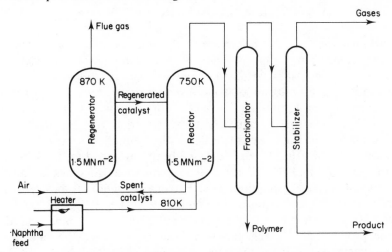

Fig. 27. *Catalytic reforming with regeneration of catalyst.*

In modern plants, the majority of catalytic reformers are of the fixed bed, semi-regenerative type in which feed is processed over the catalyst after which period the catalyst must be regenerated by means of a controlled burn. The feed is usually straight run naphtha from the crude distillation column which has been desulphurized in a separate unit by passing over a different catalyst in the presence of hydrogen. The older type platinum on alumina catalysts are gradually giving way to bimetallic catalysts comprising platinum and rhenium on alumina which allow for much longer operating periods (Dawson 1981). The feed is mixed with recycle hydrogen, heated by interchange with the product and then raised to the reaction temperature, typically 775 K at 3·4 MN m^{-2}, in a preheater. The vaporized mixture is passed over the first catalyst bed where dehydrogenation of most of the naphthenes takes place. This reaction is highly endothermic and the reactants are reheated in a furnace before being introduced into a second reactor where hydrogenation of the remaining naphthenes and some isomerization takes place. A third reactor is used to complete the isomerization and the hydrocracking. The final product is cooled and flashed to recover hydrogen which is compressed and recycled, thus providing a protective atmosphere which minimizes coke deposition on the catalyst. The separated liquid is fractionated to recover high-octane material which goes on to gasoline blending or aromatics production.

IV. OTHER CONVERSION PROCESSES

In cracking processes, the prime aim is the reduction in molecular mass of heavy components. One difficulty is that, although a high yield of gasoline components is obtained, some of the reactions in a sense "overshoot" the desired endpoint and products break down to form gases, particularly the unsaturated olefins such as ethylene and propylene. Whilst there is a considerable demand for these materials (indeed, they have become the indispensable raw materials of the synthetic petroleum chemicals industry), specialized processes have been developed for the production of ethylene, and the unsaturated gases produced in cracking are to some extent surplus to requirements. Fortunately there are processes of reforming which, although more complicated than those outlined in Section III, provide a means of producing a "synthetic"gasoline from the gaseous products of cracking. In a way these processes may be thought of as the reverse of cracking in that molecules are built up rather than broken down and in addition products can be "tailor-made" for a particular requirement. For example, branched-chain paraffins can be produced which have an important bearing on the performance and octane rating of a particular fuel. The additional reforming operations are classified according to the principal chemical reaction involved and the most important are isomerization, polymerization and alkylation.

A. Isomerization

Isomerization, the conversion of a straight-chain hydrocarbon to a branched-chain molecule or isomer having the same molecular weight, has already been mentioned as one of the reactions occurring in catalytic reforming processes. As explained in Chapter 6, the more desirable type of molecule for a high-grade gasoline is compact and has a branched-chain structure. Therefore, any process which converts straight-chain paraffins to isomers is most important in the production of a high-grade gasoline.

Typical of an isomerization reaction is the conversion of normal butane into isobutane:

$$
\begin{array}{cccc}
H & H & H & H \\
| & | & | & | \\
H-C-C-C-C-H \\
| & | & | & | \\
H & H & H & H
\end{array}
\quad \longrightarrow \quad
\begin{array}{c}
H \\
| \\
H-C-H \\
\\
H \qquad H \\
| \qquad | \\
H-C-C-C-H \\
| \quad | \quad | \\
H \quad H \quad H
\end{array}
$$

In the production of high octane number iso-paraffins for gasolines, the feedstock would be pentane or hexane obtained from crude oil, natural gas or hydrogenation processes, or the pentene and hexene fractions from cracking and reforming processes. If, however, unsaturated hydrocarbons are present in the feed, then the isomerization is carried out in the presence of hydrogen in order to avoid the formation of high-boiling polymers resulting from complicated side reactions.

For the conversion of normal into isobutane, the catalyst is usually aluminium chloride on an alumina chloride base, activated with hydrochloric acid. For heavier feeds such as pentane and hexane, a platinum catalyst in the presence of hydrogen is used and the operating conditions are more severe, up to 750 K and 7 MN m^{-2}. The yield of the isomerized product is usually greater than 90% of the feed (Guiness 1951).

B. Polymerization

Polymerization reactions, in which many thousands of identical molecules link together to form a long-chain polymer, are commonplace throughout the plastics industry. Well known examples include the polymerization of styrene to form polystyrene or the production of polyvinyl chloride (PVC) from vinyl chloride. Polymerization can be carried out under controlled conditions to give a desired product, say a molecule twice the size of the molecules in the feed. In this way, polymerization may be thought of as reversed cracking in which products which are obtained by "over disintegration" can be rebuilt to attain the desirable components required in a high-grade gasoline. Of particular interest are the gases leaving the cracking processes. These are rich in unsaturated olefins which can be polymerized to form liquid hydrocarbons of higher molecular weight. These new products are also unsaturated but may be converted to the equivalent saturated iso-paraffin by a hydrogenation stage, which is promoted by a catalyst. A typical reaction is:

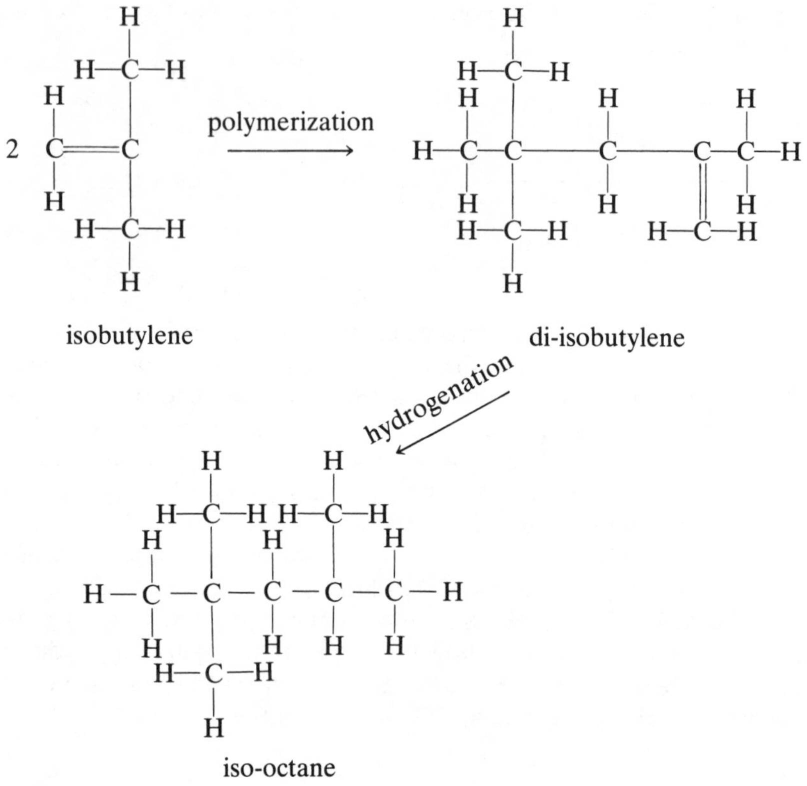

isobutylene

di-isobutylene

iso-octane

The reactions are promoted by phosphorus, either as phosphoric acid on quartz particles (Langlois 1952) or as a pelleted calcined mixture of phosphoric acid with kieselguhr (Weinert 1948, Nash 1938). The process conditions depend on the desired product and 450–500 K and 3–8 MN m^{-2} are typical with a yield of 95–98% (Shanley 1939).

C. Alkylation

A further way in which desired molecules can be synthesized is the addition of an alkyl group (CH_3, C_2H_5, for example) to a straight-chain hydro-carbon, a branched-chain or an aromatic molecule—a process known as alkylation (Thornton 1970). Again, this process provides a means of tailoring molecules to form a particular end product. One important example of this process is the coupling of an unsaturated hydrocarbon such as butylene with isobutane to form octane, in particular the branched-chain isomer, trimethylpentane.

$$C_4H_8 + C_4H_{10} \rightarrow C_8H_{18}$$

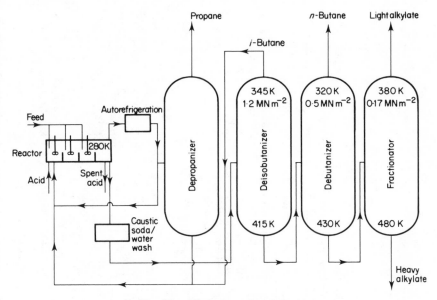

Fig. 28. *Alkylation of isobutane.*

It is important to note that the product is saturated, thus alleviating the need for hydrogenation stages. The feed mixture of isobutane and butylene contains an excess of isobutane (from 4:1 to 15:1 ratio) to suppress any polymerization and the reaction takes place in the presence of 98% sulphuric acid at 280 K. The catalyst may be dispensed with if the reaction is carried out at higher temperatures and pressures (800 K and 27 MN m^{-2}) (Mackenzie 1939). The reaction is highly exothermic and its temperature is controlled by autorefrigeration (cooling resulting from evaporation of the isobutane/butylene from the reactor) as shown in Fig. 28. In the reactor, the isobutane/butylene mixture, which is pre-cooled in contact with the acid catalyst and the alkylate product is then cooled and passed to a caustic soda/water wash to remove any excess acid. Isobutane, which is recycled to the reactor, is then removed in a column after which the product is passed to a second column in which *n*-butane is removed as overheads. Finally, the alkylate is separated into light and heavy fractions used for blending into aviation and motor gasolines respectively. Gases removed from the auto-refrigeration unit are separated into propane and the isobutane/butylene mixture in a column; the latter being returned to the reactor (Oden 1950).

The processes discussed in this section in no way represent the limits of the ingenuity of the organic chemist, and many more reactions are carried out in order to produce fuels to a particular specification or, perhaps more

TABLE 20. *Important products from crude petroleum*

	Boiling range (K)	Composition	Manufactured by	Principal uses	Notes
Natural gas	–	Mainly methane, some nitrogen depending on source	Natural sources	Fuel gas, also reformed to synthesis gas (Chapter 5)	Calorific value 38 MJ m^{-3}
Liquefied petroleum gas (LPG)	–	Propane, butane	Stripped from "wet" natural gas or from cracking operations (Chapter 3)	Domestic and industrial fuel—production of coal gas, synthetic chemicals	Calorific value 100 MJ m^{-3}
Primary flash distillate (PFD)	varies	Propane and butane dissolved in gasoline–kerosene range of liquids	Preliminary distillation of crude petroleum	Manufacture of synthesis gas	
Gasoline	300–450	Complex mixture of materials. Petrol contains additives to improve performance but no sulphur or polymerizable components	Primary distillation, cracking and reforming processes	Spark ignition internal combustion engines	Octane number—indication of performance (Chapter 6) SG 0·795
Kerosene	410–575	Paraffinic hydro-carbons with substantial pro-portion of aromatics low	Distillation, cracking	Agricultural tractors, lighting, heating and aviation gas turbines	Tractor vaporizing oil (TVO)—aromatics are an advantage—not the case with diesel engines. SG 0·793, calor-

(Gas oil)		Saturated hydro-carbons	hydrodesulphurization	and furnaces. Feed to cracking units	absorbing benzol from coal gas
Diesel fuel	450–650	Saturated hydrocarbons, often with high sulphur	Distillation cracking	Diesel engines, furnace heating	Quality of fuel and boiling point range are a function of the duty. Low-speed engine, high-sulphur, high boiling point. SG 0·870
Fuel oils	500–700+	–	Residue of primary distillation, blended with distillates	Large-scale industrial heating	Require atomizing—wide range of viscosities SG 0·89–0·95
Lubricating oils	wide range	Three types: mainly aromatic, mainly aliphatic or mixed	Vacuum distillation of primary distillation residue solvent extraction	Lubrication	Wide variation in quality from say grease in marine applications to sewing machine oil. Control of viscosity important (Chapter 6)
Wax	–	Paraffins	Chilling residue from vacuum distillation	Toilet preparations, food, candles, petroleum jelly	
Bitumen	–	Wide variation	Residue from vacuum distillation or oxidation of residue from primary distillation ("blown" bitumen)	Road surfacing, water-proofing	Wide variation in softening point. NB. "asphalt" in UK is bitumen + mineral filler

importantly, starting materials for the complex synthetic chemicals industry based on crude petroleum. The reactions discussed are, however, of
great significance and perhaps indicate to some extent the importance of
crude petroleum as a basic source of chemicals—a role previously occupied
by coal.

V. PRODUCT TREATMENT PROCESSES

It has been shown that a vast range of products can be produced from
crude petroleum both by physical separation alone and by processes
involving chemical reactions. Very few of these products, however, are
immediately useful and most of them are subjected to some form of final
processing treatment. This may involve either the removal of unwanted
components in further refining operations, such as aromatics from an
aliphatic stream, or the removal of contaminants such as sulphur, both
operations being carried out with a view to producing a product to a closely
defined specification. For example, factors other than technical performance or combustion characteristics are important in the utilization of a
particular fuel or lubricant. Such factors include smell, colour, stability on
storage and, a very important parameter, sulphur content. The effect of
sulphur in fuels, especially in connection with air pollution and corrosion of
plant has already been discussed in Chapter 2.

In product treatment, whether the removal of unwanted components
which exist in significant proportions is involved, or merely traces of
undesirable contaminants, both physical and chemical methods are used.
A good example of the former is that of liquid (or solvent) extraction
outlined in Chapter 3, of which a specific application is the Edeleanu
process (Cottrell 1933) for removing aromatics from aliphatic hydrocarbons using liquid sulphur dioxide as the solvent. Similar processes are used
in the final refining of kerosenes and lubricating oils. For example, sulphur
is removed from kerosene by washing with sulphuric acid, followed by
sodium hydroxide to neutralize the excess acid. This is known as "sweetening", a treatment which also improves the colour of a product. Indeed,
sulphur removal is one of the main forms of product treatment and various
chemical processes have been evolved which depend on the molecular
weight of the product and the amount and form of sulphur present.
Sulphur exists as either hydrogen sulphide, present in the original crude or
formed during early processing stages, or as mercaptans, which are
thioalcohols of the type C_2H_5SH or C_4H_9SH. The compounds exist in a
wide range of molecular masses and are characterized by a very strong,
repugnant smell.

A. Removal of Hydrogen Sulphide

When the product stream contains low concentrations of hydrogen sulphide, these can be removed with an alkali wash, which is usually discarded when saturated. This limits the concentration of hydrogen sulphide which can be handled and hence, where large amounts of H_2S are to be removed, a process in which the absorbent is regenerated must be adopted. Such an operation is used in the Girbotol process, where H_2S is absorbed from either a vapour or liquid stream in diethanolamine at 310 K, the solvent being stripped of the H_2S by heating to 365 K before re-use. The H_2S recovered is highly concentrated and can be converted to sulphur for use in petrochemicals syntheses or converted to sulphuric acid for use in sweetening operations (Espach 1950, Miller 1953).

B. Removal of Mercaptans

Evil-smelling mercaptans or thiols of low molecular mass can be removed by aqueous alkaline washes, though this treatment leaves the high molecular mass mercaptans largely unaffected. Although acid washing is used in these cases, especially with paraffinic products, modern processes for removal of mercaptans employ a solutizer which is added to the alkaline wash. This catalyses the absorption process. Such additives include phenols, methanol and salts of fatty acids and the absorbant is usually regenerated by blowing air through it (MacKusick 1944, Duval 1954).

C. Hydro-desulphurization

Products which have a high boiling point cannot be treated satisfactorily by the methods outlined above and hydro-desulphurizing processes have been developed which use hydrogen from catalytic reforming plants. Such processes can handle distillates which boil at temperatures up to 620 K (McKinney 1971).

In a typical process, the material is heated with hydrogen under pressure and passed through a fixed-bed catalyst, usually cobalt and molybdenum oxides on an alumina base. The reaction conditions depend on the nature of the feed and the hydrogen sulphide and excess hydrogen are separated from the purified product by scrubbing (Abbott 1955, Morbeck 1955).

These processes for the removal of sulphur are fairly typical of product treatment operations, and illustrate the complexity of the processes involved in producing a finished product using crude petroleum as the starting material.

A brief summary of the manufacture and uses of the important products discussed in this chapter is included as Table 20.

VI. FURTHER READING

American Petroleum Institute (1952). "Petroleum Facts and Figures". 10th Edn. A.P.I., New York.

Brooks, B. T. and Dunstan, A. E. (1955). "Science and Petroleum". Vol. 5, Part 3, Refinery Products. Oxford University Press, London.

Coulson, J. M., Richardson, J. F., Backhurst, J. R. and Harker, J. H. (1979). "Chemical Engineering", Vol. 2, 3rd Edn. Pergamon Press, Oxford.

Dumas, T. and Bulani, W. (1975). "Oxidation of Petrochemicals". Applied Science Publishers, New York.

Evans, E. B. (1959). "Modern Petroleum Technology". The Institute of Petroleum, London.

Goldstein, R. F. (1958). "The Petroleum Chemicals Industry". Pitman, Bath.

Gould, R. F. (ed.) (1964). "Advances in Chemistry", No. 51. American Chemical Society.

Kobe, K. A. and McKette, J. J. (1961). "Advances in Petroleum Chemistry and Refining". Vol. IV. Wiley, Interscience, New York.

Nelson, W. L. (1970). "Petroleum Refinery Engineering". 4th Edn. McGraw-Hill, New York.

Van der Have, J. H. and Verver, C. G. (1967). "Petroleum and its Products". Pitman, London.

Waddhams, A. L. (1962). "Chemicals from Petroleum". John Murray, London.

Williams, D. A. and Jones, G. (1963). "Liquid Fuels". Pergamon Press, London.

Secondary Fuels: Carbonization and Gasification Processes

5

I. INTRODUCTION

Gaseous fuels have many advantages compared with solid and liquid fuels especially in relation to ease of transmission and utilization, coupled with efficient combustion. As a result, complex networks of gas lines have been developed in many parts of the world serving both domestic and commercial consumers. A wide range of gas types and compositions are used and this chapter is concerned with the various processes for making gaseous fuels from primary fuels.

The traditional method for the manufacture of coal gas involves a process of destructive distillation of coal, a process known as carbonization. Carbonization plants have been operated for almost a century and apart from increasing the thermal efficiency by improved insulation and making better use of heat recovery, the process has remained virtually unchanged. A major step forward in gas-making has been the development of processes for the gasification of hydrocarbon fuels derived from crude petroleum, particularly naphtha and natural gas. Such processes have many advantages compared with carbonization operations and in the UK, the entire gas-making industry was converted to an oil-gasification basis. In turn this has been superseded by the advent of natural gas, although oil-gasification and natural gas reforming are still very important in the production of synthesis gases for the manufacture of petrochemicals. It may be that as the abundance of natural gas diminishes, oil-gasification will regain some of its former significance and almost certain that carbonization or gasification of coal will eventually take over once again as the prime gas-making process. Indeed, several research and development program-

91

mes are being undertaken into new processes for coal gasification at the present time. A general survey of gasification processes has been presented by Littlewood (1977) and Robson (1977).

The production of gas from oil is cheaper than gas from coal, mainly because the amount of gas purification required is greatly reduced. For example, after cooling and detarring, gas from coal contains up to 1·75% hydrogen sulphide and 0·5–1·5% hydrogen cyanide and ammonia. The corresponding concentration in gas produced from petroleum feedstocks is 0–0·5% with negligible amounts of nitrogen compounds, and hence few after-treatment operations are necessary. It must be noted that the Rochdale process, in which the product gas is recycled through the coal charge, and the steaming of the charge in vertical retorts have been attempts to improve the carbonization process, but these steps are quite insignificant compared with the advantages of oil-gasification. These include reduced space for plant of equivalent output, cleanness and ease of operation, reduced manpower and virtually fully automatic control. Nevertheless, in parts of the world where there are abundant supplies of coal, carbonization will continue to be a source of gas for many years, and it is worth considering the salient features of the process at this stage.

II. CARBONIZATION OF COAL

A. Gas Making

In carbonization, coal is heated to a temperature of 1200–1300 K, at which almost all the volatile matter is driven off, leaving a residue of coke. The coal is charged into refractory retorts, which are heated by producer gas in a surrounding flue to about 1600 K. The mass of coal in a retort varies between 500 and 30 000 kg and this is usually arranged in a bed some 0·3 m thick. Carbonization takes about twelve hours.

In the older types of gas-making plant, horizontal retorts lined with a silica refractory are used; typical dimensions are shown in Fig. 29. The retorts are arranged in two vertical rows of four or five on either side of a combustion chamber in which preheated producer gas is burnt. The waste

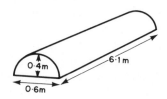

Fig. 29. *Typical dimensions of a horizontal retort.*

gas passes first to a recuperator and then to a waste heat boiler. In this type of plant, a retort is recharged every 10–12 hours with about 700 kg coal, taking care that the retort is incompletely filled to allow space for expansion during coke formation. This plant is capable of handling a wide range of coals and the by-product coke is suitable for domestic purposes, though it has the disadvantages of requiring a large labour force and occupying a considerable amount of ground space.

More modern plant utilizes continuously fed vertical retorts which are again lined with a silica refractory and are usually 7·5 m long and 1·2–2·5 m by 0·25 m in cross section. The capacity of a retort varies between 1500 and 4500 kg coal which is fed continuously by gravity. The coke is removed from the bottom of the retort and heat is recovered by using either an air or a steam blast. This type of plant has a higher thermal efficiency than horizontal retorts and the problem of atmospheric pollution is less severe. The labour and ground space requirements are also less, and the coke produced is very porous and soft and thus suitable for the domestic market. Unfortunately, the range of coal types which can be handled is limited and only small quantities of tar, a valuable by-product, are produced. In addition, a large quantity of breeze is formed and maintenance costs are high.

On carbonization, 100 heat units of coal normally yield 25 heat units of gas and 59 heat units of coke and tar; the difference represents the heat used for carbonization. A typical coal gas analysis is as follows:

$$CO_2 \ 2 \cdot 0\%, \qquad H_2 \ 51 \cdot 8\%,$$
$$O_2 \ 0 \cdot 5\%, \qquad CH_4 \ 27 \cdot 0\%,$$
$$C_nH_m \ 3 \cdot 5\%, \qquad C_2H_6 \ 1 \cdot 2\%,$$
$$CO \ 7 \cdot 5\%, \qquad N_2 \ 6 \cdot 5\%$$

Relative density (air = 1·0), 0·422, Calorific value = 20·9 MJ m^{-3}

The gas leaving the retorts in a gas-making plant contains many impurities, some of which are valuable by-products. Sale of these renders the process a viable proposition, and the gas therefore undergoes extensive purification operations. The principle stages are shown schematically in Fig. 30(a). From the retort, the gas is first transferred to a long horizontal hydraulic main, which acts as a water seal and prevents gas passing back when a retort is opened. In this main some of the ammonia liquor and tar is recovered and the crude gas, usually at 330–350 K, then contains 0·7–1·5% ammonia, 0·8–1·75% hydrogen sulphide, up to 0·2% hydrogen cyanide and 0·03% carbon disulphide, which have to be removed in further stages. The condenser, which is either a series of vertical pipes over which water is sprayed or, more simply, air, removes ammonia liquor and tar which are collected in the tar well. The gas is then passed through exhauster fans, which maintain a slight vacuum back to the retorts and force the gas through the rest of the plant to the gas holder. At this stage, the gas passes through a tar separator, which is often a simple baffled-tank in which the tar droplets are removed by impingement on a metal surface. Hence the so-called "tar fog" is removed. The rest of the ammonia is removed in a

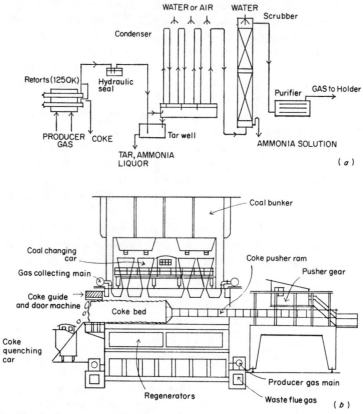

Fig. 30. *Carbonization of coal. (a) Coal gas manufacture. (b) Coke Oven layout.*

conventional scrubber (or absorbing tower) with a water wash or sometimes dilute sulphuric acid. The packing in the tower is ideally wooden slats, though coke is most usually employed. At this stage the gas still contains carbon dioxide, hydrogen sulphide and carbon disulphide, and it now passes over trays of hydrated ferric oxide (or "bog iron ore") in a purifier. The oxide is converted to ferric sulphide by a reaction of the type:

$$2Fe(OH)_3 + 3H_2S \rightarrow Fe_2S_3 + 6H_2O$$

When the activity of the oxide falls below a certain limit, the material is regenerated by exposure to air, during which sulphur is formed:

$$2Fe_2S_3 + 3O_2 + 6H_2O \rightarrow 4Fe(OH)_3 + 6S$$

Sulphur is a valuable by-product, which in bigger plants is converted to sulphuric acid. At one time, this was reacted with the ammonia to form ammonium sulphate—an important fertilizer material. Carbon disulphide may be left in the gas or removed by passing over a nickel catalyst at 700 K:

$$CS + 2H_2 \rightarrow 2H_2S + C$$

Hydrogen sulphide is then removed in a second purifier. Cyanides are removed by passing the crude gas through either a wash of ferrous sulphate in alkali or through ammonia liquor containing a suspension of ammonium sulphide and sulphur. The products are ferrocyanide and ammonium thiocyanate respectively.

After these purification stages, the gas may be mixed with water gas in order to reduce the methane content and increase the amount of carbon monoxide present. In many works, the purified gas is dehydrated by scrubbing with concentrated calcium chloride solution before storage, and the water in the holder is covered with an oil film to prevent subsequent rewetting.

In addition to the coke which is screened, graded and sold for domestic use, a hard black deposit of gas carbon forms on the walls of the retorts. The is a fairly pure form of carbon and is chipped off and used for arc electrodes and batteries. A general evaluation of coal carbonization processes has been presented by Holmes (1977).

B. Coke-making

Although coke is a by-product in gas making, the steel and metallurgical industries require a much higher grade of coke; one which is reactive and capable of withstanding very high pressures, as encountered in a blast furnace for example, without being crushed. Such a material is produced in coke ovens and in this case, gas is a by-product. A typical plant consists of 80–100 ovens each 12·5 m long, 3·5 m high and 0·5 m wide, arranged in banks enabling the coal to be fed by gravity from a coal charging car, which traverses along the top of the oven battery. Each oven contains about 15 000 kg coal and the carbonization period is 15 hours. A simplified diagram of the layout of an oven is shown in Fig. 30(b). On completion of the carbonization period, the oven doors are removed and a ram pushes the incandescent coke into an electrically driven coke car by which it is transported to a quenching tower. During operation, heat is recovered in regenerators situated below the ovens, where it is transferred to either air or producer gas, reversal taking place every 30 min. In general, a coke oven battery has a high thermal efficiency and involves relatively low capital, maintenance costs and manpower requirements. The plant is inflexible, however, as far as the range of coals which can be processed is concerned and the coke formed is not suitable for the domestic market. In many plants coals are blended to maintain constancy of feedstock quality, an important factor in controlling the degree of coke swelling in the oven during the carbonization stage. Where the ovens are part of a steel-making plant, for example, after the removal of valuable by-products the coal gas produced is used as a fuel in other units. It is occasionally sold either to a private consumer or to the national network, though the modern trend is simply to vent the untreated gas to a flare-stack. Coke ovens are usually designed to be fired with coal gas or producer gas although instances have been reported of the use of light hydrocarbon distillates for under-firing (Didier-Werke A.G. 1961). Modern trends in coke manufacture are discussed by Bruce (1977).

C. Low-temperature Carbonization

As outlined in Chapter 2, coking coals undergo some decomposition on heating to 500 K, but the coal retains its original shape (Ellis 1953). If the carbonization temperature is raised to 550–850 K, the coal becomes plastic and the tar and most of the volatile matter are driven off leaving a material known as "semi-coke". When the temperature is raised further to 850–1250 K, the remaining hydrogen is evolved and the material left is the normal coke substance. When carbonization at these temperatures is curtailed, a type of semi-coke is formed for which there is a high demand as a "smokeless fuel". On combustion, the amount of smoke formed is greatly reduced as this has already been evolved as volatile matter in the carbonization process. The material still contains hydrogen, however, and is therefore much more easily ignited than conventional coke. Smokeless fuel is made in narrow metal retorts and the gas liberated is used for heating purposes. Special coals or mixtures of coal and low-temperature coke-breeze are used.

D. The Use of Petroleum Products in Carbonization

For many years the addition of 0·5% of oils including fuel oils to dusty coals has reduced coal handling problems. More recently, the addition of up to 5·0% fuel oil to coking coals has resulted in a 10% increase in gas output from a carbonization plant with horizontal retorts. Similar results have been obtained by the addition of 3% heavy oil to coal charged in vertical retorts and improvements in gas and benzene and to yields and coke quality have been reported as a result of adding hydrocarbon materials to coke-oven charges (Coal and Coke Industry USSR 1961).

Increases in the thermal output of a carbonizing plant of up to 30% have been obtained by reforming light distillate–steam mixtures by passage through partly carbonized coal charges in intermittent and continuous vertical retorts (Oliver and Olden 1964). Similar results have been achieved using liquefied petroleum gases (Steenstrup 1958).

III. GASIFICATION OF SOLID FUELS

A. Processes Involving Air or Oxygen

Gasification of the combustible matter in solid fuels has been a traditional method of producing low-grade fuel gases for industrial use for over a century. Processes have been extended over the years and developments include complete gasification units and what may be described as unconventional gasification processes. As in the carbonization of coal, the use of solid feedstocks has now been largely superseded by gasification or reforming of liquid fuels. It is the aim of this section to outline the important features of the various methods of producing gas by gasification of primary solid fuels. For any one general process, there are many types of plant essentially performing similar duties and it is only possible to consider here the more important types of unit presently in use.

1. *Producer gas and water gas*

Two basic reactions are involved in the complete gasification of the combustible matter in solid fuels. The first is the producer gas reaction:

$$C + O_2 \rightarrow CO_2; \qquad CO_2 + C \rightleftharpoons 2CO$$

which is highly exothermic and permits the process to be operated continuously. The water gas reaction:

$$C + H_2O \rightleftharpoons CO + H_2$$

is endothermic and it is usual to combine this with the producer gas reaction, in order to maintain the bed temperature. In the manufacture of producer gas, air is passed through a bed of incandescent coke. In water gas production, steam is used instead of air. A plant in which the producer gas reaction is operated continuously is known as a producer gas plant and where only the water gas reaction is carried out, the plant is known as a "blue water gas plant". As mentioned previously, it is usual to carry out both reactions alternately. Air and then steam may be introduced at both the bottom and top of the fuel bed in order to provide a relatively uniform temperature distribution. Most units are operated at atmospheric pressure, though several new plants work at higher pressures and oxygen is used instead of air, resulting in an increased plant output.

The gas formed from producer and water gas plants, mainly carbon monoxide and hydrogen, has a lower calorific value than that of coal gas and this is used as both industrial fuel and a synthesis gas in chemical processing. Typical analyses are given in Table 21.

TABLE 21. *Properties of gas produced by gasification of solid fuels*

		Producer gas		Blue water gas	Total gasification[†]
Process:					
Fuel:		Coke	Coal	Coke	Coal
Analysis:					
CO_2		5·7	3·4	5·0	8·0
O_2		–	0·2	–	0·2
C_nH_m		–	–	–	0·6
CH_4		0·4	2·6	0·5	6·5
H_2		10·6	16·1	50·0	52·2
N_2		56·0	47·7	3·5	4·0
CO		27·3	30·0	41·0	28·5
Calorific value $(kJ\ m^{-3})$		4658	6446	10 992	12 482
Relative density $(air = 1·0)$		0·90	0·83	0·54	0·52
Wobbé index		4914	7079	14 941	17 326

† A producer or water gas plant preceded or accompanied by carbonization of the fuel used.

In the manufacture of producer gas, the fuel, which is usually coke or breeze, is contained in vessels often arranged as an annular boiler. A continuous air blast passes through the bed and in order to control the bed temperature by the water gas reaction, the air is saturated with steam at 320 K. This feature enables the rate of ash diffusion to be controlled during operation. Coal is rarely used as a fuel because of the difficulty in dealing with tar and soot. In the case of strongly coking coals, agglomeration presents further problems. Producer gas plants have been used widely in industry, mainly because of their high thermal efficiency and low capital cost (Katell 1973).

In the manufacture of blue water gas, the bed is blown first with steam and then with air to restore the temperature of the fuel bed. During this stage, the producer gas is usually burnt in a waste heat boiler. The blue water gas makes an ideal synthesis gas for the production of ammonia, although this process has now been largely replaced by units which use hydrocarbon oils as a feedstock, because of the high cost of coke and the low efficiency of the water gas process.

2. Complete gasification processes

Gasification of solid fuels may be preceded by carbonization in the same plant, producing a mixture of coal gas and water gas, which has a lower calorific value, a higher density and a higher concentration of carbon monoxide than coal gas. Carbonization takes place in continuous vertical retorts and the coke produced falls into a water gas generator. Again, this process has now been largely superseded by oil gasification.

3. Unconventional gasification processes

The processes discussed so far may be considered as conventional in that the essential features have remained virtually unchanged until recent times. These features include operation at low pressures, usually with a fixed bed, solid ash removal and the use of air and steam as the gasifying media. More recent plants operate at high pressures and are unconventional in that the bed is often fluidized (Anderman and Haldipur 1978) with ash removal as a slag and gasifying media include oxygen, oxygen-enriched air and hydrogen. The general effect of these modifications is to speed up the reactions involved and hence increase the throughput of a given unit. Such plants have to be built on a large scale to be economic and therefore they are only suitable where the demand for gas is continuously high.

Perhaps the best known of such processes is the Lurgi process, which, though similar to a producer gas plant with solid ash removal, operates at 1000–3000 kN m^{-2} and uses a mixture of superheated steam and oxygen as the gasification medium. The gas produced has a high methane content, formed in reactions such as:

$$C + 2H_2 \rightleftharpoons CH_4$$
$$CO + 3H_2 \rightleftharpoons CH_4 + H_2O$$

The $H_2:CO$ ratio in the final gas is controlled by the steam to oxygen ratio in the blast to the bed. A typical gasification rate is 500–2000 kg fuel per m^2 of grate area per hour and, of the heat capacity in the coal feed, 81% appears in the gas and 8% in tar and other products. It should be noted that the energy required in producing the steam feed must be subtracted from the output and 67% is a reasonable value for the overall efficiency of the process compared with 62% for conventional carbonization. The calorific value of the gas is about 14 900 kJ m^{-3} (the corresponding value for carbonization is 22 350 kJ m^{-3}) and for use as a coal gas this must be upgraded by the addition of natural gas or other hydrocarbons such as propane. One advantage of a high-pressure process is that transportation through a large pipe network can be achieved without additional boosting. In recent years, Lurgi plants have been installed in the UK, Australia and South Africa, though in common with other solid-fuel gasification processes, the economics of operation are very unattractive compared with the continuous reforming of light distillate feedstocks.

Another modern development is the Winkler process. Here, the coal feed (usually 0·8–1 mm particles) is fluidized by a steam–oxygen blast and ash falls to the bottom of the bed, where it is removed continuously. It is

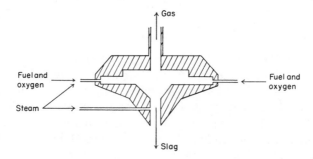

Fig. 31. *Koppers–Totzec gasifier.*

essential that the ash has a high melting point and only highly reactive fuels can be handled. A similar process (Fig. 31) is the Koppers–Totzec in which the pulverized fuel, usually 0·1 mm coal containing 2% moisture, is gasified as a suspension in oxygen at approximately 100 kN m^{-2} in the presence of steam (Anon 1972). The rapid rate of gasification is due to the high temperatures involved and the gas leaves the chamber at 1400–1600 K, enabling a large amount of heat to be recovered. The process steam is preheated by direct firing and 50% ash and 15% fuel are carried over with the gas and have to be removed. The product gas contains low concentrations of hydrocarbons and negligible amounts of tar and it is eminently suitable as a feedstock for chemical processes. This process is more flexible than the Lurgi process in terms of fuel quality, but suffers from the disadvantage of producing low-pressure gas. This also applies to a whole range of fixed-bed producers fed with oxygen and steam and which are quite uneconomic in that high-cost coke, which is in short supply, is the primary feedstock.

In the Rummel Slag-Bath Generator, fuel particles in suspension are gasified by injection with preheated steam and air or oxygen into a turbulent slag bath maintained in the base of a producer shaft. A 1·8 m diameter commercial plant of this design has produced 370 000 m³ per day of gas at 101 kN m⁻³ using brown coal with a thermal yield of some 80%. A similar concept is a double shaft generator used for the manufacture of water gas, where it has been suggested that the molten slag could be used as a heat transfer medium (MacCormac and Wrobel 1965). A similar process, in which the slag is replaced by a molten salt is the Kellogg Molten-Salt process which is designed to avoid the use of oxygen. The bath is operated at 1300 K and 3000 kN m⁻² and the product contains 7–8% methane (Cover 1971).

Brief mention may be made at this stage of underground gasification of coal, which, although still at the experimental stage in the UK, has been used extensively on a large scale in the USSR as an alternative to mining. The gasifying medium is oxygen-enriched air and the low-grade product gas is used in the generation of electricity above ground (Anon. 1972, Lamb 1977, Dorling 1978).

B. Processes Involving Hydrogasification

It seems likely that natural gas supplies to the USA will be soon inadequate (Linden 1969) and the development of plants for the production of methane is being actively pursued. Since coal and lignite are available within economic gas transmission ranges of major US centres of population, processes involving the production of the bulk of methane by reacting hydrogen directly with the coal substance are favoured. Such processes will have to be coupled with a conventional process using oxygen in order to produce the hydrogen for the hydrogenation stage. A process of this type has been developed by the Institute of Gas Technology—it is known as the "Hygas" process (Tsaros *et al.* 1967, Anon 1970). First coal is reduced to 0·07–2·4 mm and fed to a water-cooled fluidized pretreatment bed maintained at around 700 K (Davis 1977). The char produced is then treated in two fluidized beds with steam–hydrogen at 1000 K and 7800 kN m⁻² in which about 50% of the char is gasified. The gases from the hydrogasifier are purified in a hot potash wash and the remaining carbon monoxide is then reacted:

$$CO + 3H_2 \rightleftharpoons CH_4 + H_2O$$

giving after dehydration a product containing 90% methane at 7100 kN m⁻² with a calorific value of 35 MJ m⁻³. The char residue from the gasifier is used to produce hydrogen in a slagging cyclone combuster plus a fluidized bed producer, although a modification is to produce the synthesis gas by electrothermal gasification using electricity generated using an MHD device fuelled by spent gasifier char (Tsaros *et al.* 1968).

A similar process known as the carbon dioxide acceptor process, adsorbs the carbon dioxide on dolomite which is then regenerated by combustion of the char residue in air (Linden 1971, Toles 1973).

Analogous processes have been investigated in Europe and although the close parity of coal and oil prices favours the use of hydrocarbon oils for the manufacture of natural gas replacement at present, hydrogasification of coal will almost certainly provide the long-term solution.

C. Liquid Fuels from Coal

As the world's supplies of hydrocarbon fuels based on crude petroleum diminish, one fairly obvious means of providing a replacement is to produce liquid fuels from coal. Since the heart of the processes is the gasification of coal, it is convenient to present a summary of the processes involved at this stage.

1. *Principles of coal conversion processes*

The conversion of coal into liquid products involves increasing the proportion of hydrogen to carbon and this is achieved by either synthesis or degradation. In the synthesis route, the coal is broken down by gasification into carbon monoxide and hydrogen, which are then reacted to form refined products. Degradation is rather less drastic as it retains some of the original chemical structure, though it is more difficult to achieve on a large scale. In general 1 Mg of coal produces rather less than 0·4 Mg liquid fuels, because of energy losses in processing, and whereas the synthesis route produces paraffinic compounds, degradation products are highly aromatic and suitable for the production of high-octane gasoline.

In the synthesis route, the ratio of carbon monoxide to hydrogen in the raw synthesis gas can be changed by the "shift" reaction:

$$CO + H_2O \rightleftharpoons CO_2 + H_2$$

The equilibrium is determined by the operating conditions and the reaction is promoted by nickel catalysts which are prone to poisoning by sulphur compounds (Cusumo *et al.* 1978, Donath and Hoering 1977). The raw synthesis gas can be converted into a wide range of products including hydrocarbons, petrochemical feedstocks, alcohols and aldehydes by a Fischer–Tropsch reaction generalized as:

$$nCO + 2nH_2 \rightarrow (-CH_2-)_n + nH_2O$$

or

$$2nCO + nH_2 \rightarrow (\text{---CH}_2\text{---})_n + nCO_2$$

The final composition depends on the $CO : H_2$ ratio, the catalyst selectivity, the degree of conversion, the control of heat release and the extent of recycle employed. The production of methanol by a variation of Fischer–Tropsch synthesis has aroused much interest as has the direct synthesis of ethylene and other lower olefins.

In the degradation route, liquids are produced directly from coal and the higher proportion of hydrogen compared with the original coal is achieved by either removing carbon by pyrolysis or adding hydrogen. Such reactions are usually carried out in liquid solvents and are promoted by the addition of catalysts. Pyrolysis, that is heating the coal in the absence of air, may be achieved using traditional carbonization processes described earlier in this chapter, or newer techniques, particularly those based on a fluidized bed, which promotes efficient gas–solids mixing, high heat transfer and uniform temperature distribution. A further advantage is that coals other than coking coals may be used, preserving what is already a scarce commodity. Where a high conversion to liquid fuels is required, a hydrogenation stage is essential. This can be in the primary stage or alternatively the pyrolysis products can be refined with hydrogen. In general terms, the hydrogenation opens ring structures and eliminates oxygen, nitrogen and sulphur as water, ammonia and hydrogen sulphide respectively. The extent of reaction and the final products depend on the temperature, the pressure, the contact time and, most importantly, the catalyst employed.

Solvents play an important part in the production of liquids from coal since they extract hydrogen-rich materials and facilitate the reaction with hydrogen. Specific solvents can extract up to 40% of coals at temperatures up to 500 K; the extracted material is the main organic component of the volatile matter evolved when coal is heated. Degrading solvents extract up to 90% of the coal substance at around 675 K and in this way absorb the primary pyrolysis products. A typical degrading solvent is anthracene oil which does not react with the coal substance but is used as a medium for reaction with hydrogen in the presence of catalysts. Reactive solvents do, however, react with the coal substance producing smaller and more soluble materials and giving significantly different extracts compared with degrading solvents. An interesting feature of both degrading and reactive solvents is that there is very little variation in the chemical composition of the extract even with a wide range of coal feeds—much less so than with crude oils. Compressed gases in the supercritical state have important advantages as solvents for coal particularly in inhibiting polymerization.

2. Process development

Probably the first conversion of coal into liquid fuels was the production of tars and oils as by-products in carbonization processes. In 1818 coal tar distillation was first practised, followed by the refining of crude benzole in 1839. This received an enormous boost due to the demand for higher-octane gasolines in the first world war, though in recent years the economics have been dominated by the growth of the petrochemicals industry and benzole is no longer a component of motor fuels. Since the exploitation of natural gas sources and the demise of coal gas industries, tar production has approximately halved and in the UK is now less than one million tonnes per year. Whilst pyrolysis processes are ancilliary to coke production, their potential as sources of synthetic liquid fuels is very limited.

Practical processes using hydrogenation date from about 1914 when Bergius converted brown coal into a heavy crude oil. This early process did not use a catalyst, though catalysts were used in the development of commercial-scale processes by I. G. Farben industrie AG and by ICI. These processes consisted essentially of a liquid-phase hydrogenation of the coal slurried in recycled heavy oil followed by vapour phase hydro-cracking and hydrofining of the middle oil, and a commercial plant was commissioned at Billingham in 1935 with an output of 100 000 tonnes per year. The main development took place in Germany, where seven hydrogenation plants were operating in 1939 and five more were constructed between 1940 and 1943 producing about 90% of the available aircraft fuel at that time. After World War II, the development of coal hydrogenation processes centred on the United States and this ultimately led to the current work on the Conoco Synthetic Fuel process.

Synthesis processes originated in Germany at about the same time as hydrogenation of coal. In 1923, Fischer and Tropsch produced "synthol", a mixture of alcohols and fatty acids with some hydrocarbons using an iron catalyst at 15 MN m^{-2} and 700 K. By 1943, the total German production was 570 000 tonnes per year using gas produced in blue water gas generators from low-temperature cokes as the feedstock. The catalyst was cobalt–thoria–magnesia and although a high-quality diesel fuel was produced, the main interest lay in the production of detergents and edible fats. A design for a complex based on a pressurized slagging gasifier and a Fischer-Tropsch variation was proposed for the UK during the early sixties, but this was abandoned because of the availability of cheap oil at that time. The only commercial synthesis plant to have had extended operation is that erected in 1955 by the South African Coal, Oil and Gas Co. Ltd. (SASOL) at an initial cost of £55m. Two synthesis processes are integrated in SASOL—a medium-pressure fixed catalyst process known as

ARGE and the Kellogg medium-pressure entrained catalyst process, now known as SYNTHOL. The overall thermal efficiency is 56% and about 12–15% of the petrol requirements of South Africa are produced, albeit with marginal overall economics.

3. *Current research programmes*

In the United States, the Char Oil Energy Development process (COED), uses a series of interconnected fluidized beds to convert coal to char, tar, gas and oil with pyrolysis taking place at progressively higher temperatures (Anon. 1970b). In a later modification known as COGAS, the char is gasified to produce substitute natural gas. In the SRC 2, solvent refined coal process, coal is slurried with recycle and hydrogenated to give a clean fuel for combustion in power stations. The Exxon Donor Solvent Process, which is expected to be demonstrated in 1980, uses solvents together with molecular hydrogen to produce a coal extract which after hydrogenation is distilled to separate undissolved material, thereby avoiding filtration. Less than 70% of the coal is extracted in order to limit hydrogen consumption and 0·04–0·2 kg naphtha per kg coal is produced together with a low-sulphur fuel oil. The H-Coal process devised by Hydrocarbon Research Inc. is a solvent extraction process based on their commercial H-Oil process for reducing the sulphur content of fuel oil by catalytic hydrogenation. Mobil are developing a process for the production of a high-octane gasoline either from methanol or directly from synthesis gas derived from the Lurgi gasification of coal.

In the UK, the NCB Coal Research Establishment is investigating two extraction processess; one uses a process-derived solvent and the second uses supercritical gases and a plant for the hydrocracking of each extract is operated with a throughput of 0·05 tonne/day. Bergbau-Ferschung in Germany are investigating the direct hydrogenation of coal and Saarberg-werke AG commissioned a plant in 1979 in which the solution and hydrogenation stages are carried out in a single vessel using a disposable iron catalyst. A sharp decline in Soviet oil production is expected in the early 1980s and a pilot plant for the combined hydrogenation of coal and oil is being evaluated. Some research into coal liquefaction is under way in Japan although the replacement of oil as the primary energy source would require importation of large amounts of coal to supplement indigenous supplies. Nevertheless, a Japanese consortium of ten companies is sponsoring the work by Exxon on its liquefaction process. A second SASOL plant is now under construction which will include 8–10 Synthol synthesis units fed by synthesis gas from 36 Lurgi gasifiers.

The commercial exploitation of coal liquefaction processes is an important development which, while probably limited at first to say hydrogenation of coal–petroleum mixtures, must ultimately reach the stage of a fully integrated operation giving a wide range of products and not unlike the concept of a modern oil refinery (Luntz 1977, Lochmann and Hawell 1977). A useful survey of the operations involved has been presented by Shinnar (1978).

IV. THE GASIFICATION OF OIL AND HYDROCARBON GAS REFORMING

A. Introduction

The gasification of petroleum feedstocks and the reforming of hydrocarbon gases involves essentially two operations: the "cracking" of large molecules and increasing the concentration of hydrogen (Townsend 1971). As seen in Table 22, the carbon:hydrogen ratio in coal gas and natural gas is

TABLE 22. *Carbon–hydrogen ratio in various fuels*

Fuel	C/H ratio
Coking coal	15·5
Heavy fuel oil	7·8
Light distillate	5·6
Coal gas/natural gas	3·0

much less than in liquid fuels and this decrease may be brought about during reforming either by removing carbon or by adding hydrogen derived directly or indirectly from steam. It is important to prevent the formation of tar and free carbon, which increase the C:H ratio, and to achieve this and increase the gas yield, oxygen or air is added to the feedstock, with hydrogen, usually as a steam–oxygen mixture. The reactions involved are promoted at high temperatures or by the use of catalysts and these techniques superimpose partial combustion and hydrogenation processes on purely thermal cracking. It is convenient to classify the many processes which have been developed for this operation by their use or otherwise of a catalyst and whether the process is continuous or cyclic.

Compared with the gasification of solid fuels, processes involving liquid feedstocks have higher gasification efficiencies, the capital and operating costs are lower, the amount of purification of the product gas required is less and it is much easier to transport and control the flow of fluids. For these reasons, oil gasification has completely replaced the traditional solids gasification processes in the UK, both for the production of industrial and synthesis gases and also for the production of synthetic natural gas.

The gas produced from liquid fuels has very little odour because of the higher degree of purity. Where high concentrations of carbon monoxide are present, however, it is desirable to be aware of the presence of gas, especially as leaks, and 15–30 kg tetrahydrothiophen are added to every million cubic metres of the gas.

B. Thermal Cracking Processes

The first processes for the production of gas from oil used no catalyst and operation was on a cyclic basis. The feedstock was crude oil which was cracked with steam at 1400 K and 100 kN m^{-2}, producing gas with a calorific value in the range 18 600–22 400 kJ m^{-3}. However, the gas yield was only 50% of the thermal value of the oil and considerable amounts of carbon black were produced. Natural gas has also been used as a feed and this again produces carbon black and a gas rich in methane and hydrogen with a calorific value of 20 500–27 950 kJ m^{-3}. This type of process is used only where the demand for carbon black is sufficiently high to offset the low gasification efficiency.

There are three types of plant in operation:

(i) *Jones process*. In this case the main product is carbon black, and the gas, which has a calorific value of 13 400 kJ m^{-3}, is a by-product. The recovery of carbon is about 40% of that in the original feed.

(ii) *Hall process*. In this process, the cracking is much less rigorous and a gas of high calorific value (37 250 kJ m^{-3}) is produced with similar characteristics to natural gas. Distillate, residual and crude oils are used as the feed material.

(iii) *Semet–Solvay*. A simplified diagram of this process is shown in Fig. 32. The plant consists of two symmetrical chambers in which oil is vaporized above a chequer-filled section. Each chamber has combined steam and oil entries and gas and stack connections at the base. During the production stage or "run", steam is passed first into one vessel where it

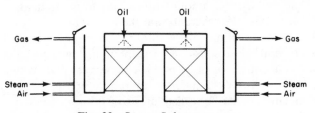

Fig. 32. *Semet–Solvay process.*

recovers heat from the chequers, and then into the second chamber where mixing with the vaporized oil takes place. Cracking is completed at this stage and carbon is formed on the chequers with the gas passing out of the plant. Air is then passed through the plant (the "blow" stage) in the reverse direction in order to burn off the carbon and heat up the chequers, and waste gases are vented to the stack. The cycle is continued with a "run" in the same direction; the total time for a "blow" and a "run" being 200–250 s.

C. Catalytic Processes

1. General considerations

The two main reasons for using a catalyst are, firstly, to manufacture gas, whether it be coal gas, lean gas or synthesis gas, without the formation of tar and carbon, secondly, to increase the gas yield compared with thermal cracking processes. In general, the catalyst employed is usually lime or some form of nickel and reactions of the water gas type are thus promoted:

$$C_aH_b + aH_2O \rightarrow aCO + (a + b/2)H_2$$

This type of process can handle a wide range of petroleum feedstocks, the limiting parameter being specific gravity. Where this exceeds 0·73, some carbon is deposited on the catalyst during processing, and it is necessary to use cyclic operation to regenerate the catalyst by burning the carbon deposit with air and at the same time restoring heat removed from the bed during the gas-making stage. In continuous processing, feedstocks with specific gravities less than 0·73 are used as it is important to avoid the formation of carbon at all times. Whereas continuous plants may have the advantage of operating at high pressures (2000–4000 kN m^{-2}), cyclic plants are limited to low pressures and the design of the plant and choice of catalyst depends on the feedstock to be used. For feeds in the gas oil to medium fuel oil range, lime is usually used and this is regenerated by air flowing in the opposite direction to the production gases. With light distillates and petroleum gases, nickel catalysts promote a high gasification efficiency and reduce the amount of carbon formed. In this case, it is advantageous to pass the reactants and the regenerative gases through the plant in the same direction: this is known as "uniflow" operation. Cyclic processes are much less sensitive to sulphur in the feedstock than continuous and concentrations of up to 3% can be tolerated. When producing a town gas of CV 18 630 kJ m^{-3}, the thermal efficiency varies from 80% with high specific gravity light distillates to 87% with LPG.

In the continuous reforming and gasification of light distillate fuels and petroleum gases, the hydrocarbon feedstock is reacted with steam at 100–4000 kN m^{-2} and 1000–1200 K in externally heated nickel–chrome alloy steel tubes packed with catalyst. The general reaction is of the form:

$$x(C_nH_m) + yH_2O \rightarrow aCO + bCO_2 + cCH_4 + dH_2 + eH_2O$$

though secondary reactions such as:

$$CH_4 + H_2O \rightleftharpoons CO + 3H_2$$
$$CO + H_2O \rightleftharpoons CO_2 + H_2$$

may also occur. The composition of the product gas depends on the C:H ratio in the feed, the ratio of steam to feed, the reaction temperature and pressure and, where the feed contains a high proportion of methane and butane, the amount of process air. An increase in the process steam to feed ratio increases the ratio of carbon dioxide to monoxide and reduces the concentration of methane in the product. The effects of increased reaction temperature and pressure on the composition of the product gas are shown in Fig. 33, from which it will be noted that increasing the former reduces the CO_2:CO ratio because of its effect on the water gas shift reaction. Increased pressure has a considerable effect on the dissociation of methane. When the feed is in the methane to butane range, process air is used and this increases the $(CO + CO_2)$:H_2 ratio and of course dilutes the product with nitrogen. An important use of the steam reforming process is in the production of a synthesis gas for the manufacture of ammonia. In this case, part of the reaction is carried out at a low temperature to form methane and the rest of the reaction is carried out after adding air to form the hydrogen–nitrogen mixture at a higher temperature. For many feedstocks some pretreatment, such as the removal of sulphur compounds with active carbon or zinc oxide, is essential. Light distillate fuels are subjected to vapour phase catalytic treatment at 700 K before the process steam is added.

Various catalysts are used (Veillat 1968) and the reforming efficiency, which is usually 80–87%, depends on the C:H ratio in the feed, the amount of air added, the amount of heat recovery and the methane content required in the final product. The catalyst is usually manufactured *in situ* and a typical plant requires two weeks each year for maintenance. This type of plant is extremely flexible and it is possible to operate with a throughput of only 40% of the maximum. One of the most important advantages of oil reforming plants over solid fuel units is the great reduction in ground space needed for a given gas output—values for the former being around 3500 m^2 for a plant producing a million cubic metres of gas a day.

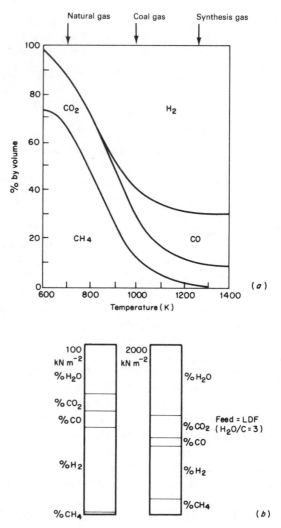

Fig. 33. *(a)* *Effect of temperature* (steam/LDF = 4:1, pressure = 2500 kN m⁻²) *and (b) of pressure on product composition.*

2. *Cyclic processes*

It is not possible to consider here all the cyclic processes which use a catalyst, though the Segas plant will be discussed in view of its importance and commercial application. The layout of the equipment is shown in Fig. 34. The catalyst, in the form of hollow cylindrical pellets, consists of magnesia with 1% free lime and it has to be replaced every three years. The cycle of operation is as follows. First, during the "blow", air which is heated in chamber 3 passes through the catalyst into chamber 1, where it consumes carbon and raises the temperature. This takes 250 s and the flue gas passes to a waste heat boiler. The plant is then purged with steam followed by the "run" in which steam, preheated in chamber 1 is mixed with the oil and passed through the catalyst bed, where the reactions take place, the product gas being withdrawn from chamber 3 in which it is cooled. The cycle is then repeated after a second steam purge. During the run, carbon is deposited in chambers 1 and 2 and in burning this during the

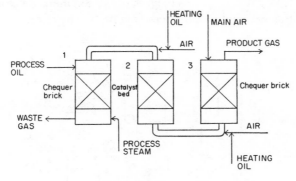

Fig. 34. *Segas process.*

blow, insufficient heat to restore the temperatures is liberated. To overcome this, 5% of the feedstock is used to provide auxilliary heating during the blow and also to control the product calorific value, which is a function of the operating temperature. This type of plant is easy to control and a wide range of feedstocks can be handled.

3. *Continuous catalytic steam reforming*

Cyclic processes have several advantages compared with thermal cracking processes and, indeed, for gas quantities of up to 300 000 m³/day made from high-sulphur feeds, they can compete on economic grounds with continuous processes especially where the product is required at low pressure. For larger gas throughputs, however, at high pressures, using low-sulphur (800 p.p.m.) light distillate or gaseous feedstocks, the more complex continuous reformers operating at 1000–3500 kN m^{-2} are very much more economical for the production of town gas, synthesis gas or hydrogen. With the addition of carbon dioxide or carbon monoxide to the reactants, synthesis gases can be made with $CO:H_2$ ratios in the range

0·5–4·0:1. With steam as the gasifying medium, a stream containing in excess of 99% hydrogen can be produced after carbon monoxide conversion and removal of the dioxide and residual monoxide. Feedstocks include natural gas, refinery gases and LPG and also low-sulphur light distillates, which usually undergo a vapour phase catalytic hydrosulphurization at about 675 K before addition of steam. For many years nickel on alumina catalysts was used in reforming low molecular mass hydrocarbons, though for light distillates, ICI have developed a potassium alkali activated form of the nickel catalyst. In its latest form a non-volatile alkali has been substituted for the potassium base (Nicklin *et al.* 1970).

The ICI lean-gas process was the first of the commercial naphtha–steam reforming processes and a simplified diagram is shown in Fig. 35 (Bridger

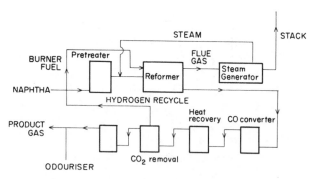

Fig. 35. *ICI continuous LDF reformer.*

1972). The catalyst is nickel oxide, with added potassium alkali and superheated steam is added to the feed to give a ratio of 3 kmol steam per kmol of carbon in the feed. Before entering the reactor, the feed is vaporized with hydrogen and desulphurized at 650 K over a zinc oxide catalyst. The reformer consists of three rows of 125 mm ID tubes, 8·5 m long, which are heated externally and the flue gases raise steam at 2000 kN m⁻². The product gas leaves the reformer at 1000 K and 1800 kN m⁻² and contains 16% CO_2, 11% CO, 12% CH_4 and 61% H_2, with a calorific value of 12 100 kJ m⁻³. This is treated catalytically in a converter in which the carbon monoxide concentration is reduced to 3%. The gas is finally enriched with LPG or natural gas and delivered for use at 1200 kN m⁻².

The production of the lean gas element of town gas has become less important as natural gas resources have become more widespread. At the same time, increased quantities of lean gas are required for ammonia, methanol and other syntheses and as a source of hydrogen for oil refining.

Regardless of the feedstock, the technique adopted for the main reforming process is varied according to the type of gas required. For the production of ammonia, the tubular reformer is followed by a secondary reformer in which the reformed gas, steam and some added air react in the presence of a nickel catalyst in order to reduce the methane content to the desired level. The air used provides the nitrogen for the ammonia synthesis. In the synthesis of methanol, a $CO:H_2$ ratio of $1:2$ is achieved by adding carbon dioxide. The production of hydrogen cannot be achieved by a secondary reformer since the presence of nitrogen cannot be tolerated. Instead the main reformer is operated at 1220 K with a higher steam:carbon feed ratio in the presence of a nickel–urania catalyst (Nicklin et al. 1970). At these high temperatures, close control of the tube wall temperature is important and the SELAS and Foster Wheeler designs have proved to be successful in this respect. Where the required production rate of hydrogen is less than $0.01 \text{ m}^3 \text{ s}^{-1}$, it is more economical to produce hydrogen by the catalytic splitting of ammonia, the reforming of methanol or the electrolysis of caustic soda or caustic potash.

A further important continuous gasification process is the UK Gas Council's Rich-Gas Process which is used for the production of "high-speed" coal gas or for supplementing or replacing natural gas (Cockerham et al. 1965). Analogous processes have been developed in other countries and these include Lurgi Gasynthan, BASF Lurgi and Japan Gasoline Osaka MRG. In the process, the light distillate fuel, which usually boils below 460 K, is vaporized, mixed with 0.01–$0.06 \text{ m}^3 \text{ kg}^{-1}$ of recycled product gas and passed at 625 K to a vessel containing a nickel–molybdenum catalyst where all the sulphur is converted to hydrogen sulphide which is then removed. Steam in the ratio $2:1$ is added and the mixture is reacted at 715 K in the presence of a highly active alkalized nickel catalyst. The product, which contains about 60% methane, 20% carbon dioxide and 18% hydrogen leaves at 760 K with a thermal yield of 94%. In the production of coal gas, this rich gas may be processed in a conventional tubular reformer operated at 920–970 K to give 34% methane and 48% hydrogen. In producing a substitute natural gas, the calorific value of the rich gas is raised by methanation (Davies et al. 1969), that is, reacting the carbon oxides and hydrogen over a nickel catalyst to form methane in two stages:

$$CO + 3H_2 \rightarrow CH_4 + H_2O$$
$$CO_2 + 4H_2 \rightarrow CH_4 + 2H_2O$$

An alternative to the first of these two exothermic stages is to place two CRG reactors in series. Where LPG is substituted for IDF as a feedstock, a

◄

richer gas is formed in the CRG process and in the manufacture of natural gas substitute a single methanation stage will suffice (Anon. 1971).

D. Partial Combustion Processes

In these processes, the feedstock is reacted with a limited quantity of either air or a mixture of oxygen and steam. The former is used to achieve light cracking, producing a gas with a calorific value of $18\,500-41\,000\,kJ\,m^{-3}$. Heavy cracking produces a mixture of hydrogen and carbon oxides. Capital costs are low and feedstocks ranging from LPG to heavy fuel or tar can be used (Berg 1970). There are many types of plant available of which the Shell process, shown in Fig. 36, may be cited as a typical example. The

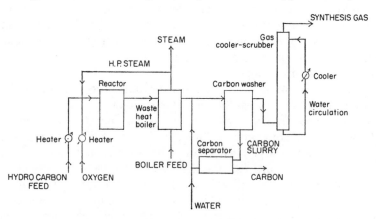

Fig. 36. *Shell partial combustion process.*

reactants are preheated to 550 K and heat is recovered in a waste heat boiler in which process steam is generated. The gas which leaves the reactor at about 1500 K contains 40% CO and 50% H_2 after carbon removal and water scrubbing, and as such is used as a synthesis gas. It is possible to produce a coal gas by converting the carbon monoxide to dioxide, which is then removed by absorption. This treatment improves the combustion characteristics, reduces the toxicity of the product and converts any carbonyl sulphide present to hydrogen sulphide. The reactions usually take place at about $3100\,kN\,m^{-2}$ and, with a naphtha feed, the gasification and thermal efficiencies are 82% and 94% respectively.

E. Hydrogasification of Hydrocarbon Oils

The presence of sulphur in crude oil and heavy fuel oils limits their use as feedstocks in catalytic processes. These materials can be hydrogenated, however, and the rich gas produced is then reformed to give a coal gas and particularly a substitute natural gas. In this way, such processes provide alternatives to the gasification of solid fuels and the CRG processes described earlier.

In the UK Gas Council's Fluidized-Bed Hydrogenator (Murthy and Edge 1963), the reactor contains a circulating bed of $0 \cdot 1$–$0 \cdot 4$ mm coke particles onto which the atomized oil is sprayed with the hydrogenating gas, which is formed by the steam-reforming of naphtha. The oil and hydrogen react at 5000–7000 kN m^{-2} and 1020 K in an exothermic process. The thermal yield is 85–90% and the rich gas contains 36% hydrogen, 46% methane, 14% ethane with a calorific value of 31 MJ m^{-3}. The final natural gas substitute is then made by propane enrichment of this rich gas. The gas-recycle hydrogenator (Conway 1973) is an ancillary to a continuous reformer in which the lean gas is used to hydrogenate thermally cracked light distillate vapour. The hydrogenation temperature depends on the degree of preheat of the reactants which is 720–820 K for a product at 1025 K and 2500 kN m^{-2}. The substitute natural gas is again obtained by propane enrichment of the hydrogenated product.

V. CARBURETTED WATER GAS

The manufacture of carburetted water gas is a combination of solid fuel and oil gasification. The generator is fed with coke and blown alternatively with steam and air to make blue water gas and producer gas respectively. The producer gas made during the blow is burned with secondary air in a second chamber into which light distillates or heavy oils are sprayed during steaming of the main bed. The mixture of blue water gas and thermally cracked oil-gas so formed passes into a superheater where cracking is completed. The thermal yield is 60–65% with no oil addition, 95% with the addition of light distillates and 65% with heavy oils which give some 25–30% tar as a bonus. The process was developed for meeting seasonal and peak gas loads. This end is now achieved more economically by oil gasification, though many plants have been modified in recent years to reform hydrocarbons, generally by a partial combustion process.

VI. FURTHER READING

American Institution of Chemical Engineers (1978). "Fluidization—Application to Coal Conversion Processes".

British Petroleum Ltd. (1965). "Gasmaking". British Petroleum Co. Ltd., London.

British Petroleum Ltd. (1972). "Gasmaking and Natural Gas". British Petroleum Co. Ltd., London.

Byrom, C. (1952). "Modern Coking Practice", 2 Vols. Technical Press Ltd., London.

Claxton, G. (1961). "Benzoles—Production and Uses". Heffer, Cambridge.

Coe, A. (1934). "The Science and Practice of Gas Supply", 3 Vols. The Gas College, Halifax.

Coke Oven Managers Association (1961). "The History of Coke-making". London.

Dixon, E. C. (1939). "Coke and By-products Manufacture". Griffin, London.

Ellington, R. T. (1977). "Liquid Fuels from Coal". Academic Press, New York and London.

Gould, R. F. (ed.) (1974). "Coal Gasification". Advances in Chemistry, No. 131, American Chemical Society.

Lavrov et al. (1963). "Thermodynamics of Gasification and Gas Synthesis Reactions". Pergamon Press, Oxford.

Lom, W. L. and Williams, A. F. (1976). "Substitute Natural Gas". Applied Science Publishers, New York.

Lupton, H. P. (1960). "Industrial Gas Engineering", 3 Vols. Walter King, London.

Lurgi Gesezlschaften (1961). "The Lurgi Manual". Lurgi, Frankfurt.

Seglin, L. (1975). "Methanation of Synthesis Gas". American Chemical Society, New York.

Fuel Testing

6

I. INTRODUCTION

The production and characteristics of fuels have been dealt with in previous chapters and it is appropriate at this stage to deal with the testing of combustible materials, a topic of vital significance throughout the consumer and power industries. It is of paramount importance, for example, that an oil refinery produces materials to a closely defined and consistent quality. A user of coal in bulk must be able to carry out tests to determine the predicted performance of fuel purchased, and hence be able to calculate the cost per unit energy and the efficiency of the entire process with an acceptable degree of accuracy.

In this chapter, the basic principles of fuel testing are considered together with an outline of the various tests available and, perhaps more important, the significance of the data obtained. It should be noted at the outset that, especially in the case of liquid fuels, a great many of the standard tests are empirical in nature and provide data in non-absolute units, often referred to some arbitrary datum. A good example of this is viscosity, for which data for petroleum products are obtained in Redwood seconds, the time taken for a standard volume of oil to flow under a given head through a capillary of standard dimensions. Such units are well understood and accepted throughout the fuel industries and the conversion to absolute units, in this case $N s m^{-2}$, is rarely carried out. The main reason for the empirical nature of the tests is that, in many cases, they were developed in the early days of the modern petroleum industry at a time when the scientific background was not fully understood and modern facilities such as electronic instruments were not available. As the science of materials testing has been developed, so the equipment involved in the testing of fuels has been improved, and although the units and the principles are basically empirical, the accuracy and reproducibility of the methods are completely acceptable.

It is necessary to confine the present discussion to those properties of fuels which are readily and most frequently measured in the laboratory and which have the greatest significance. The analysis of solid fuels has been discussed in Chapter 2 and will not be considered here and the calculation of properties from experimental data forms a major part of Chapter 9.

II. CALORIFIC VALUE

The calorific value of a fuel is the number of heat units evolved when unit mass (or unit volume in the case of a gas) of a fuel is completely burned and the combustion products cooled to 288 K. With solid and liquid fuels, the mass sufficiently defines the quantity of fuel present, but with gaseous fuels it is necessary to specify both temperature and pressure in order to define the quantity. The British system uses a temperature and pressure of 288 K and 101·3 kN m^{-2} as the conditions to which the calorific value of a gas should be referred.

In many respects the calorific value of a fuel is the most important parameter required before a fuel can be used efficiently in combustion and furnace plant. A knowledge of both the heat requirements of the process and the calorific value of the fuel to be used enables the quantity of fuel required for that particular duty to be calculated. Only when this quantity of fuel, per unit time, is known, can pipework and storage facilities by sized and costed and the operating costs of the plant be calculated. It will be appreciated that accurate evaluation of the calorific value is vital to the economic operation of furnace and boiler plant, and care in experimental determination is of the utmost importance.

A. Gross and Net Values

The definition of calorific value includes the provision that the products of combustion are cooled to 288 K and hence the sensible heat and the latent heat of condensation of the water produced during combustion are included in the heat liberated. The calorific values determined by the Mahler Bomb and Boys' Calorimeter which are described later, include this heat and are designated "gross calorific values".

In many industrial applications, however, the products of combustion leave the plant at temperatures well in excess of 288 K so that the water formed remains in the vapour state. The latent heat of condensation is thus not given up and the total heat liberated per unit mass (or volume) of fuel is less. Calorific value in the case where the water remains as vapour is designated "net calorific value".

The net calorific value is rarely determined directly but it may be calculated from the gross calorific value and a knowledge of the analysis of the fuel, which enables the quantity of water formed per unit mass or volume of fuel to be calculated as shown in Example 9.4 (Chapter 9). This quantity multiplied by the latent heat of condensation of water plus the reduction in sensible heat of the water in cooling from the dew point to 288 K must be subtracted from the gross calorific value to give the net value. The net value is of greater significance in practical applications as this represents the actual heat which is available. British Standard 526 (1961) considers gross and net calorific values at both constant pressure and constant volume and their determination.

B. Calculation of Calorific Values from Fuel Analyses

It is possible to obtain an estimate of the calorific value of a fuel by multiplying the percentage of each component in the fuel by the known calorific value of the component and summing the results.

For a gaseous fuel, the calculated calorific value is often within 2% of the experimental value, although the accuracy of the calculated value depends on the accuracy and scope of the analysis. Often, analytical tests group several components together as one percentage of the total fuel, so that an estimated average calorific value for that group must be used (e.g. unsaturated hydrocarbons are often grouped together). For many gases, however, the analysis is known in terms of the permanent gases, lower hydrocarbons and oxides of carbon, in which case the calorific values may be determined from the percentage composition and the standard calorific values given in Table 23. Calorific values of some gaseous fuel mixtures are shown in Table 24.

The calorific value of a liquid fuel can be calculated by a similar method to that used for a gaseous fuel provided that the composition is accurately known. Table 25 lists properties of a range of commonly encountered liquid fuels. It is far more difficult, however, to obtain an accurate estimate of the calorific value of a solid fuel, since the ultimate analysis of coal, for example, gives the percentage composition in terms of elements rather than compounds. Several workers have derived empirical relationships for the calculation of calorific values of solid fuels whose ultimate analysis is known. Such relationships are based on the assumption that each element makes the same contribution to the calorific value as it would make if it were present in a mixture and not in chemical combination with other elements. Since this is not true, the calorific value calculated from each formula is merely an estimate.

The oldest and best known relationship is the Dulong Formula:

$$CV = 338 \cdot 2\,C + 1442 \cdot 8(H - \tfrac{1}{8}O) + 94 \cdot 2S \quad kJ\ kg^{-1}$$

where C, H, O, and S are the percentages of these elements, on a dry ash-free basis, in the ultimate analysis. Dulong has assumed that the oxygen present is combined with hydrogen as water and hence this reduces the amount of combustible hydrogen correspondingly. Experience has shown that this formula gives very good results for carbon contents up to 86%, but is of little use where this value exceeds 90%.

TABLE 23. *Properties of pure gases*

Gas	Formula	Relative density†	Calorific value (MJ m^{-3}) Gross	Net	Note
Carbon monoxide	CO	0·967	11·97	11·97	
Hydrogen	H$_2$	0·070	12·10	10·22	
Methane	CH$_4$	0·554	37·71	33·95	
Ethane	C$_2$H$_6$	1·038	66·07	60·43	
Propane	C$_3$H$_8$	1·522	93·94	86·42	
n-Butane	C$_4$H$_{10}$	2·006	121·8	112·4	
n-Pentane	C$_5$H$_{12}$	2·490	149·7	138·4	1
n-Hexane	C$_6$H$_{14}$	2·974	177·6	164·4	1
n-Heptane	C$_7$H$_{16}$	3·458	205·4	190·4	1
n-Octane	C$_8$H$_{18}$	3·942	233·3	216·4	1
n-Nonane	C$_9$H$_{20}$	4·426	261·2	242·4	1
n-Decane	C$_{10}$H$_{22}$	4·911	289·1	268·4	1
Ethylene	C$_2$H$_4$	0·968	59·72	55·96	
Propylene	C$_3$H$_6$	1·452	87·09	81·45	
Butylene	C$_4$H$_8$	1·936	114·6	107·1	
Acetylene	C$_2$H$_2$	0·910	55·85	53·95	

† Relative density is the density of the gas divided by the density of air, both at 288 K and 101·3 kN m^{-2}.
1. Where the "gas" is a liquid at 15°C and 101·3 kN m^{-2}, values are based on ideal gas volumes.

The most reliable formula over a wide range of fuel compositions is that due to Grumell and Davies (1933):

$$CV = (15 \cdot 22\,H + 937)(\tfrac{1}{3}C + H - \tfrac{1}{8}(O - S)) \quad kJ\ kg^{-1}$$

In addition it is possible to estimate the calorific value of a solid fuel from its proximate analysis (see Example 9.2). The result obtained is not as accurate as those above, due to the uncertain nature of the components

TABLE 24. *Properties of fuel gases—gas mixtures*

Gas	Composition (% by volume)												Relative Density	Calorific value (MJ m^{-3})		Note
	O$_2$	CO$_2$	CO	H$_2$	N$_2$	CH$_4$	C$_2$H$_6$	C$_3$H$_8$	C$_4$H$_{10}$	C$_5$H$_{12}$	C$_5$H$_{14}$	C$_n$H$_m$		Gross	Net	
Natural gases																
North Sea		0·2			1·5	94·4	3·0	0·5	0·2	0·1			0·589	38·62	34·82	
Groningen		0·9			14·0	81·8	2·7	0·4	0·1	0·1	0·1		0·784	33·28	30·00	
Algeria		0·2			5·5	83·8	7·1	2·1	0·9	0·4				39·10		1
Synthetic†		2·0	0·1	0·7		95·2		2·0					0·589	37·88	34·13	
Commercial propane							1·5	91·0	2·5			5·0	1·523	93·87	86·43	2
Commercial butane							0·5	7·2	88·0			4·2	1·941	117·8	108·7	2
Blue water gas		4·7	41·0	49·0	4·5	0·1							0·55	11·14	10·19	
Carburetted water gas	0·4	5·6	30·5	37·0	5·5	14·0						7·0	0·63	18·95	17·31	3
Blast furnace gas		17·5	24·0	2·5	56·0								1·04	3·18	3·13	
Coal gas	0·4	4·0	18·0	49·4	6·2	20·0						2·0	0·48	17·97	16·14	4
Producer gas		5·0	29·0	11·0	54·5	0·5							0·89	4·99	4·77	
Lurgi crude gas		25·6	24·4	37·3	1·8	10·3							0·732	11·76	10·64	5
Lean reformer gas		16·7	2·2	46·4		34·7							0·499	18·96	16·79	
Rich reformer gas		21·0	1·0	17·0		61·0							0·678	25·18	22·57	
Sewage gas													0·79	24·96		

† SNG is CRG + 2-stage methanation. 1: 0·4% in composition refers to C$_5$+. 2: C$_n$H$_m$ = C$_3$H$_6$. 3: C$_n$H$_m$ = C$_{2\cdot5}$H$_5$; take CH$_4$ as C$_{1\cdot1}$H$_{4\cdot2}$. 4: C$_n$H$_m$ = C$_4$H$_8$. 5: C$_n$H$_m$ = C$_{2\cdot5}$H$_5$O

TABLE 25. *Properties of liquid fuels*

Fuel	Relative Density	Composition (% by mass)				Calorific value (MJ kg^{-1})	
		C	H	S	O+N+ash	Gross	Net
Light distillate	0·68	84·10	15·85	0.05		47·8	44·5
Kerosine	0·78	85·8	14·1	0·1		46·5	43·5
Gas oil	0·83	86·1	13·2	0·7		45·6	42·8
Light fuel oil	0·93	85·6	11·7	2·5	0·2	43·5	41·1
Medium fuel oil	0·95	85·6	11·5	2·6	0·3	43·1	40·8
Heavy fuel oil	0·96	85·4	11·4	2·8	0·4	42·9	40·5
Methanol	0·796	37·5	12·5		50·0†	22·69	19·94
Ethanol	0·794	52·2	13·0		34·8†	30·15	27·23
Petrol	0·72–0·76	850–885	11·5–15·0	0·1		44·8–46·9	41·9–44·0
T.V.O.	0·815	86·9	12·9	0·2		46·0	43·2
Diesel fuel	0·840	86·5	13·2	0·3		45·7	42·9

† Oxygen only.

quoted. The most important relationship is due to Goutal (1902) and modified by Taylor and Patterson (1929):

$$CV = 4{\cdot}19(82FC + a\,VM) \quad kJ\ kg^{-1}$$

where FC is the fixed carbon content, VM the volatile matter content and a an empirical constant, which varies with the volatile matter content, calculated on a dry ash free basis as shown in Fig. 95.

Table 26 shows the calorific values for various solid fuels and an indication of their ultimate analysis and the use of the above relationships is illustrated in Example 9.7.

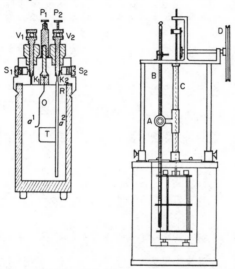

Fig. 37. *Bertholet–Mahler bomb calorimeter.* A, *thermometer telescope;* B, *10–25° thermometer;* C, *stirrer shaft;* D, *drive pulley;* K_1, K_2, *oxygen outlet and inlet;* O,R, *electrical terminals;* S, *screw plugs;* T, *crucible;* P, *electrical connections;* V, *oxygen needle valves;* a, *crucible supports and connections for iron wire.*

C. Experimental Determination

The first experimental determinations of the calorific values of fuels were made by Lavoisier and Laplace (1780) using a calorimeter and the development of techniques has been discussed by Poole (1918).

Present day methods used to measure calorific value are all based on calorimetry and vary according to the type of fuel being tested and also the degree of accuracy required. It is usual to determine the calorific value of solid and liquid fuels with the Mahler Bomb Calorimeter, illustrated in Fig. 37. Essentially, the solid or liquid fuel sample is explosively detonated by

TABLE 26. *Properties of solid fuels*

Fuel	NCB rank code No.	C	H	N	S	O	Moisture	Ash	Calorific value (MJ kg^{-1}) as fired Gross	as fired Net	dry, ash-free basis Gross	dry, ash-free basis Net
Coals												
Anthracite	101	78·2	2·4	0·9	1·0	1·5	8·0	8·0	29·66	28·94	35·82	
Dry steam	201	77·4	3·4	1·2	1·0	2·0	7·0	8·0	30·59	29·67	36·52	
Coking steam	202	77·1	3·5	1·2	1·0	2·2	7·0	8·0	30·70	29·75	36·63	
Medium Volatile coking	301a	75·8	4·1	1·3	1·2	2·6	7·0	8·0	30·82	29·75	36·75	
Low volatile heat altered	206	75·0	3·6	1·7	1·2	2·5	8·0	8·0	30·00	29·00	36·29	
Medium volatile heat altered	305	74·4	4·2	1·7	1·2	3·5	7·0	8·0	30·35	29·26	36·29	
High volatile coking coals												
Very strongly coking	401	71·6	4·3	1·6	1·7	3·8	9·0	8·0	29·54	28·38	36·05	
Strongly coking	501	71·0	4·3	1·4	1·7	4·6	9·0	8·0	29·19	28·03	35·70	
Medium coking	601	67·8	4·2	1·4	1·7	5·9	11·0	8·0	27·80	26·61	34·42	
General purpose coals												
Weakly coking	701	65·7	4·0	1·4	1·7	6·2	13·0	8·0	26·75	25·54	34·42	
Very weakly coking	802	61·3	4·0	1·3	1·7	7·7	16·0	8·0	25·24	23·96	33·72	
Non-coking	902	59·0	3·7	1·2	1·7	8·4	18·0	8·0	23·84	22·59	32·80	
Other solid fuels		**C**	**H**	**N+S**		**O**	**Moisture**	**Ash**				
Wood		42·5	5·1	0·9		36·5	15·0	Trace	15·82	14·35	18·63	17·28
Peat		43·7	4·2	1·5		26·6	20·0	4·0	15·91	14·49	20·93	19·72
Lignite		56·0	4·0	1·6		18·4	15·0	5·0	21·45	20·19	26·80	25·70
Charcoal		90·2	2·4	1·5		2·9	2·0	1·0	33·70	33·12	34·75	34·22
Coke		82·0	0·4	1·7		0·9	8·0	7·0	28·63	28·35	33·70	33·59
Low temp. coke		79·0	2·6	1·7		1·7	8·0	7·0	29·19	28·42	34·33	33·66
Mixed wood waste											20·88	
Mixed rags											18·35	
Mixed paper											16·26	

electrical ignition in a stainless steel bomb, containing a known weight of fuel in oxygen at a pressure of about 2500 kN m^{-2}. The bomb is immersed in a known mass of water in a calorimeter, so that the heat released on combustion is transferred to the water. The temperature of the water is measured accurately as a function of time so that the actual rise in temperature due to the burning of the fuel may be interpolated, allowing for heat losses from the calorimeter. Corrections are made to allow for divergence from the standard operating conditions and the calorimeter is surrounded by a water or air jacket to minimize heat losses. An example of the method of calculation is included as Example 9.5.

The Mahler Bomb Calorimeter is typical of a range of bomb calorimeters, so called because they use oxygen at a high pressure for combustion of the fuel. Other calorimeters, such as the Griffin-Sutton, the Emerson, and the Scholes Bombs, differ only in the physical form of the bomb and the arrangement of the ancillary equipment.

The calorific value of a gas is determined by burning the gas continuously at a known rate within a vessel so that the heat is transferred to water, also flowing at a known constant rate. Thermometers are used to measure the inlet and outlet water temperatures and the calorific value of the fuel gas is determined from a simple heat balance.

A section of Boys' Calorimeter, first introduced by Boys (1906) is shown in Fig. 38, since this represents the most widely used and perhaps most reliable gas calorimeter. Again, as in the case of bomb calorimeters, the experimental readings are corrected to allow for any divergence from the standard operating conditions. A known volume of the gas sample is burned in a chamber surrounded by a coil, through which a known flow rate of water is passed. It is important to ensure that the following standard conditions are observed in carrying out the test.

   (i) The inlet water temperature is not more than 5 deg K below room temperature.

  (ii) The rise in water temperature in passing through the calorimeter is approximately 20 deg K.

 (iii) The water flow rate is between 6 and 10 cm^3 s^{-1}.

 (iv) The gas flow rate is between 30 and 40 cm^3 s^{-1}.

  (v) The equipment is left between a half and one hour to attain a steady state once the flows have been adjusted.

Example 9.6 illustrates the calculation of the calorific value of a gas from experimental data.

The water-flow calorimeter is a simpler version of the Boys Calorimeter. This has no provision for the collection of water formed in the products of combustion, but because of its smaller overall size the system reaches thermal equilibrium more quickly giving a more rapid, but less accurate, determination of the calorific value. The calorimeter has the advantage, however, of providing data on the relative density of the gas so that the Wobbé Index may be calculated directly.

The Wobbé Index of a gas (Chapter 7, III. B.3) is the ratio of calorific value to the square root of the relative density. The relative density of a gas is determined by measuring the times taken for equal volumes of gas and air to flow through a small orifice. With the water-flow calorimeter, it is

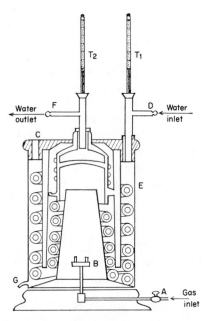

Fig. 38. *Section of Boys' calorimeter. A, gas inlet connection; B, gas burner; C, flue gas exit; D, water inlet; E, formed water tube; F, water outlet; G, condensate outlet;* T_1, T_2, *thermometers.*

possible to measure these times by fitting an orifice at the exit from a gas holder. By an extension of Graham's Law of diffusion, and by making various approximations it can be shown that:

$$\text{Relative density of gas} = t_g^2/t_a^2 \quad \text{(relative to air} = 1)$$

where t_g and t_a are the effusion times for equal volumes of gas and air, respectively, through the same orifice.

III. TESTS ON LIQUID FUELS

In order to select a fuel for a particular application and to design burners and associated equipment, it is necessary to be aware of properties which influence the way in which the liquid can be handled, the way it can be stored, and problems in its utilization. Such properties include surface tension, viscosity, relative density, volatility and flash-point, and empirical data such as octane number or cetane number.

It is the purpose of this section to show how such properties may be measured and how a knowledge of that property affects the utilization of the fuel. No specific practical details are given since these are available in the Institute of Petroleum Standards (1978) on liquid fuel testing.

A. Relative Density

The calorific value of a liquid fuel is normally quoted on a mass basis, so the relative density of the liquid must be known to enable the volume associated with the corresponding mass of oil to be calculated. Relative density also provides a rough check on the consistency of quality in a series of batches. It is defined as the ratio of a mass of a given volume of oil to the mass of the same volume of water at a given temperature. Since oils expand on heating, it is important to quote relative density at a datum which is usually 288 K. Relative density is also important in assessing the volume of a given mass of material (or vice versa) for transport and storage purposes.

The most convenient method of measuring relative density involves the use of a hydrometer. This instrument floats in the oil at a depth of immersion which is proportional to the relative density of the oil. The major disadvantage of the hydrometer is that the scale is not linear and the instrument requires calibration, which limits the accuracy obtainable. Arising from the use of a hydrometer is the °API scale of relative density (American Petroleum Industry):

$$°\text{API} = \left(\frac{141 \cdot 5}{\text{Relative density at 288 K}}\right) - 131 \cdot 5$$

This scale was drawn up in order to correct values of relative density which had been measured by incorrectly calibrated hydrometers, and it is still widely used in the oil industry.

A more accurate value for the relative density can be obtained from a Westphal balance or a relative density bottle. Of these methods, the Westphal balance is the more convenient as it gives a direct reading. The balance is shown in Fig. 39 and consists of a beam supported on a knife edge. At one end of the beam is a fixed balancing weight on which is a pointer, lying parallel to the beam. Attached to the support of the knife edge is a second pointer, positioned such that the beam is horizontal when the pointers are aligned. The second arm of the beam is notched at 1 cm intervals. From the end notch is hung a plummet, normally made of glass. A fine adjustment screw on the end of the beam enables the operator to level the beam with the plummet hanging in air. The plummet is then immersed first in freshly distilled water and then in the sample. For each liquid the balance of the beam is restored by positioning riders on the numbered notches. Three riders are normally used, each being one tenth the mass of the next largest rider, so that the numbers on the notches in which the riders are placed to restore the balance correspond to three

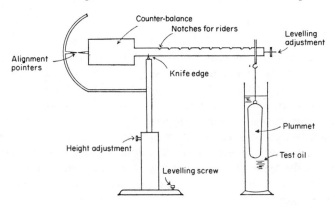

Fig. 39. *The Westphal balance.*

decimal places of the relative density, the largest rider giving the first point and so on. The reading on the beam with the plummet immersed in oil divided by the reading in water is the relative density of the oil. Ideally, both oil and water should be at 288 K but corrections can be made to compensate for divergence from this temperature.

In general, petroleum fuels have relative densities less than unity and coal tar fuels have values greater than unity, typical values for the former being given in Table 28. Because the components of a petroleum fuel are generally a narrow range of organic compounds, certain properties may be related empirically to the relative density. For example, the US Bureau of Mines (Cragoe 1929) gives an estimation of the gross calorific value of petroleum oil as:

$$CV = 51\,916 - 8792\,d^2 \quad kJ\,kg^{-1}$$

where d is the relative density at 288 K. Use of this equation is illustrated in Example 9.9.

B. Viscosity

The viscosity of a liquid is a measure of its resistance to flow. It is an important property of all liquid fuels since it affects for example, the rate of flow through pipes and other plant items, the rise of kerosene up a wick, the atomization of fuel oils and the performance and wear of diesel pumps.

A liquid in laminar flow (i.e. without any transverse mixing) may be considered as a series of playing cards sliding over one another when the bottom card is stationary. A certain force is required to produce this motion, depending on the resistance between the layers of liquid (or playing cards, in this analogy). Absolute viscosity is defined as the force required to move one square metre of plane surface at the rate of 1 m s^{-1} relative to a second plane surface, parallel to the first and separated 1 m from it by a layer of liquid. The units of viscosity are N s m^{-2}. A further viscosity term, the kinematic viscosity, is defined as the ratio of the absolute (or dynamic) viscosity to the density, the units being $\text{m}^2 \text{ s}^{-1}$.

1. *Absolute viscosity*

Absolute viscosity is commonly measured with either an Ostwald or an Ubbelohde Suspended Level Viscometer. The Ostwald viscometer is shown in Fig. 40. Sufficient liquid is poured into the U-tube to fill the region between marks b and c. This liquid is then drawn up the left-hand

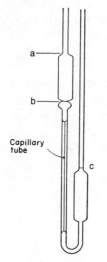

Fig. 40. *The Ostwald viscometer.*

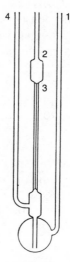

Fig. 41. *Ubbelohde suspended level viscometer.*

arm until the liquid level is above mark a. The time taken for this level to fall from a to b is then noted. This time is multiplied by the instrument constant (usually obtained with a standard liquid such as water) to give the absolute viscosity of the liquid.

The viscometer is immersed in a constant temperature bath, since, for the majority of liquids, viscosity decreases with increase in temperature. The instrument is designed with bulbs A and B identical in order to minimize errors due to surface tension, and is designed to give laminar flow conditions between b and c.

The Ubbelohde Suspended Level viscometer is shown in Fig. 41. This is intended for routine use as it provides a value for the viscosity more quickly than the Ostwald type, since it does not require a measured volume of liquid. Oil is poured into the instrument down tube 1. A portion is then drawn up to mark 2 while the operator closes tube 4. On opening tube 4, air enters the tube and the oil breaks away from the lower end of the capillary, thereby forming an inverted meniscus or "suspended level". The time for the liquid level to fall from mark 2 to mark 3 is noted and the viscosity calculated as for the Ostwald type. Again the viscometer is suspended in a constant temperature bath so that the viscosity may be determined over a range of temperatures.

2. *Kinematic viscosity*

Kinematic viscosity may be calculated from the absolute viscosity by dividing by the density of the liquid. In the early days of fuel testing a number of empirical viscometers were used, giving rise to viscosity measurements in arbitrary units, which were intended to be proportional to the kinematic viscosity of the oil. Unfortunately, the fundamentals of viscous flow were not well understood at that time and the values obtained are not directly proportional to kinematic viscosities. Tables are available for converting from one set of arbitrary units to another and to absolute values.

Consider a liquid flowing under laminar conditions, in which two parallel surfaces of area A and distance dx apart are moving relative to one another in the same direction; if a force F is applied to one surface, it will move with a speed dx relative to the other.

Therefore the velocity gradient is

$$\frac{dv}{dx}$$

and for laminar flow,

$$F \propto \frac{dv}{dx} \quad \text{and} \quad \frac{dv}{dx} \propto \frac{1}{A}$$

Therefore,

$$\frac{dv}{dx} \propto \frac{F}{A}$$

The constant of proportionality is denoted by $1/\eta$ for Newtonian liquids where η is the dynamic (or absolute) viscosity of the liquid. Therefore

$$\eta = \frac{F}{A} \frac{dx}{dv} \tag{1}$$

For liquid flowing in a pipe under the conditions shown in Fig. 42 where the liquid velocity along the inner surface of the sheath, radius x, is v and

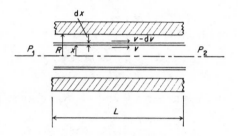

Fig. 42. *Liquid flow in a pipe.*

the velocity along the outer surface, radius $x + dx$, is $v - dv$, if the pipe is of diameter R and length L and the pressure differential between inlet and outlet is $P_1 - P_2 = \Delta P$, then from (1)

$$\frac{dv}{dx} = \frac{F}{A\eta}$$

The force $F = (-\Delta P \times$ cross sectional area of fluid within the sheath) $= -\Delta P \pi x^2$ and therefore

$$\frac{dv}{dx} = \frac{-\Delta P \pi x^2}{2\pi x L \eta} = \frac{-\Delta P x}{2L \eta}$$

Since v decreases as x increases,

$$-dv = \frac{\Delta P x}{2L \eta} \, dx$$

Integrating,

$$-v = \frac{\Delta P x^2}{4L \eta} + \text{constant.}$$

When $x = R$, $v = 0$ (i.e. at the surface of the pipe). So that

$$v = \frac{\Delta P(R^2 - x^2)}{4L\eta} \qquad (2)$$

which is the equation of a parabola.

The volume dV of liquid passing along the sheath in time t is given by the velocity of the sheath multiplied by its cross sectional area. Therefore

$$dV = v\pi[(x + dx)^2 - x^2]$$

taking v as the average velocity across the sheath, since dv is very small. Hence

$$dV = v\pi 2x \, dx$$

ignoring second order small quantities.

Substituting for v from (2):

$$dV = \frac{\Delta P(R^2 - x^2)\pi 2x \, dx}{4L\eta}$$

Integrating between the limits $x = 0$ and $x = R$, i.e. over the whole pipe,

$$V = \frac{\pi \Delta P}{2L\eta} \int_0^R (R^2 x - x^3) dx$$

Therefore

$$V = \frac{\pi \Delta P R^4}{8L\eta}$$

which is Poiseuille's Law. So for fixed tube dimensions the volume of oil is directly proportional to the pressure differential ΔP and inversely proportional to the viscosity η.

If the pressure differential is due to a head h of liquid then the hydrostatic pressure is $h\varrho$, where ϱ is the liquid density, and

$$V \propto \frac{h\varrho}{\eta}$$

If V is the volume of liquid flowing in time t:

$$\frac{V}{t} \propto \frac{h\varrho}{\eta}$$

For a viscometer, the head of the oil is constant at the start of each run and the volume of oil passing through the capillary is also constant so that

$$\frac{1}{t} \propto \varrho/\eta \quad \text{or} \quad t \propto \eta/\varrho$$

which is the kinematic viscosity. Thus, the time for the volume of oil to pass through the capillary in seconds is directly proportional to the kinematic viscosity.

The instrument most commonly used in the UK to measure viscosity is the Redwood Viscometer illustrated in Fig. 43. The viscosity is measured in Redwood seconds, which is the time taken for a fixed volume of oil (50 cm^3) to flow under gravity through an orifice of fixed dimensions. The two standard instruments are the No. 1 and No. 2 Redwood viscometers.

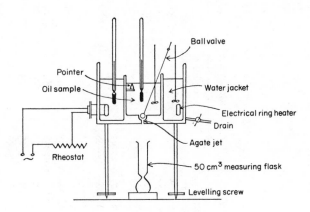

Fig. 43. *Redwood viscometer.*

The former is used for thin oils having viscosities of less than 2000 Redwood seconds, and the latter for more viscous oils. The viscometers vary in the dimensions of the orifice.

	Diameter	Length
Redwood No. 1	1.62 mm	10·0 mm
Redwood No. 2	3·50 mm	5·0 mm

Other empirical viscometers are used in the USA and in Europe. The Saybolt and Furol (US) and the Engler (continental) viscometers all operate on the same principle as the Redwood but have different geometries. New devices are being continuously developed and for example an automatic viscometer for use at high pressure has recently been described by Irving (1971). The general selection of a viscometer is discussed by Zientara (1972). Conversion between the various viscosity measurements may be carried out with the values shown in Table 27.

TABLE 27. Conversion from arbitrary viscosity units†

Kinematic viscosity (centistokes)	Equivalent Redwood No. 1 viscosity (seconds)			Equivalent Saybolt Universal viscosity (seconds)			Equivalent Engler viscosity degrees all temps.
	70°F‡	100°F	200°F	100°F	122°F	210°F	
2	30·22	30·65	31·22	32·62	32·67	32·85	1·141
3	32·72	33·15	33·72	36·03	36·08	36·28	1·225
4	35·33	35·65	36·33	39·14	39·20	39·41	1·309
5	37·94	38·25	38·94	42·35	42·41	42·65	1·401
6	40·55	40·85	41·55	45·56	45·62	45·88	1·482
7	43·26	43·55	44·21	48·77	48·84	49·11	1·565
8	46·07	46·25	46·97	52·09	52·16	52·45	1·655
9	48·93	49·05	49·73	55·50	55·58	55·89	1·749
10	51·79	51·95	52·64	58·91	58·99	59·32	1·840
12	58·01	58·07	58·86	66·04	66·13	66·50	2·024
14	64·49	64·54	65·39	73·57	73·68	74·09	2·224
16	71·32	71·39	72·37	81·30	81·41	81·87	2·439
18	78·29	78·40	79·54	89·44	89·57	90·06	2·650

Kinematic viscosity (centistokes)	Equivalent Saybolt Furol viscosity at 122°F (seconds)
50	26·1
55	28·3
60	30·6
65	32·8
70	35·1
75	37·4
80	39·6
85	41·9
90	44·1
95	46·4
100	48·6
110	53·2
120	57·8

20	85·02	85·75	87·15	97·77	97·91	98·43	2·877	140	67·0
22	93·15	93·28	94·75	106·4	106·6	107·1	3·108		
24	100·7	100·8	102·5	115·0	115·2	115·8	3·344	150	71·7
26	108·4	108·6	110·3	123·7	123·9	124·5	3·584	160	76·3
28	116·1	116·3	118·3	132·5	132·7	133·4	3·830	170	81·0
								180	85·6
30	123·9	124·1	126·4	141·3	141·5	142·3	4·081	190	90·3
35	143·7	144·0	146·6	163·7	163·9	164·9	4·708		
40	163·7	164·1	167·2	186·3	186·6	187·6	5·350	200	95·0
45	183·8	184·3	188·1	209·1	209·4	210·5	5·993	220	104·3
50	203·9	204·4	208·9	232·1	232·4	233·8	6·650	240	113·7
								260	123·0
55	224·0	224·6	229·8	255·2	255·6	257·0	7·260	280	132·4
60	244·2	244·8	250·8	278·3	278·7	280·2	7·920		
65	264·4	265·0	271·6	301·4	301·8	303·5	8·580	300	141·8
70	284·8	285·4	292·6	324·4	324·9	326·7	9·240	320	151·2
75	304·7	305·4	313·4	347·6	348·1	350·0	9·900	340	160·6
								360	170·0
79·9	324·5	325·3	333·9	370·3	370·8	372·9	10·547	380	179·4
								399	188·3

† From Spiers (1945).
‡ 70°F = 295 K; 100°F = 311 K; 122°F = 323 K; 210°F = 370 K. 1 Stokes = 10^{-4} m^2 s^{-1}.

3. Effect of temperature on viscosity

Temperature has a marked effect on the viscosity of most oils, the viscosity decreasing with increased temperature as shown in Table 28 and Example 9.10. The viscosity–temperature relationship is expressed on an arbitrary viscosity index scale. The change in viscosity of the sample oil over the range 311 K to 372 K is compared with the corresponding change for two standard oils: a Pennsylvanian oil with a high VI and hence little change in viscosity; and a Gulf Coast oil with a low VI and hence a large change in viscosity. Both have the same kinematic viscosity as the sample at 372 K.

The viscosity of the sample is determined at known temperatures over the range 311–372 K. Values interpolated from the results are used, together with standard viscosity–temperature data for the Pennsylvanian and Gulf Coast oils to calculate the viscosity index, as outlined in Example 9.10.

A high viscosity index is desirable for lubricating oils in particular, since these are required to maintain their viscosity when the moving parts of the machine have reached their operating temperature. For fuel oils, a knowledge of viscosity index is important in determining temperature to which an oil must be heated before it can be easily pumped.

4. Effect of pressure on viscosity

Pressure has an appreciable effect on viscosity only at pressures in excess of 100 MN m^{-2}, such as may be encountered in a bearing, for example. Experiments have shown that viscosity increases very rapidly according to the relationship:

$$\log (\eta_1/\eta_2) = a (P_1 - P_2)$$

where η is the dynamic viscosity of the oil, P the pressure above the oil and a is a constant depending on the chemical structure of the oil. Pressure variation is usually lower for paraffins than for aromatic hydrocarbons.

Viscosity is generally measured at elevated pressures only for specialized lubricating oils.

C. Flash-point

The flash-point of a liquid fuel is the temperature at which the oil begins to evolve vapours in sufficient quantity to form an explosive or flammable mixture with air. This temperature is an indirect measure of volatility and serves as an indication of the fire hazards associated with storage and application of the fuel. Regulations governing the safety aspects of fuel storage dictate that the flash-point of fuel should not be lower than 339 K. Flammable products having flash-points below 339 K are governed by special regulations for storage and handling. In the latter category, kerosenes in the UK are required to have flash-points above 296 K and in normal practice have flash-points above 311 K.

Two types of apparatus are used in the UK to determine the "closed" flash-point of a fuel ("closed" denotes that the vapour and air mixture is in a confined space above the liquid). The Pensky-Martens apparatus (Fig. 44) is used when the flash-point is higher than 322 K and the Abel apparatus is used for fuels whose flash-point is lower than this temperature. Each apparatus operates on the same principles. The oil under test is

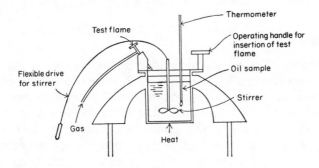

Fig. 44. *Pensky–Martens apparatus for closed flash-point.*

heated at a constant rate in a covered metal cup, and at intervals a small test flame is introduced through an opening in the lid of the cup. The temperature of the oil at which insertion of the flame causes the vapour–air mixture above the oil in the cup to ignite is the flash-point, equivalent to the lean limit of flammability of the vapour–air mixture.

If the test flame is introduced when the oil is heated above its flash-point, a temperature is reached at which the oil burns continuously—this is known as the "fire point". Its significance is somewhat uncertain.

A flash-point may also be determined when liquid fuel is heated in an open crucible and a test flame is periodically applied above the surface. This is the "open" flash-point and is usually several degrees higher than the corresponding closed flash-point, since ignition takes place when there is just sufficient vapour in excess air rather than in a restricted space as with the "closed" flash-point. The open flash-point has the disadvantage that traces of very volatile material may be lost in draughts of air across the surface.

When it is anticipated that the closed flash-point of the fuel is less than 322 K, the Abel apparatus is used. This differs from the Pensky–Martens apparatus in that the sample is heated by a water bath and an air jacket is interposed between the bath and the sample vessel so that a very slow rate of heating may be employed. Provision is made for cooling the sample and apparatus below room temperature before a test is made if the flash-point is lower than 291 K.

It should be noted that to check a flash-point value, a fresh sample of oil must always be used as volatiles are lost from the mixture during a determination. Flash-point tests are used to identify products and also to detect contamination with gasolines or kerosenes for example. More recent developments include the Setaflash Tester described by Handley (1970) and typical values of flash-points are given in Table 28.

D. Volatility

It was stated that flash-point is an indirect measure of volatility. Generally, flash-point is important for fuel oils since it refers to a temperature above normal room or ambient temperature, and volatility is important for gasolines whose flash-point is lower than ambient temperature. Volatility is of particular importance in the specification of a gasoline fuel for a spark ignition, internal combustion engine. It is desirable that an engine should be easy to start under varying temperature conditions, ranging from a maximum in summer to a winter minimum. By increasing the proportion of

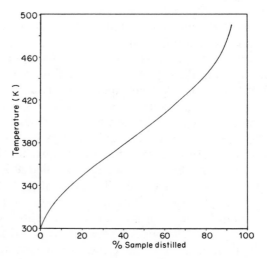

Fig. 45. *Typical curve for petrol distillation test.*

light hydrocarbons in a fuel ease of starting is improved but evaporation losses and problems of vapour lock are increased.

These conflicting factors mean that a compromise must be made. The oil companies, therefore, change the proportion of light hydrocarbons in petrol from summer to winter to give acceptable starting characteristics.

A distillation test can be carried out to show the temperature range over which various portions of the fuel are vaporized. It is usual to distil a 100 cm^3 sample of the fuel and to note the temperature at which the first drop of distillate is collected and also the volume of distillate collected at convenient intervals of vapour temperature. The distillation is stopped when 90% of the sample has been collected and the results plotted as shown in Fig. 45. The 10% distillation point gives an approximate indication of the starting characteristics. Typically, 10% of the sample will have distilled over at 328 K for a winter grade fuel and at 338 K for a summer grade.

The range 50–70% distillation is indicative of the warm-up and acceleration performance and the 50% point is usually less than 385 K as shown in Table 28.

Details of a method for the determination of distillation characteristics of liquids have been specified by the British Standards Institution (1971).

E. Octane Number

In the UK motor gasolines are sold commercially according to their octane number and the grade appropriate to the compression ratio of a particular engine. Octane number is an empirical rating of the anti-knock quality of a fuel. "Knock" is caused by secondary ignition of fuel unburned after normal spark ignition which gives rise to a fast moving flame front in the cylinder. Pressure waves are set up which vibrate against the cylinder walls, giving rise to a "knocking" sound. This feature of a fuel is undesirable because it accelerates wear in the engine bearings and causes overheating in the cylinders.

The tendency of a fuel to knock increases as the compression ratio increases. Certain fuels have better anti-knock characteristics than others because of their molecular structure, branched structures having better characteristics. On the arbitrary octane number scale, iso-octane (C_8H_{18}) is given an octane value of 100; the paraffin, n-heptane (C_7H_{16}), is given a value of zero. The octane number of a fuel is determined by comparing its performance in a standard spark-ignition engine with the performance of various mixtures of iso-octane and n-heptane. The behaviour of the fuel under test is carefully matched by a known mixture of iso-octane and *n*-heptane. The percentage of iso-octane in this mixture is then taken as the octane number of the fuel.

When a fuel has an octane number in excess of 100, a mixture of tetraethyl lead (an anti-knock additive) and iso-octane is matched to the performance of the fuel in the standard engine. The octane number of the fuel is then 100 + the quantity of tetraethyl lead in the mixture measured cm^3 per gallon.

F. Cetane Number and Diesel Index

The cetane number is used to evaluate fuels used in compression-ignition (Diesel) engines and is analogous to octane number (Sellschopp 1971). Cetane (*n*-hexadecane, $C_{16}H_{34}$) is designated 100 and α-methyl-naphthalene ($C_{11}H_{10}$) zero, so that the cetane number of a fuel is the proportion of cetane in a mixture of these having the same ignition delay after injection of the fuel as the test fuel. A high-speed diesel fuel may have a cetane number between 52 and 54 and a relative density of 0·84.

The Institute of Petroleum has proposed a method for the calculation of cetane number given by:

cetane number = 175·4 log (mid-boiling point °F) + 1·98 (°API) − 496

(Goodger 1953). The Diesel index gives an estimation of ignition quality based on the aniline point and the relative density of the fuel:

Diesel index = aniline point (°F) × relative density (°API)

The aniline point of a fuel is the temperature at which equal volumes of fuel and aniline are just miscible. The index indicates the paraffinicity of the fuel and, since paraffins ignite more readily than any of the other components present, it gives an indication of ignition characteristics. It is only applicable to petroleum fuels when there are no additives present.

G. Carbon Residue

The tendency for a diesel oil to form carbon is an important property and is determined by a carbon residue test. Solid carbon may be formed by many oils when they are burned in the absence of a large excess of air or when they are subjected to evaporation and pyrolysis. Carbon residue may be measured empirically by either the Conradson or the Ramsbottom test. Each test involves heating a known mass of the oil in a covered container (a crucible or a special capsule) in a bath, which may be of air or of molten metal. The Conradson test is used for fuel oils while the Ramsbottom test is applied to lubricating oils.

The Ramsbottom test produces the more accurate and reproducible results and, for carbon residues of 1–10%, the two tests are related approximately by the formula

$$\text{Ramsbottom} = 0\cdot8 \times \text{Conradson}$$

The apparatus used for the Conradson test is shown in Fig. 46. There are standard specifications for the shape, size and material of the crucibles, insulator and hood. The sample is heated indirectly by a Meker type burner as shown in the figure; 10 g of oil is used for those oils having carbon residues of less than 5%, and 5 g is used when the higher residues are anticipated. During the test, the crucible is heated strongly, with the burner top some 5 cm below the crucible, so that the pre-ignition time is 600±90 seconds. When smoke appears above the hood, the burner is

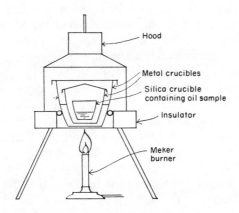

Fig. 46. *Conradson apparatus.*

moved so as to play the flame on the side of the crucible and to ignite the vapours. The rate of heating is adjusted to maintain a steady flame between the top of the hood and the bridge. This heating is continued for 780±60 seconds from the time of igniting the vapours.

When the vapours have ceased to burn, the burner is replaced in its original position so as to heat the lower part of the crucible to a cherry-red colour. This heating is continued for exactly 420 seconds after which the apparatus is left to cool for 900 seconds before the crucible is transferred to a dessicator for final cooling and weighing. The total heating time should not exceed 1800±120 seconds.

When distillate fuels, such as gas oil for high-speed diesel engines, are used, the test is carried out on the 10% residue after distilling 90% of the sample. Such gas oil residues should yield less than 1% carbon residue by the Conradson test, so that accumulation of carbon on the injector nozzles is avoided.

Medium- or slow-speed diesel engines can tolerate much higher carbon residues (up to 10%). Pressure jet and blast atomizing burners, described in Chapter 7, are virtually insensitive to carbon residues, but vaporizing burners are greatly affected by deposits of carbon, which should not exceed 0·05% on the 10% residue.

H. Contaminants in Oil

1. Sulphur in oil

The presence of sulphur in an oil is undesirable for the reasons given in Chapter 2. The sulphur content can be conveniently measured at the same time as the calorific value is determined using the Mahler bomb calorimeter. The method is modified in that 5 cm^3 of sodium carbonate solution is placed in the bottom of the bomb and spread over as large an area as possible so that the sulphur dioxide produced by combustion of the sulphur in the fuel forms a solution of sodium sulphate. At the end of the calorific value determination, the solution is removed and the sulphur precipitated as barium sulphate by mixing the solution with barium chloride. The sulphate precipitate is then filtered off, dried and weighed. The mass of sulphur from the oil sample is then 13·73% of the weight of the barium sulphate formed.

Diesel fuels for road vehicles contain about 0·5–1% sulphur and for low-speed diesel engines, this value may be as high as 2%. Heavy furnace oil from Middle East crude oils, can contain as much as 4% total sulphur.

The corrosiveness of a fuel oil is directly related to the organic sulphur content. This corrosiveness may be determined by observing the colour bands of a strip of copper immersed in the oil.

2. Water in oil

Water in an oil is undesirable because the presence of globules of water at the outlet of an oil burner may lead to flame failure, either by interrupting of the oil supply or quenching the flame by the sudden evolution of a mass of steam. Also globules of water may freeze in supply lines during cold weather.

The method of Dean and Stark is commonly employed for determining the water content of an oil. During this test the oil sample is heated under reflux with an organic liquid which is immiscible with water, such as xylene or petroleum ether. The normal form of apparatus is shown in Fig. 47. The sample and organic liquid are heated gently in a round-bottomed flask. The water and some of the organic liquid are boiled off and the reflux from the condenser is collected in a graduated vessel below the condenser. The water separates below the organic liquid and its volume may be measured directly. The water content is usually quoted on a volume basis for liquid

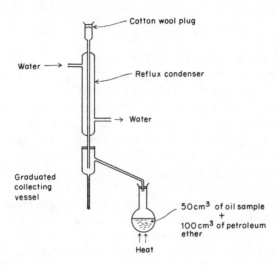

Fig. 47. *Dean and Stark apparatus for the determination of water in oil.*

fuels. The Karl–Fischer technique which involves titration of an extract of the oil with a special reagent can be quicker and is more sensitive to low water concentrations.

I. Other Tests

1. *Surface tension*

The surface tension of a liquid is important as a measure of its "wettability", or the way in which it forms drops and globules on a flat surface. It is usually measured by means of a du Noüy tensiometer, in which a wire ring, suspended from one arm of a beam, is positioned just below the liquid surface. Weights are placed on the pan suspended from the other arm of the balance until the ring just breaks free of the liquid. The ring is shaped so that the perimeter, placed perpendicular to its eventual direction of motion, is 1 cm. Since surface tension is defined as the force acting on a 1 cm length in the surface, the weight required to cause the ring to break the surface is directly proportional to the surface tension ($N\ m^{-1}$). Direct-reading instruments are also available in which the force to lift the ring from the sample is applied by twisting a wire, the torque being calibrated in units of surface tension. A technique for the calculation of the surface tension of hydrocarbon mixtures has been presented by Bagzis and Maddox (1970).

2. Pour point

The pour point of an oil fuel is defined as the lowest temperature at which the oil will flow, or pour, when cooled without agitation under standard conditions. The oil sample is placed in a $3 \cdot 20$ cm diameter tube surrounded by a wider bore tube to provide an air jacket. The sample is warmed to 320 K to ensure that any wax crystals are dissolved. The tube is then placed in an ice–water or freezing bath, according to the pour point anticipated. The sample is cooled slowly and the tube is withdrawn from the bath at 3 deg K intervals and tilted gently. Eventually a temperature is reached when the tube can be held horizontally for 5 s without any movement of the oil. The pour point is taken as the temperature 5 deg K above the point of solidification and indicates the resistance of the oil to congealing at low temperatures. The point is related to the viscosity of the oil and to the formation of a delicate structure of wax crystals within the fluid oil. In the latter case, the oil may be pumpable at temperatures below the pour point but will not flow spontaneously under a small pressure head, especially in narrow-bore tubes. The pour point is therefore important in the design of heating jackets for liquid fuel lines from the storage vessel to the burner. Apparatus for the automatic determination of pour point has been described by Campbell (1970).

This discussion of the various tests on liquid fuels has necessarily been brief. Fuller details are given in the appropriate Institute of Petroleum Specification (1978) and the more important tests are:

IP Serial	Test
1/74	Acidity of Petroleum Products
2/78	Aniline point
12/73	Heat of combustion of liquid fuels
13/78	Conradson residue of petroleum products
15/67(75)	Cloud and pour points
21/53(75)	Diesel Index
33/59(78)	Flash-point—Abel
34/75, 35/63(75)	Flash and fire point—Pensky–Martens
41/60	Ignition quality of diesel fuels

IV. FUEL AND FLUE GAS ANALYSIS

Mention has been made already of methods used to determine the relative density and calorific value of a fuel gas. In addition to these properties, the hydrogen, hydrocarbon and carbon monoxide contents are also very important as the composition of a fuel gas greatly influences its properties and combustion characteristics. Gas burners are generally designed for one particular fuel and they will not operate satisfactorily or safely with a fuel of a significantly different composition.

A flue gas contains fewer components than the majority of fuel gases, the important constituents being carbon dioxide, carbon monoxide, nitrogen, water, water vapour and often oxygen, with possibly excess fuel. Because there is no technical advantage to be gained from a high degree of precision in flue gas measurements, the presence of minor constituents, such as sulphur dioxide, is normally ignored. A flue gas analysis serves to indicate the completeness of combustion by the presence or absence of carbon monoxide, for example, and in the case of coal, it leads to an estimate of the carbon and hydrogen content of the fuel. The presence of nitrogen oxides in exhausts is important and their analysis is reviewed by Allen (1973).

In general, then, a fuel gas may contain more components than a flue gas and it is important that the analysis of the former be known accurately. The same methods can be used to analyse both fuel and flue gases but, in addition, there are some less accurate methods available for analysing flue gases, often giving continuous monitoring of one component.

Methods of gas analysis are classified according to the means by which the components are separated for individual measurement. The two important techniques used for such separation are selective chemical and selective physical absorption. Once isolated, each component is determined, either qualitatively or quantitatively, by measurement of a physical property such as volume, pressure, density, thermal conductivity, refractive index, paramagnetic susceptibility, or energy absorption in the infra-red, visible or ultraviolet electromagnetic spectrum. Many of these

TABLE 28. *A summary of the important properties of liquid fuels. Recalculated data based mainly on Spiers (1945).*

		Gasoline	Methanol	TVO	Kerosine	Diesel oil	Light fuel oil	Heavy fuel oil
Relative density	(288/288 K)	0·745	0·796	0·780	0·793	0·870	0·895	0·950
Composition	°API	58·4	46·3	50	47	31	26·6	17·5
	C	85·4	37·5	86·2	86·3	86·3	86·2	86·1
	H	14·6	12·5	13·8	13·6	12·8	12·4	11·8
	S	0·03	0	0·01	0·08	0·9	1·4	2·1
Calorific value (MJ kg⁻¹)	gross	46·0	22·7	46·7	46·6	46·0	44·8	44·0
	net	43·8	20·0	43·6	43·6	43·2	42·1	41·4
Flash point (K)	Abel	–	–	310	312	–	–	–
	Pensky–Martens	–	–	–	–	349	352	383
Volatility Vapour pressure (kN m⁻²) at	300K	23	–	0·9	1·3	–	–	–
	400K	303	–	40	36	6·7	5·0	1·3
	500K	1425	–	401	272	80	53	19
	600K	4000	–	1879	1032	411	253	119
	700K	8350	–	5570	2715	1330	783	430
Boiling point (K)	initial	307	338	388	413	450	475	525
	mid	383	338	440	469	573	620	–
	final	463	338	469	588	–	–	–
Spontaneous ignition temperature (K) (in oxygen)		558	730	540 000	532	545	535	535
Viscosity (Redwood s) at	70°F	–	–	–	–	38	203	4850
	100°F	–	–	–	–	35	89	1215
	140°F	–	–	–	–	–	51	360
	200°F	–	–	–	–	–	37	102
(m²s × 10⁻⁴) at	294 K	0·0076	0·0075	0·0139	0·0160	0·049	0·50	12·0
	310 K	0·0062	0·0055	0·0110	0·0120	0·033	0·21	3·0
	333 K	–	–	0·0080	0·0090	0·020	0·095	0·88
	336 K	–	–	0·0059	0·0065	0·013	0·043	0·24

determinations require sophisticated apparatus and may demand considerable operative skills.

A. Selective Chemical Absorption

Selective chemical absorption is the most widely used of the manual methods of gas analysis. Generally these employ two successive stages: firstly, direct absorption from the sample, and secondly, oxidation (often combustion) of the sample followed by a further absorption stage. During the primary absorption stage, the sample is mixed in turn with a series of reagents which selectively absorb one, or possibly two, of the components present. The reagents used are as follows:

CO_2, SO_2 and H_2S absorbed by caustic alkali solution (KOH),
O_2 absorbed by alkaline pyrogallol solution,
CO absorbed by ammoniacal cuprous chloride solution,
Unsaturated hydro-
    carbons absorbed by bromine water or various concentrations of sulphuric acid.

The reagents are used in the order shown above, since alkaline pyrogallol will absorb CO_2, SO_2 and H_2S together with O_2, if these components have not been removed previously.

After these absorptions the residual gas sample often contains hydrogen, the lower paraffin hydrocarbons and nitrogen. These components can be determined quantitatively by combustion and subsequent absorption of carbon dioxide and water formed. The combustion may be carried out either by mixing a known volume of residual gas with a known volume of air, exploding the mixture and noting the volume change after explosion and the volume of CO_2 formed, or by oxidizing the gas through contact with hot copper oxide at a series of progressively higher temperatures. At 550 K, hydrogen in contact with hot copper oxide is completely oxidized to water, which condenses when the residual gas is cooled. Hence the volume change is proportional to the hydrogen removed. At 1025–1075 K, the saturated paraffin hydrocarbons, C_nH_{2n+2}, are completely oxidized. For example:

$$CH_4 + 2O_2 \rightarrow CO_2 + 2H_2O$$
$$C_nH_{2n+2} + \tfrac{1}{2}(3n + 1)O_2 \rightarrow nCO_2 + (n + 1)H_2O$$

When the residual gas is cooled, there is no volume change if methane only has been oxidized and the volume of methane originally present in the sample is given by the carbon dioxide volume absorbed from the cooled residual. If higher hydrocarbons are present ($n > 1$), there is an expansion after oxidation. This expansion, and a measure of the carbon dioxide formed, allows the original proportion of hydrocarbon in the sample to be calculated and a non-integer number be assigned to n, indicating the possible presence of higher paraffins (e.g., C_3H_8, C_4H_{10}).

Gas analyses are normally expressed on a volume basis. These may be obtained by measuring either the volume change accompanying an absorption or the pressure change. The former involves constant pressure apparatus in which the temperature and pressure are maintained at the

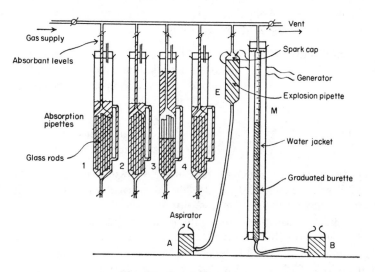

Fig. 48. *Orsat apparatus.*

same value throughout the measurements of volume. The pressure change due to absorption of a component is measured in constant volume equipment. Since each component in a gas mixture exerts a partial pressure which is in proportion to its proportion by volume in the mixture, the composition determined in constant volume apparatus is also on a volumetric basis.

The Orsat apparatus shown in Fig. 48 is the commonest constant pressure apparatus used for fuel and flue gas analysis. The apparatus is available in a variety of forms, ranging from elaborate laboratory equipment to simple portable equipment for on-site work; the more refined the apparatus, the better the accuracy attainable. Even the portable Orsat has the facility of determining hydrogen and paraffin hydrocarbon content by combustion or explosion with air, although for flue gas analyses only the

CO_2, O_2 and CO contents are measured directly—N_2 is obtained by difference.

The reagents in the absorption pipettes are as follows:

Pipette	Gas absorbed	Reagent	Concentration
1	unsaturated hydrocarbons	bromine water	sat. bromine water + 2 vols water
2	CO	cuprous chloride	16% solution in conc. HCl
3	O_2	pyrogallol	5% solution in KOH
4	CO_2	potassium hydroxide	25 g/100 cm^3 water

Analysis of fuel gases by this method has now been largely superseded by more modern techniques such as gas chromatography, though it is still used widely in analysing flue gases, where an accuracy of 1% is adequate. In Chapter 9, Example 9.3, typical data from an Orsat are used to calculate the composition of a gas, and in Example 9.8 the Orsat analysis is used to calculate the calorific value of a gaseous fuel.

The Bone and Wheeler apparatus gives a more precise analysis than the Orsat. This apparatus is of the constant volume type, using mercury as the containing fluid, and demands some degree of skill in its use. The changes in sample pressure following the removal of successive components, necessarily removed in the same order as with the Orsat, are accurately measured.

More accurate analyses may be performed on more complex equipment, although such equipment uses somewhat complicated measurements of electromagnetic absorption, ionization or density.

B. Selective Physical Absorption

The commonest type of selective physical absorption for the analysis of fuel and flue gases is gas chromatography. This relies on the ability of certain materials, solid or liquid, to absorb the components in the sample gas on to the surface of the material for a length of time which depends on the properties of the gas components, the absorptive material and the physical conditions of the system. Since the various components in the sample are retained by the absorbent for differing periods of time, it is possible to separate the components by passing the sample in a stream of inert carrier gas (nitrogen or argon) into a column containing the active material, either in the form of a solid or as a non-volatile liquid absorbed in a porous solid. Factors such as the length and diameter of the column, the flow rate and type of carrier gas, the number and type of components, and the temperature at which the separation is carried out, influence the efficiency of separation.

A small sample (10^{-3} to 10 cm³) is injected into the carrier gas stream at the entry to the adsorbent-packed column as near instantaneously as is possible. The carrier gas leaving the column of packed adsorbent is contaminated with traces of each component of the sample in turn. The presence of these traces can be detected by instruments which measure physical properties of the stream, such as gas density, thermal conductivity, or thermal ionization. Each type of detector is constructed so that the electrical signal which it produces is directly proportional to the amount of contaminant (gas component) in the carrier gas stream passing from the packed column. The detector output signal is fed to a chart recorder where each component is displayed as a peak in the pen trace (see Fig. 49), the

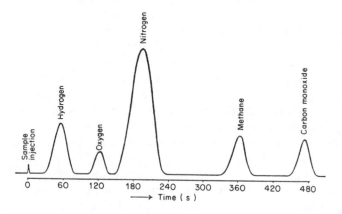

Fig. 49. *A typical chromatogram.*

quantity of component being proportional to the area under its characteristic peak.

Once the parameters of the chromatographic system have been fixed so as to give complete and rapid separation of the components in the small fuel or flue gas samples, the system requires calibration. This can be done most conveniently with known-volume samples of pure components or standard mixtures of all the components expected in the samples. The area under the characteristic peak for each component can then be calibrated to give a direct measure of the amount of component present. Under a fixed set of operating conditions, the components will leave the column at times after injection which are constant for each individual component.

Gas chromatographs can be arranged to carry out complex separations in a matter of 10–20 minutes and simple separations in a matter of seconds. They are very well suited to analysis of fuel gases where there are six or more components and several are hydrocarbons which are not measured separately in an Orsat analysis, for example. Gas chromatographs are being used increasingly in industrial application and new developments include an automatic device described by Stockwell (1970). A general guide to the selection of equipment and techniques for the analysis of gases by chromatography is given by the British Standards Institution (1970).

C. Industrial Automatic Analysis

On an industrial plant it is desirable to have a continuous monitoring of certain parameters. Very precise measurement is not required but an indication is needed of the efficiency of the combustion of a fuel, in the case of a flue gas analyser.

The examples given in Chapter 9 show the importance of a knowledge of flue gas composition. The majority of gas analysers employed on combustion equipment are used to measure the concentration of one component or more in the flue gas. These analysers are often automatic, and tend to be specific in their determination, measuring a unique level of thermal conductivity or paramagnetic susceptibility.

Instruments are available to measure the thermal conductivity of carbon dioxide in a sample. It is possible to do this because CO_2 has a much lower thermal conductivity than the other main components of flue gas (O_2 and N_2). The method involves passing the dried, or fully saturated (since water has a thermal conductivity very similar to that of carbon dioxide) sample stream through one of two identical cells containing a platinum resistance wire, heated by a stabilized AC supply, while a stream of air is passed through the second cell. The two resistances are connected into a Wheatstone bridge circuit and the off-balance of the bridge is indicative of the cooling effect of the flue gas stream on the platinum wire, whose resistance decreases with reduction in temperature. The extent of cooling is due to the carbon dioxide content so that the off-balance shown on a chart recorder is a measure of the carbon dioxide content.

This meter gives tolerably accurate readings except when hydrogen is present in the gas stream, as the thermal conductivity of hydrogen is eleven times that of carbon dioxide. It can be adapted to measure $(CO + H_2)$ concentrations by the addition of a combustion stage followed by a second Wheatstone bridge.

Of all the usual flue gas components, only oxygen is paramagnetic, i.e. it responds to an imposed magnetic field and is attracted towards the strongest region of the field. If a flue gas is free of nitric oxide (also paramagnetic), then its response to an imposed magnetic field is due only to the oxygen present. Various instruments have been devised to record

such a response. One such (Fig. 50) is in the form of an annular gas passage
having a gas inlet and outlet diametrically opposed, and a connecting
passage across the perpendicular diameter. The connecting tube is wound
with a centre-tapped coil of platinum wire which acts as two arms of a
Wheatstone bridge circuit. One arm of the bridge is surrounded by a
permanent magnet. On entering the magnetic field the oxygen is heated by
the platinum coil and its paramagnetic susceptibility is lowered. The
pressure of cool oxygen being attracted towards the magnetic field causes a
flow of oxygen into the connecting tube at the end where the magnet is

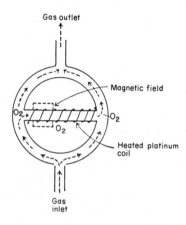

Fig. 50. *A paramagnetic oxygen indicator.*

placed and out into the annular passage at the other. This flow causes a
cooling of the heating coil at the magnetic end and its resistance decreases.
The off-balance of the Wheatstone bridge is proportional to the oxygen
content of the flue gas and may be displayed on a chart recorder.

These instruments give acceptable accuracy, but should be recalibrated
at regular intervals by a manually operated Orsat apparatus. More recent
developments in gas analysis have been described by Schwartz (1971).

V. FURTHER READING

Brame, J. S. S. and King, J. G. (1955). "Fuel, Solid, Liquid and Gaseous".
    Arnold, London.
Brooks, A. E. and Dunstan, A. E. (1950). "The Science of Petroleum",
    Vol. 15, Part 1, Crude oils—chemical and physical properties. Oxford
    University Press, London.

Brooks, A. E. and Dunstan, A. E. (1955). "The Science of Petroleum", Vol. 5, Part 3, Refinery products. Oxford University Press, London.

Campbell, J. R. (1961). "Methods of Analysis of Fuels and Oils". Constable, London.

Dinsdale, A. and Moore, F. (1962). "Viscosity and its Measurement". Chapman and Hall, London.

Gallant, P. W. (1970). "Physical Properties of Hydrocarbons". Gulf Publishing Co., Houston.

Himus, G. W. (1946). "Fuel Testing". Leonard Hill, London.

Hude, C. G. and Jones, M. W. (1960). "Gas Calorimetry". Benn, London.

Institute of Petroleum (1964). "Standards for Petroleum and its Products". The Institute of Petroleum, London.

Institute of Petroleum (1978). "Methods for Analysis and Testing", 37th Edn. Heyden, London.

Lodding, W. (1967). "Effluent Gas Analysis", Vol. 1. Edward Arnold, London.

Maxwell, J. B. (1950). "Data Book on Hydrocarbons". Van Nostrand, New York.

Popovich, M. and Hering, C. (1959). "Fuels and Lubricants". Wiley, New York.

Pugh, B. (1966). "Fuel Calorimetry". Butterworths, London.

Tine, G. (1961). "Gas Sampling and Chemical Analysis in Combustion Processes". Pergamon Press, London.

Tranchant, J. (1969). "Practical Manual of Gas Chromatography". Elsevier, London.

Energy Conversion with Combustion

7

I. INTRODUCTION

Previous chapters have been concerned with the production and properties of fuels. This section is devoted to a discussion of the utilization of fuels and, in particular, energy conversion by the combustion process, the most important feature being the production and the control of a flame. Flames are associated with the combustion of a flowing stream of fuel, whether it be solid, liquid, or gas. In general terms, combustion denotes any fast (<1 s) exothermic gas phase chemical reaction (the combustion of solid carbon may be a heterogenous reaction), and a flame is defined as a combustion reaction which propagates subsonically through space, usually accompanied by visible radiation (Akita 1971).

A combustion reaction, whether in a furnace or an engine, is accompanied by the release of energy, principally in the form of heat, which may be used to generate steam, to heat a process stream or a space, or to produce mechanical power directly. The heat from the combustion process stems from the release of energy when the carbon and hydrogen atoms in a carboneous fuel react with oxygen or with air. It is evolved irrespective of whether a solid, liquid, or gaseous fuel is used in any of these applications.

The physical form of the fuel, however, will affect the method by which fuel and oxidant are mixed and ignited. In many respects, gaseous fuels are the easiest to deal with since they are miscible in all proportions with the oxidant, i.e. oxygen or air. This goes some way towards fulfilling the first condition for efficient combustion—that the fuel and oxidant be thoroughly mixed.

It is convenient to consider one or two important routes for the direct

154

conversion of energy in this chapter, since magnetohydrodynamics, thermionics and so on involve a combustion stage and fuel cells may be thought of as a means of achieving slow combustion. Before discussing these topics however, attention is devoted to the principles of combustion, burner design and a description of combustion plant.

II. COMBUSTION

A. Gaseous Fuels

1. *General principles*

Because mixing of a gaseous fuel with air for combustion may be achieved relatively easily, it is comparatively simple to produce an oxidizing, a neutral, or a reducing environment within the flame gases. An excess of combustion air will produce an oxidizing flue gas, and a fuel-rich mixture (too little air for stoichiometric combustion) produces a reducing flue gas. A neutral atmosphere may be produced by burning the fuel in its stoichiometric proportion of air.

Gaseous fuels have the advantage that complete combustion can be obtained with very little excess air in the mixture, although gas mixtures containing large proportions of hydrocarbons (such as propane or butane) require a rather greater excess of air for combustion than do hydrogen or carbon monoxide. The rate of output of heat from a gas flame can be easily controlled by varying the flow rate of the gas, within certain limits, and the rate and mode of introducing the air for combustion.

The behaviour of a fuel gas on combustion is dictated by a combination of several factors, including the volumetric ratio of fuel gas to air, and the velocity at which the neat gas, or a gas–air mixture, emerges from the burner nozzle. The temperature of the gas–air mixture is also important, and so are the proportions and type of constituents in the mixture. The important parameters of the system, such as ignition temperature, limits of flammability and burning velocity, are all influenced by these factors.

2. *Ignition temperature*

The ignition temperature of a mixture of a combustible gas with air, or oxygen, is the lowest temperature at which combustion becomes self-propagating. At this temperature the rate of heat release from the initial combustion just exceeds the rate at which heat is lost to the surroundings. If, for example, a mixture of hydrogen and oxygen were gradually heated, the temperature rise of the mixture would be approximately proportional to the rate of heat input. A slow combination reaction,

$$H_2 + \tfrac{1}{2}O_2 \rightarrow H_2O(vap.) + 241 \cdot 2 \quad kJ,$$

would take place, but most of the heat released would be dissipated to the surroundings and would not be effective in raising the temperature of the mixture. As the temperature is increased, the rate of reaction, or combustion, increases until, at 855–865 K, the rate of combustion becomes very rapid. Below the ignition temperature of 860 K, the combustion reaction slows down and gradually stops if the external heating is terminated. Above this temperature, however, the reaction becomes self-supporting and continues until all the hydrogen, has been consumed. The ignition temperatures of common fuel gas components are shown in Table 29.

TABLE 29. *Ignition temperatures of common fuel gas components in air at atmospheric pressure*

Component	Ignition temperature (K)
Hydrogen	860
Carbon monoxide	925
Methane	925–945
Ethane	850
Propane	820
Butane	800
Ethylene	820
Propylene	830

Similar data for gaseous and liquid petroleum products have been presented by Goodger (1979). The general topic of self-ignition of hydrocarbons is discussed by Penchenkov (1972).

An increase in total pressure in the system lowers the ignition temperature because the concentrations of the gases are increased—a matter of some significance in internal combustion engines. The presence of inert components, such as moisture, raises the ignition temperature, since the system is thereby diluted.

3. *Limits of flammability*

A mixture of a combustible gas and air cannot be ignited, that is it cannot achieve self-supporting combustion, if there is either too little or too much combustible present. All combustible gases have these two limits of flammability and each gas has a different range of fuel–air mixtures which can be ignited. The limiting values of flammability are called the lower, or lean limit, and the upper, or rich limit, respectively, according to whether there is too little or too much combustible gas present for ignition to be possible. Table 30 shows values for the limits of flammability of

TABLE 30. *Approximate limits of flammability of gases in air at STP and with upward propagation*

Gas	Lower limit (v/v %)	Upper limit (v/v %)
Hydrogen	4·0	75
Carbon monoxide + water vapour	12·5	74
Methane	5·3	15
Ethane	3·0	12·5
Propane	2·2	9·5
n-Butane	1·9	8·5
Ethylene	3·1	32·0
Propylene	2·4	10·3
Coal gas†	5·3	31
Water gas†	6–9	55–70
Natural gas†	4·8	13·5

† Depending on the composition of the fuel.

common gases and gas mixtures. These values are only approximate since the limits are greatly influenced by the size and shape of the environment in which combustion takes place, by the direction in which the flame propagates through the gas mixture and by the volumetric composition of the fuel gas mixture. A good review of flammability limits has been presented by Lovachev (1973).

4. *Flame speed*

The flame speed is the speed at which flame will travel in a mixture of a combustible gas and air. Flame speed has an important bearing on the design and operation of gas burners.

Flame may travel in one of three ways in a combustible mixture, depending on the condition of ignition. It may travel with a relatively slow uniform velocity, with a faster, accelerating, velocity, or the latter may reach such proportions that the velocity becomes very high and the combustible mixture is said to "detonate".

It is with the slow uniform velocity of flame propagation that the designer is primarily concerned and this can be altered by changing the proportion of combustible gas in the gas–air mixture, provided that the composition remains within the limits of flammability. The flame speed has its lowest value for mixtures near to either of the limits and has a maximum value for mixtures which contain slightly more combustible gas than the stoichiometric mixture (i.e. fuel-rich). Typical values for the maximum flame speed of the common gases under laboratory conditions are given in Table 31.

TABLE 31. *Maximum flame speeds and the corresponding mixtures of gases in air*

Gas	Mixture (vol. % combustible)	Flame speed (cm s^{-1})
Hydrogen	42	252
Carbon monoxide	45	43
Methane	9·96	33·8
Ethane	6·28	40·1
Propane	4·54	39·0
Butane	3·52	37·9
Ethylene	7·40	68·3
Propylene	5·04	43·8
Town gas	–	100

No relationship has yet been established between flame speed and the chemical structure of a gas.

B. Liquid Fuels

There are several important liquid fuels, ranging from volatile fuels for internal combustion engines to heavy hydrocarbon fractions, sold commercially as fuel oils. Fuels for spark-ignition and compression-ignition internal combustion engines and for gas turbines will be described later in this chapter and the combustion of fuel oils, in particular, will be discussed in this section.

Fuel oils comprise a range of liquid combustibles, mainly hydrocarbons, which are obtained either as distillates in the working up of petroleum or as residues after the lighter fractions have been removed. Efficient combustion of a fuel oil takes place when the hydrocarbons in the fuel are burned under such conditions that they combine with the oxygen in the combustion air to form carbon dioxide and water vapour. As in the case of gaseous fuels, good mixing between fuel and oxidants is essential for complete combustion. The liquid fuel and combustion air are intimately mixed in a suitable burner, which either vaporizes the oil or disperses it into droplets which then vaporize before burning. It is important that the vapour or spray is brought into intimate contact with the air at a sufficiently high temperature and for a sufficient time to permit the combustion reactions to go to completion. There must be sufficient air to complete the combustion of the oil but not too large an excess, which will cool the products of combustion. In addition, the air must be present in every part of the combustion chamber, otherwise pyrolysis of the fuel oil will take place instead of combustion, giving rise to solid carbon, which is undesirable both because of the waste of heat which it represents and because it appears as black smoke in the waste gases.

The combustion of a liquid fuel takes place in a series of stages: atomization (where applicable), vaporization, mixing of the vapour with air, ignition and maintenance of combustion (flame stabilization). The factors which control these stages can be altered to regulate the rate of heat release according to the particular application.

The viscosity of a fuel oil is the property which governs the method by which a liquid fuel is burned. Each type of atomizing burner can handle oils of a narrow viscosity range with which it gives satisfactory performance. A combination of viscosity and surface tension dictates the size of droplet formed by passage through a particular hole. Consequently it is often necessary to preheat the fuel to a temperature at which the viscosity falls within the prescribed range for the burner.

Flame stabilization requires that the combustion mixture be heated to a temperature at which the reactions persist. It is common practice for radiation from the surroundings and some recirculation of the flame gases to be used to supply sufficient heat to the fuel–air mixture to raise it to the required temperature. The form of recirculation pattern varies with the types of burners used.

An excellent survey of the combustion of liquid fuels in sprays has been presented by Williams (1976).

C. Solid Fuels

1. Pulverized fuel

A very high proportion of coal mined now is used for steam raising in conventional power stations. In the majority of these steam generators, the coal is supplied as a finely ground powder, known as pulverized fuel, which is blown into a large combustion chamber by a blast of air. The fine coal particles then burn while suspended in air, in much the same manner as atomized oil droplets. It is possible, therefore, to obtain complete combustion with only a small excess of air, thus reducing the heat loss in the flue gases, giving a higher flame temperature which means that smaller ducts are required for venting the flue gases to atmosphere.

Coal is pulverized to obtain a very high specific area (surface area per unit mass). This promotes a fast reaction between air and volatile matter which is released as the particles are heated, and fast combustion of the solid residue. Because of the higher specific surface obtainable by pulverizing a coal, it is possible to burn a wide range of coals in this way; examples are lignite, bituminous coal, anthracite, coke and even peat. Considerations such as the initial cost of the fuel and the wear of the hammers or balls in the pulverizing mills will often dictate which type of fuel is most suited to a particular application.

The shape and size of the combustion chamber depends very much on the application. Chambers as large as 500 m³ are in use, and the shape is governed by the design of the entry port for the air-borne pulverized fuel and secondary air streams. Experience has shown that the combustion process is accelerated when the air supply is made to form a vortex in which there is intense agitation of the particles of burning fuel. The primary air, which carries pulverized coal into the furnace, is used to establish this vortex; secondary air is admitted to provide more oxygen for combustion and to stabilize the flame. Often tertiary air is introduced at some point remote from the main combustion zone in order to complete the combustion process.

When pulverized fuel burners were first employed, they were used in conventional furnaces with solid refractory walls. This resulted in serious erosion of the walls by abrasion by particles of fused ash from the intense combustion. Pulverized fuel furnaces are now built sufficiently large to ensure that the burning fuel does not impinge upon the walls, which are water-cooled. The walls are constructed of tubes in the main water-system of the unit, and may be either bare and exposed to direct radiation from the furnace, or embedded in refractory bricks, which are thus cooled and prevented from overheating.

Combustion of coal particles has received extensive attention in recent years, ranging from studies with a single particle to the performance of pulverized fuel burners on a commercial scale. Typical of the many contributions to the literature is a paper by Baum and Street (1971).

2. Combustion on a grate

Coal is also burned in boilers on grates made up of series of individual firebars placed parallel to one another and only a short distance apart. A bed of coal, at various stages of combustion, rests on top of this grate and air is passed upwards between the bars into the bed of coal. When combustion has taken place for some time, the solid on the grate is arranged as shown in Fig. 51. The incombustible ash forms a narrow layer (20 mm thick) immediately above the bars of the grate. On the top of this

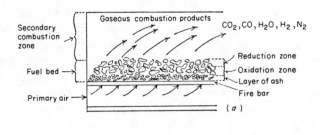

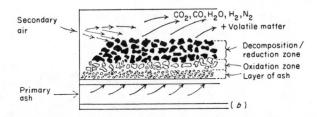

Fig. 51. *Combustion of coal on a grate. (a) Firebed before refuelling.*
(b) Firebed immediately after refuelling.

ash lies a mixture of coke and any fresh coal which has been added. Fresh coal is heated rapidly and decomposes to evolve volatile matter which rises up through the bed into the combustion space above it, where it is burned with secondary air, supplied directly to the space above the bed of solid. When all volatile matter has been evolved, the fresh coal has been converted to coke. This coke forms the bulk of the bed above the ash layer on the grate and burns on the firebed.

As soon as the primary air, passing up between the bars of the grate, contacts the bed of hot coke, the oxygen reacts with the coke to produce carbon dioxide:

$$C + O_2 \rightarrow CO_2$$

This reaction is exothermic and the temperature of the bed is therefore maintained. Oxygen from the primary air is completely consumed by this oxidation reaction in the bottom region of the coke layer (up to 100 mm is used) and the carbon dioxide begins to react with the hot coke:

$$C + CO_2 \rightarrow 2CO$$

This is a reduction reaction and is complemented by two reactions between the coke and any moisture in the air:

$$H_2O + C \rightarrow CO + H_2$$
$$2H_2O + C \rightarrow CO_2 + 2H_2$$

These last two reactions are endothermic and tend to cool the top, reduction, zone of the firebed, in opposition to the heating from the oxidation zone. The proportion of carbon monoxide in the gaseous products immediately above the bed is governed by the temperature of the firebed, the flow rate of air through the bed, and the contact time between air and coke, which is proportional to the thickness of the bed.

The variation in composition of the combustion gases as they pass through the bed has been determined experimentally and has the form shown in Fig. 52. The higher the bed temperature and the longer the

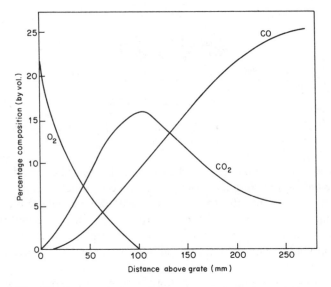

Fig. 52. *Variation of combustion gases through a coal bed.*

contact time, the greater the proportion of carbon monoxide in the combustion gases. Consequently, the use of a minimum thickness of firebed to give a hole-free layer will diminish the production of carbon monoxide in the reduction layer on top of the bed.

The gases in the combustion space above the firebed include nitrogen, water vapour, hydrogen, carbon dioxide, carbon monoxide and volatile matter, during a period after fresh coal has been added to the bed. In order to release the heat from the combustible components (H_2, CO and volatile matter) of this gas mixture, secondary air is fed into the hot gases in sufficient quantities to oxidize the gases completely. The composition of the volatile matter from the coal will change as the pyrolysis reaction proceeds, and also the amount of volatile matter evolved depends upon the rank of the coal fired. Lower-rank coals yield more volatile matter and produce less coke than high-ranked coals. The successful combustion of coal on a grate depends on the successful provision of just sufficient primary and secondary combustion air. Since the amount of secondary air required depends on the nature and amount of volatile matter and the amount of carbon monoxide and hydrogen resulting from a reduction of carbon dioxide and a partial oxidation of the coke with water vapour, the more uniformly the fresh coal feed is introduced on to the bed, the more easily can the supply of secondary air be matched to the needs of the system.

Pulverized coal has several advantages over the combustion of coal on a grate. These may be summarized as follows.

(i) Combustion is complete and smokeless, if the plant is well designed and operated.

(ii) There are no difficulties with the ash fusing as clinker, since there is no fuel-bed.

(iii) Low-grade fuels can be burned efficiently, even if they contain comparatively large quantities of mineral matter, which reduces the capacity of a furnace when the fuel is burned on a grate.

(iv) Because the fine powder can be intimately mixed with air, complete combustion can be maintained with a minimum of excess air.

(v) Distribution and handling of pulverized fuel is easier than for coal, so that costs are reduced.

Combustion on a grate is not limited to coal and indeed the system is used extensively in the field of waste incineration. This is discussed by Corey (1969) and a recent development is the combustion of fuel cylinders reported by Lee (1978).

3. *Fluidized bed combustion*

A relatively new way of burning solid fuels and wastes is in a bed of inert material such as sand or ash, in which passage of the combustion air is such that the solids–air mixture behaves as a fluid. Such a system has many important advantages, such as a high degree of mixing and high rates of heat transfer, and the system is being developed for steam raising on a very large scale and for the incineration of domestic refuse (Hickman 1978). The system can also cope with low-grade coals (Hodgkinson and Thurlaw 1977), that is, coals with high ash and sulphur concentrations, because of the low bed temperature of 1075–1225 K compared with a grate. A general survey of the field has been presented by the Institute of Fuel (1975) and pilot units of a rating around 0·5 MW have been operated with units of up to 30 MW in the course of construction.

The particle size in the bed is in the range 500–1500 μm and during operation, the bed consists essentially of ash from the coal and additives such as lime or dolomite to remove the sulphur. Ash is removed continuously from the bottom of the bed which is limited to a depth of about 0·6 m in order to limit power requirements. The coal, which represents some 5% by mass of the bed, is fed with a size up to 25 mm thus eliminating the crushing required for pulverized fuels.

For steam raising, tubes are immersed in the bed and also located above the free surface. Radiative heat transfer is high and the general design of fluidized bed boilers has been discussed by Hansen (1977). Fluidized bed combustion gives less pollution because of a reduced formation of nitrogen oxides and absorption of sulphur dioxide by dolomite in the bed.

Beds have been operated at pressures in the range 0·6–1·0 MN m^{-2} which permits the use of smaller beds and the possibility of generation of power by the flue gases in a gas turbine, which is important to the economics of the system. Fluidized bed combusters are of increasing importance and it is likely that they will be incorporated into a large proportion of new coal-fired generating stations. A general review of fluidized bed combustion technology has been presented by Rao (1977).

III. BURNER DESIGN

A. Oil Burners

1. Introduction

The combustion of a liquid fuel takes place in a series of stages (atomization, vaporization, mixing of the vapour with air, ignition and maintenance of combustion) as discussed in Section II. B. The function of an oil burner is to atomize the oil, to aid the mixing of the vapour with air and to maintain a stable flame once the mixture has been ignited.

Oil may be burned in one of two ways. It may be vaporized before ignition so that it burns as a gas, or it may be broken into fine droplets (atomized) which are injected into hot air so that they evaporate while burning. Burners of the former, vaporizing, type are not commonly used in industrial applications because they require a highly volatile non-charring fuel such as paraffin or gas oil.

Consequently, atomizing burners form the majority of industrial oil burners. They may be classified according to the source of energy used to disintegrate the fuel.

(a) Pressure jets, in which pressure energy is employed directly.

(b) Rotary atomizers, in which centrifugal energy is imparted to the fuel.

(c) Blast atomizers, in which a gas is impinged on to the liquid.

These atomizers differ also as to the size of droplet and the shape of the burning zone. Pressure jets give a conical spray, rotary atomizers give a very uniform droplet size ($\approx$ 20 μm) over a wide area, and blast atomizers a narrow jet and a long pointed flame, with a more variable droplet size than either of the other types (Williams 1976).

2. Pressure jets

Oil is pumped at high pressure (700–3500 kN m^{-2}) through a fine nozzle to produce a spray of droplets. In order that the nozzle behaves satisfactorily, heavy oils are pre-heated to reduce their viscosity to between 70 and 100 Redwood seconds, depending on the size of the nozzle.

An atomizing burner is shown diagrammatically in Fig. 53. Pre-heated oil enters the swirl chamber B through tangential ports A, rotates in the

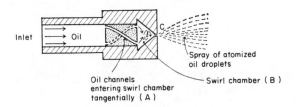

Fig. 53. *Pressure jet atomizing burner.*

chamber around an air core and passes through the orifice C in the form of a hollow conical film. The core expands because of centrifugal force and the film gets thinner until it finally disintegrates into droplets. The size and size range is determined by the operating conditions, the physical properties of the oil and the nature of the surface of the nozzle material.

The flow rate through a nozzle is proportional to the square root of the pressure. Consequently this type of burner has only a narrow throttling range, because doubling the pressure increases the rate by only about 40%. Droplet size is directly proportional to viscosity and inversely proportional to the cube root of pressure, which determines a minimum pressure at which the droplets become too large to burn completely.

The parameter used to characterize the flexibility of a burner is the turn-down ratio. This is defined as the ratio of the maximum to the minimum load or throughput. An atomizing burner has a low turn-down ratio but this difficulty may be overcome by using systems in which individual burners may be turned off or wide-range pressure jets may be employed. Such modifications give claimed turn-down ratios of 10:1, although these burners give poorer atomization than the less complex types.

3. *Rotary atomizers*

In this type of burner, atomization of the oil is achieved by centrifugal force. The oil flows through a central pipe to the inner surface of a revolving hollow tapered cup. It spreads over the surface and is thrown off the periphery of the free end, or lip. Because of the uniformity of the surface of the cup, the thickness of the oil film and the velocity of the oil are the same over the circumference of the rim of the cup. Good atomization is obtained and the droplet size is more uniform for this atomizer than for any other type.

The cup is usually rotated by an electric motor or a turbine, driven by a proportion of the atomizing air, as shown in Fig. 54. The proportion of air

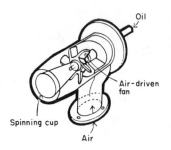

Fig. 54. *Air-driven rotary cup burner.*

used to drive the turbine is about 15% of the air required for combustion and is supplied at a pressure of 200–350 kN m^{-2}. This air then passes around the outside of the cup to prevent oil droplets being dispersed from the rim along a plane at right angles to the axis of the cup and to exert additional atomizing forces on the droplets.

Rotary atomizers require fuels with a viscosity in the range 100–400 Redwood seconds. These viscosities are markedly higher than those for pressure jet atomizers and the turn-down ratio of 5:1 compares very favourably with that associated with simple pressure jet atomizers. The rotary atomizer is much less sensitive to changes in viscosity and is much less liable to be blocked by grit than the pressure jet. It is, however, susceptible to deposition of carbon formed by cracking caused by radiation from the hot surroundings when the burner is shut down.

Fuel oil burners are described by the Belgian Standards Institution (1972).

4. *Blast atomizers*

Blast-atomizing, or twin-fluid, burners operate at low, medium, or high pressures. They are further classified as either internal mixing or external mixing blast burners, according to whether the steam or air and oil impinge within the burner assembly, or the oil is released into the atomizing fluid at the outlet from the burner. In the former type, the oil–air, or steam, mixture leaves the burner as a foam or as a fog, depending on whether the atomizing fluid is sprayed into the oil or vice versa.

The internal-mix burner is the more common type and is used for all three pressure classes. The general form is that shown in Fig. 55, modified

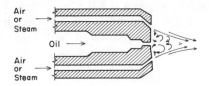

Fig. 55. *Internally mixed blast atomizing burner.*

in particular applications to give finer atomization or improved mixing of fuel and air, and enhanced turn-down ratio.

(a) *Low-pressure blast atomizers, using air at* 105–115 kN m^{-2} *as the atomizing medium.* These use a large proportion and sometimes all of the combustion air as the atomizing medium. The turn-down ratio of such burners is between 2 and 5:1, but where these low values are acceptable, low-pressure (LP) burners are probably the most economical, efficient and reliable. Because of the low pressure involved, air can be supplied from a single-stage centrifugal fan.

When all the combustion air is used for atomization, mixing of the oil and air is efficient and combustion with little requirement for excess air results, but the turn-down ratio rarely exceeds 2:1. Higher turn-down ratios are obtained when some 20% only of the combustion air is used for atomization. In the latter situation, the remaining combustion air is introduced through ports around the burner.

As with all blast-atomizing burners, the low-pressure burner is most effective when the viscosity of the fuel is in the range 70–150 Redwood seconds.

(b) *Medium-pressure blast atomizers, using air at* 230–300 kN m^{-2}. The medium-pressure blast atomizers differ from low-pressure ones in that less than 10% of the combustion air is required to atomize the fuel. A turn-down ratio of 10:1 can therefore be obtained, as the secondary air is controlled seperately from that entering the burner. It is possible to obtain higher flame temperatures with medium-pressure burners because the secondary air may be preheated without danger of cracking the fuel within the burner.

The air is supplied by a rotary compressor whose power requirement may well be less than that for the low-pressure fan, although the compressor itself is more expensive.

(c) *High-pressure atomizing burners, using air of steam at pressures greater than* 300 kN m^{-2}. High-pressure air burners are very similar to the medium-pressure burners but require a more expensive compressor. High-pressure steam burners are used only where a large amount of cheap steam is available, since between 0·3–0·5 kg is required per kg of oil. If such steam atomizers are used in steam-raising plant, the atomizing steam accounts for 2·5% of the steam generated (Williams 1976).

B. Gas Burners

1. *Diffusion flames*

There are two important classes of gas burners. One is the type in which gas and air flow separately into the combustion chamber and intermix as burning proceeds. The flames produced are referred to as "diffusion flames". In the other type, gas and air are intimately mixed whilst cold, and burned as they leave the mixing chamber. The flames from such burners are known as "pre-mixed flames". Within these two classes there is a wide range of individual burners designed to give complete combustion of the particular fuel. Gas properties such as relative density, calorific value, flame speed and limits of flammability affect the design of a particular burner. The flame speed, for example, will dictate the size of burner orifice used to stabilize a desired flow rate of either the fuel gas or a pre-mixed gas-air mixture. If the linear velocity of the gas through the orifice is higher than the flame speed, the flame will tend to "lift off" the burner and be very unstable (Harris and South 1978).

Combustion in diffusion flames takes place when gas is allowed to burn at an orifice by reaction with the surrounding air, or when gas and air streams are passed separately into a furnace, either parallel or impinging. The combustion reactions proceed at rates which depend on the turbulence and degree of mixing within the system. The more turbulent the gas streams, the more efficient is the mixing, the higher the rate of combustion and the hotter the flame.

When "diffusion" burners, or "non-aerated" or "neat gas" burners, are used to burn gases containing a high proportion of hydrocarbons, the flames produced are very luminous because of the incandescence of carbon particles produced by thermal cracking of a proportion of the hydrocarbons. Such flames have high emissivities so that the radiative heat transfer is also high. The presence of solid carbon in the flame gases persists as long as there is insufficient air in the bulk gases to permit secondary combustion of the carbon.

In a simple diffusion burner, the gas is burned at the outlet from a straightforward circular or square-sectioned pipe. Usually, the air for combustion initially fills the combustion space and as combustion proceeds further air is drawn into the chamber through an annulus around the burner tube by the partial vacuum caused by the fuel gas effusing from the pipe. The flame from such a burner is normally large and of an ever-changing shape and has a relatively low flame temperature. The flame may be lengthened considerably by introducing combustion air at a series of ports downstream from the burner mouth. This arrangement is useful in giving fairly uniform heating along the length of a narrow extended furnace.

A smaller, hotter diffusion flame may be produced by arranging the gas exit ports so that several jets impinge on one another, giving rise to a flat or fan-shaped flame. There is a high degree of turbulence in restricted regions which gives rise to improved diffusion of gas and air and to the formation of a short stable flame—e.g. the flame on the Bray jet burner of domestic gas fires (Roper 1978).

Diffusion burners are particularly useful where large volumes of low calorific value gases are to be burned and where both gas and air must be preheated to produce a high flame temperature. In the latter situation it is not possible to mix the fuel and the air within the burner because of the dangers of pre-ignition.

Diffusion flame burners cannot backfire, because there is no air within the burner to sustain combustion, and combustion is silent, which is not the case with aerated burners. There is no necessity for accurate adjustment of the gas and air ports since air is normally drawn in according to the flow rate of gas from the nozzle. The characteristics of the gas have little effect on burner operation, except that a reduction in relative density causes a corresponding change in the thermal input to the burner. Diffusion flame burners normally use gas at low pressure (up to $110\,kN\,m^{-2}$) which is limited by a governor. Their construction is simple and their operation flexible in response to demand.

2. Pre-aerated flames

Burners of this type may be divided into two important groups according to the pressure at which air is supplied to the mixing chamber: low-pressure burners in which air is supplied at atmospheric or slightly higher pressure, and air-blast burners in which combustion is at pressures significantly higher than atmospheric and is blown into the gas stream.

The best known example of a low-pressure aerated burner is the laboratory bunsen burner, shown in Fig. 56. Air is entrained by gas issuing

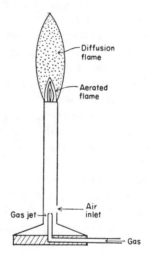

Fig. 56. *Bunsen burner.*

from a jet situated opposite the air valve, into the mixing chamber, which is simply a short length of tube. The mouth of the burner is designed so that the velocity of the gas–air mixture leaving the tube is slightly higher than the flame speed of the mixture involved. If the gas velocity is less than the flame speed of the mixture, the flame will flash back down the tube and seat on the neat-gas nozzle, thus acting as a diffusion flame (Plee and Mellor 1978).

If the gas velocity exceeds the flame speed, the flame lifts off the burner rim and takes up some position above the burner, at which it is very unstable. A stable flame is produced when the velocity is equal to the flame speed. Because the gas velocity at the rim is zero, the parabolic form of the flame front is due to the velocity distribution across the burner tube of the gas in laminar flow. The stabilizing effect of the rim is also dependent on the cooling of the gases by the rim, since the flame will strike back if the rim is allowed to get too hot.

Bunsen burners are designed to entrain approximately half of the air required for complete combustion. The remainder of the combustion air is entrained from the surrounding air into the flame to produce a diffusion flame downstream from the aerated flame, as shown in Fig. 56. Bunsen burners are very sensitive to changes in the relative density of the fuel and each burner is designed to give satisfactory performance over a different narrow range of relative densities according to the fuel gas to be employed.

Low-pressure aerated burners give hotter, smaller flames than do the corresponding diffusion burners. In, for example, the Bunsen burner the diffusion flame makes the system bulky and spreads the heat release over a larger area than is desirable in certain applications. When all the combustion air is pre-mixed with the fuel in the air-blast burner, the flame produced has only the inner cone of the bunsen flame formed by a region of intense combustion and high temperatures. Since the fuel and air may be metered separately, the mixture in the burner is near to stoichiometric. The flame speed is near to its maximum value and the linear velocity of the gas–air mixture must be maintained above this value to avoid the dangers of "flash back".

The "blast" of compressed air may be supplied at pressures in the range 100–3500 kN m^{-2} and is injected into the gas stream whose pressure is much lower, at between 100–2000 kN m^{-2}. The resultant high-pressure mixture permits high gas velocities in the burner tube and gives rise to a high turn-down ratio before the flame strikes back. These high velocities, however, increase the possibility of the flame lifting off the burner rim and blowing out, leaving an explosive mixture in the combustion space.

A simple air-blast burner is shown in Fig. 57, in which the gas and air are mixed at the burner itself. In more complex burners the gases are mixed upstream from the burner before entering the burner tube. These devices are potentially dangerous because of the highly explosive nature of near-stoichiometric fuel gas–air mixtures and flame traps are often incorporated into the fuel lines to obviate the dangers of explosion.

By modifying the design of the burner tunnel itself to minimize the risk of flame "blow-off", it is possible to build air-blast burners capable of very intense combustion over a short flame length.

Recent developments in burner design have included the production of dual fuel burners (Lombardi 1972) and investigations into oscillation combustion (Baade 1978) with its inherent high rates of heat transfer.

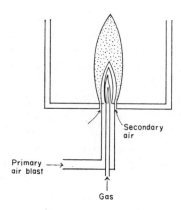

Fig. 57. A simple air-blast burner.

Tearle (1972) describes gas burners for use in furnaces and a general review is presented by Gas World (Anon. 1972c). Future trends in burner design are discussed by Taylor and Hughes (1978) and the problem of burner control is considered by Uram and Crull (1972).

3. Combustion characteristics

At various stages during this discussion of gas burners the importance of the relative density of the fuel gas has been emphasized. At constant pressure, the volume of gas passing through an orifice is inversely proportional to the square root of the relative density (air = 1) by Graham's Law of Diffusion. If the relative density of the fuel gas is reduced, then the volume of gas from a constant pressure supply passing through the orifice of a diffusion-flame burner, for instance, is increased.

Calorific value is the most important property of a fuel gas and is expressed on a volumetric basis. In view of the dependence of volumetric flow rate through an orifice on relative density, it is desirable to combine both parameters into one term. This term is known as the Wobbé Index, or Wobbé Number, of the gas and is defined as:

$$\text{Wobbé Index} = \frac{\text{Calorific value}}{\sqrt{(\text{Relative density (air} = 1))}}$$

This represents the potential heat flow through an orifice at constant pressure and its method of calculation is discussed in Chapter 9, Section VI. D.

The importance of Wobbé Index in the specification of a burner is shown in Fig. 58, which relates Wobbé Index and a flame speed factor (relative to a hydrogen flame speed of 100) for satisfactory performance on coal gas burners or natural gas burners.

In order that a gas may burn satisfactorily on a burner, the following conditions must be satisfied:

(i) Combustion must be complete, i.e. sufficient air must be pre-mixed or entrained to give a low CO content in the flue gases.

(ii) The flame speed must be low enough to prevent "flash back".

(iii) The flame speed must be high enough to prevent "blow off".

In Fig. 58, two areas are shown; the upper zone refers to satisfactory combustion on a burner designed for natural gas and the lower zone refers

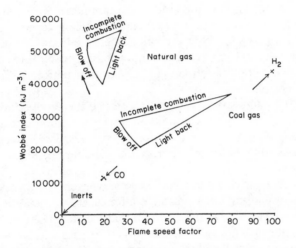

Fig. 58. *Diagram showing the limits of satisfactory combustion of gases burned on appliances adjusted for gas having a Wobbé index between* 26 000 *and* 28 300 kJ m^{-3} *and* 47 600 *to* 50 000 kJ m^{-3}.

to the combustion of coal gas. It will be seen that a given gas mixture can be brought into one of the two zones by addition of hydrogen, which increases the flame speed and Wobbé Index, or of carbon monoxide, which decreases the Wobbé Index. An increased hydrocarbon content reduces flame speed but increases the Wobbé Index.

In the UK, all burners were designed to burn coal gas satisfactorily until the advent of natural gas when every burner was changed to cope with the new fuel. This conversion took place at considerable expense and the factors taken into account at the time may be summarized as follows.

Coal gas normally has a calorific value of 18 630 kJ m^{-3} and a flame speed factor within the range 32–45 (relative to $H_2 = 100$). It is known as a high-speed gas, because its comparatively high hydrogen content (at least 40% by volume) gives it a high flame speed. Methane and natural gas, however, are termed "low-speed gases" because their flame speed factor falls within the range 13–15.

Natural gas is different from coal gas in two other important respects: its calorific value of about 37 000 kJ m^{-3} is nearly twice that of coal gas, and its stoichiometric air requirement is much higher. Thus it is not possible to obtain satisfactory combustion of natural gas on coal gas burners, either aerated or non-aerated.

Several methods were tried to overcome this difficulty. As mentioned, the addition of proportions of particular types of constituents to the gas can alter its flame speed and Wobbé Index. It is not possible, however, to bring the operating point for natural gas within the triangular area for coal gas burners, shown in Fig. 58, by making small additions to the gas. The properties of natural gas can be suitably modified by reforming it in a manner similar to that described in Chapter 4 for petroleum fractions but this is very costly.

Even if the flame speed were enhanced and the Wobbé Index reduced by reforming natural gas, it is unlikely that the combustion air requirements would be very similar to those of coal gas. Consequently, it was necessary to modify the air inlet ports to aerated burners to give the correct air–fuel ratio.

Since such a modification was necessary even if the gas had been reformed, it was decided to exchange all coal gas burners for burners to handle natural gas. These new burners have enlarged air–entry ports to give the higher air–fuel ratio and enlarged nozzles to give a slower gas velocity and minimize the chance of flame lift-off. In non-aerated burners (diffusion flame burners), however, the lower gas velocity and the higher air requirements of natural gas make it impossible to obtain complete combustion so that all natural gas burners are aerated burners and domestic gas fires no longer operate with a complete absence of combustion noise.

IV. COMBUSTION PLANT

A. Boilers and Furnaces

In industrial applications combustion takes place in furnaces of many types designed for a wide range of duties. Furnaces fall conveniently into three classes according to the mode by which the heat of the combustion reaction is transferred to the process stream or stock: these are internally and externally heated furnaces and blast furnaces.

1. *Internally heated furnaces*

Internally heated furnaces are those in which the flames and/or the hot products of combustion come into direct contact with the material to be heated. Such furnaces utilize solid, liquid or gaseous fuels and are typified by open-hearth steel furnaces, metallurgical heating furnaces, and pottery, cement or brick kilns. The physical form of the furnace depends on the form of the material to be heated (the load) and on whether the material is fed through the furnace continuously or in batches.

The majority of kilns are operated continuously and are such that the load is passed through the furnace chamber countercurrently to the flow of hot combustion gases. Often gas or liquid fuel burners are mounted along the length of the kiln to control the heat input and the temperature distribution. A tunnel kiln is one in which the material is transported through the hot zones on bogeys or some similar form of conveyance and the residual heat of these conveyors is used to preheat the secondary combustion air. A rotating kiln is a long cylinder which is inclined to the horizontal and rotates about its longitudinal axis so that granular material fed in at the higher end is transported along the length of the hot space by gravity and by the rotation of the kiln, in opposition to the hot combustion gases from burners at the lower end.

Such furnaces expose the load to impurities in the fuel such as sulphur or ash, unless a gaseous fuel is used. Recent developments include the rotary hearth furnaces described by Scharbrough (1971) and a general survey of open flame furnace design has been presented by Ward (1971).

2. *Externally heated furnaces*

Externally heated furnaces are those in which the process stream is heated primarily by radiative heat transfer from the flames and hot gases. They are known as muffle furnaces when used as gas retorts, coke ovens or metallurgical crucible furnaces, and as steam generators or steam boilers when used to raise steam. The latter application is of paramount importance because of the widespread use of steam, at various pressures, in modern industrial practice.

There are three types of boiler. Small units are used for such purposes as central heating and consist of a combustion space and flue to a stack, surrounded by a jacket containing water, at the top of which wet steam is collected. Such furnaces are cheap, easily operated and maintained, but are not very efficient. They are not suitable therefore for large-scale operations.

A more refined type of boiler is the shell-type, typified by the

Lancashire boiler shown in Fig. 59. This boiler is capable of producing larger quantities of steam at moderately high pressures. The construction is very straightforward and consists of two wide flues which pass right along the length of a cylindrical boiler drum, back along outside the bottom of the drum and then along two side flues to the stack. The two wide flues within the drum contain the combustion space and permit some transfer of heat from the hot combustion products to the water in the drum. More heat transfer takes place during passage of the gases around the outside of the drum but much of the heat evolved during combustion is lost as sensible heat in the gases at the base of the stack.

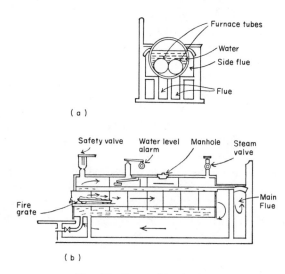

Fig. 59. *Lancashire boiler.*

In order to improve the heat transfer from the hot gases to the water, the Lancashire design has been modified to that of the Economic boiler, (Gunn 1972/1973, Moore 1978). Because of the reduced length of the Economic boiler, combustion is not completed within the two wide flues inside the drum and secondary combustion takes place in a chamber outside one end of the water drum. The hot gases are drawn forward through fine bore tubes immersed in the water shell which provide a large surface area for heat transfer.

Where higher steam pressures and throughputs are required, a water tube boiler is used. The water tubes are arranged mainly in parallel vertical planes and in banks around the combustion space and in the path of the hot gases to the stack. Water drums are mounted, one above and one below the tube banks as shown in Fig. 60. The upper drum acts as a separator between the circulating water and the wet steam and the lower contains water and any solids which have separated out from the circulating water (sludge drum). Water circulation is either by natural convection or by a pump (forced circulation). The water first receives heat from the very hot combustion zone by radiation and then sensible heat is removed by

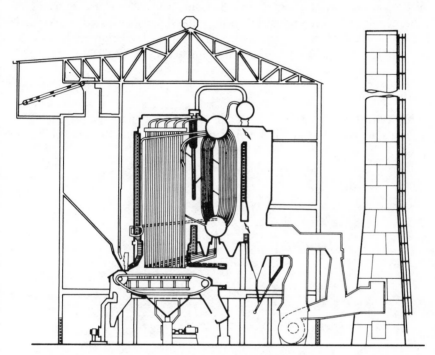

Fig. 60. *Water-tube boiler installed at UKAEA Springfield works. The unit generates* $7 \cdot 6$ kg s^{-1} *steam at* 1380 kN m^{-2} *and* 500 K. (Reprinted by courtesy of Clarke Chapman and Co. Ltd.)

convection from the combustion products. A suitable arrangement of the radiative and convective tube leads to a high degree of superheat in the steam generated. The boiler feed-water is preheated by passage through an economizer and often the combustion air is similarly preheated.

The overall efficiency of any steam raising equipment can be improved by the use of an economizer. This takes the form of a tube bank positioned at the entry to the stack in order to remove the sensible heat from the gases and to preheat the water fed to the shell. The water feed rate through the economizer is adjusted so that the gases are not cooled to below their dew-point, to minimize corrosion. This condition necessarily reduces the overall efficiency of the economizer.

There is an abundance of literature on boiler performance and design and a useful survey of packaged boilers has been presented in Heating and Air Conditioning Journal (Anon. 1977, 1972b); the economics of steam raising are discussed by Lock (1972) and Goodall (1980). The design of oil-fired boilers is considered by Clayton (1971) and a useful paper on combustion safety in industrial boilers has been presented by Monroe (1971). Typical of many papers on corrosion and deposits in boilers are those of Diamant (1972) and an excellent text by Reid (1971).

3. Blast furnaces

In blast furnaces, material to be heated is mixed with the (solid) fuel. The furnaces are essentially cylindrical or rectangular shafts through which the

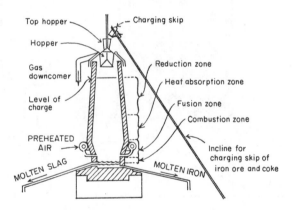

Fig. 61. Simplified view of blast furnace.

solid charge flows downwards under gravity into the space vacated either by removal of solids or liquids from some lower part of the shaft, or by gasification of some part of the charge. The fuel, which is usually coke, is included in the charge and is preheated as the charge descends by a stream of hot gas (N_2 and CO) rising from the burning coke below. The air for combustion is introduced through parts around the lower end of the shaft.

Blast furnaces for the manufacture of iron, such as that shown in Fig. 61 can operate very efficiently not only as heating units but also as high-temperature reaction chambers. They may be up to 30 m high and as much as 10 m in diameter at the base. Heat transfer in this counter-current operation is potentially very high but depends on matching the available heat in the gases to the demand of the stock. Thus efficient heat transfer demands a uniform permeability of the charge from the feed distributor and the highest practicable combustion temperature.

B. Internal Combustion Engines

The two types of internal combustion piston engine, spark-ignition and compression-ignition engines, are commonly known as petrol and diesel engines respectively.

1. *Spark-ignition engines*

In this type of engine, the fuel is mixed with air to form a flammable mixture, compressed in one of the engine cylinders and then ignited by a spark. The mixture burns and the resulting increase in pressure moves the piston and provides the power stroke. The main factor in determining the efficiency of this type of engine is the compression ratio. The higher the compression ratio (ratio of the volume of gas when the piston is at the bottom of its stroke to that when the piston is at the top of its stoke), the greater the efficiency. Unfortunately, the compression ratio is limited by the characteristics of the fuel (octane number being the most important) described in Chapter 6. Above the maximum "useful" compression ratio, "knocking" or pre-ignition occurs and this leads to a decrease in power output and overheating of the engine.

During the normal combustion, the burning takes place in a narrow flame-front which travels through the mixture at a moderately fast subsonic rate. There is a gradual increase in pressure and there are no surges or vibrations in the cylinders. A slow oxidation of the unburned fuel takes place ahead of the flame front in which oxygen combines with some of the hydrocarbon molecules to enhance their energy. These energized molecules then react with adjacent molecules and a chain reaction is set up so that very few unstable compounds are formed and combustion is smooth.

Under certain conditions, combustion starts in the normal manner and then the remaining unburned fuel ignites spontaneously. This happens because the chain reactions just described proceed very rapidly, so that unstable products are formed and the mixture detonates, giving rise to pressure waves which "knock" against the cylinder walls. Small amounts of certain compounds reduce the tendency of a fuel to knock by reacting with activated oxygenated intermediate compounds whose decomposition products lead to knocking. The most effective is tetraethyl lead (TEL) and this is added to the extent of about $0.5 \text{ cm}^3/1000 \text{ cm}^3$ of motor gasoline.

Recently, fuel injection engines have been developed in which the fuel is injected directly into the cylinders and mixed there with the combustion air before the mixture is sparked. The Wankel engine, another important development, has been discussed by Mortimer (1972) and the combustion of methane and LPG as motor fuels is described by Karim and D'Souza (1972) and Anon. (1971b).

2. *Compression-ignition engines*

In contrast to spark-ignition engines, the fuel for a compression-ignition engine is injected into the engine cylinders containing a highly compressed charge of air. The heat of compression raises the air temperature to 875 K and ignites the atomized fuel spontaneously. The oil first absorbs heat from the air and attains its ignition temperature before burning. The interval between the start of injection and ignition of the fuel is termed "ignition delay". Fuels having a short ignition delay are defined as high-quality fuels or fuels having high cetane numbers (Chapter 6). The ignition delay must, however, be sufficiently long for the compression stroke to be completed.

After ignition, fuel is injected into the burning mixture and burns at the rate at which it is injected. It is necessary to obtain complete combustion to give maximum power output and minimum fuel consumption. Excess air is essential for complete combustion but unless the air is in sufficient excess and turbulence, some of the hydrocarbons will be only partially oxidized and will be emitted as a dense black smoke and carbon will be deposited within the cylinders. This deposition causes blockage of the injection nozzles leading to maldistribution of the fuel droplets and increased fuel consumption. For this reason, fuels with low carbon residues (Chapter 6) are desirable as diesel fuels.

As with oil burners, the viscosity characteristics of the fuel greatly influence the size of droplets produced at the nozzles and therefore the time required for complete combustion.

The characteristics of a fuel for a diesel engine depend on factors such as the engine size, speed and load ranges, and the frequency of speed and load changes. The higher the operating speed and the smaller the size, the more critical is the fuel quality so that road vehicles and diesel locomotives demand much higher quality fuels than marine main-propulsion engines, for example.

A useful article dealing with the thermodynamics of diesel, gasoline and Stirling engines has been presented by Wilson (1978).

3. *Gas turbines*

Strictly, a gas turbine is an internal combustion engine which does not use a piston to transmit the power released from combustion of the fuel. It relies on the principle that a jet of gas moving rapidly will move the object from which the gas issues in the opposite direction and that energy of a high velocity gas stream may be converted into shaft power by a turbine. The advantages of a gas turbine for power production and propulsion are:

  (i) Relative simplicity of design.
 (ii) High power/weight ratio.
(iii) Cheap and simplified lubrication.
 (iv) Low capital costs.
  (v) Swift development of full power at start up.
 (vi) No cooling water requirements.

The essential components of a simple gas turbine as shown in Fig. 62 are a centrifugal air compressor, one or more combustion chambers in

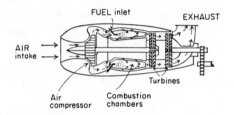

Fig. 62. *A simple open-cycle gas turbine.*

which fuel (usually kerosene) is burned continuously and a turbine, revolving on a common shaft with the compressor (Anon. 1978). Because the work which a stream of gas can perform is proportional to the mass and the velocity of the gas, and because gas densities are low, it is necessary that large volumes of combustion products are available to produce a useful amount of work. This is done by pumping large volumes of air into and around the combustion chamber, where a high throughput of fuel is burned (Winkler 1977). The air, at 420 kN m^{-2}, passing into the combustion chamber, mixes with liquid fuel sprayed in continuously at a pressure of 540 kN m^{-2}, at an air:fuel ratio of about 14:1. The remaining 45 or so volumes of air per volume of fuel is passed around the outside of the combustion chamber to cool the wall and is then mixed with the hot products of combustion issuing from the chamber. This mixing dilutes the hot gases and cools them from 2070 K to between 1200 K and 950 K, depending on the ash content of the fuel. The cooling of the gases is necessary to protect the metal of the turbine blades from excessive temperatures.

The cooled gases pass through the turbine where rapid expansion of the gases cause the shaft to rotate. The turbine supplies mechanical power to the centrifugal compressor at the air inlet to the extent of 60% of the total energy in the fuel burned.

The turbine can be designed to operate in one of two ways (McDonald 1978, Institution of Mechanical Engineers 1978). The turbine may be large enough to produce only enough power to drive the compressor, while the excess energy in the jet of gases issuing from the turbine drives the machine forward. This is known as a "turbo-jet", giving jet propulsion. Alternatively, the turbine may be so large that it takes most of the energy from the gases and can be connected to a shaft to provide shaft power for turning alternators to generate electricity, or for turning airscrews in "turbo-prop" aircraft or providing traction.

The system shown in Fig. 62 is the simplest form. In more efficient systems, the hot waste gases are used to preheat the compressed air before it enters the combustion chamber. This waste heat recovery can raise the efficiency of the "open cycle" (in which the hot gases are vented to atmosphere) from 25% to 40%.

C. Control of Combustion Systems

Most burner systems are designed to give complete combustion of fuel supplied at a predetermined rate. It is necessary, however, to match the supply of heat from the fuel to the demands of the system, either by increasing the flow rate of fuel above or by decreasing it below the design value for the burner. Because of the nature of flame stabilization, there is a maximum throughput of fuel above which complete combustion is not possible and a minimum throughput below which continuous combustion is not possible. The ratio of maximum to minimum fuel throughput is known as the "turn-down" ratio for the burner (Section III. A. 2).

The way in which the feed rate of fuel to a burner is changed depends primarily on the type of fuel concerned. Solid fuels are normally fed mechanically on to the combustion grate so that the feed rate may be easily altered. The quick, easy regulation characteristics of gas burners make them simple to control and this is normally done automatically by controllers activated by changes in pressure, temperature or rate of flow. The control of oil burners is a more difficult operation, especially in the case of mechanically atomizing burners, which are generally operated by an "on-off" controller. For air- and steam-atomizing burners, the atomizing fluid must be proportional to the oil rate for satisfactory operation. In many installations, this proportioning is carried out manually, although devices are available for proportioning low-pressure burners (Anderson 1971).

If an oil or gas flame is extinguished and the fuel supply is not shut off, the combustion chamber rapidly fills with a combustible or an explosive mixture. Ignition of this mixture can take place by contact with the hot furnace walls or through an attempt to relight the burner. Consequently, burners are normally fitted with flame-failure devices which are positioned to "see" radiation from either the flame or the hot, combustion gases. These devices shut off the supply of fuel once the temperature they detected falls below a given value. The former type is preferred as the flue gas temperature may be maintained for a short period of time by radiation from the walls of the furnace.

It has been shown that there is a wide variety of applications for fuels whether they be solid, liquid or gas. It must be re-emphasized that, no matter what the application, the burner and chamber within which the combustion takes place must be designed to give intimate mixing between the fuel and air. In the majority of applications, air must be supplied in quantities which are in excess of the stoichiometric requirements of the fuel in order that combustion may be complete. The amount of excess air and the method of its introduction into the fuel–air mixture will vary with the type of fuel used. Solid fuels require more excess air than do liquid fuels and gaseous fuels can be burned completely with only slightly more than stoichiometric quantities of air.

In all applications, the rate of heat release can be controlled by altering the rate at which the fuel is supplied and by the positioning of the entry ports for the primary, secondary and, sometimes, tertiary combustion air.

The supply of excess air and its mode of introduction influences the combustion process and alters the composition of the flue gases. Analysis of flue composition permits the system to be quantified as described in Chapter 9.

V. DIRECT CONVERSION OF ENERGY

A. Thermal to Electrical Conversion

1. Introduction

In Chapter 1, it was pointed out that the most convenient form of energy in civilized society is probably electrical energy generated on a very large scale by turbo-generators driven by steam produced by either nuclear or chemical combustion. Such an operation is a relatively inefficient conversion route because of the production of large amounts of low-grade heat. Attempts are being made to utilize this heat in district heating schemes or for horticultural purposes, though these are at present on a limited scale.

In addition proposals are being considered in which the waste heat will be upgraded to a more useful quality by limiting the electrical demand, although this is probably only feasible with new installations. All these considerations are aimed at converting more of the energy in fossil and nuclear fuels into electrical power. Another approach is to investigate the direct conversion of thermal energy to electrical, without the intermediate step of mechanical energy; that is to exclude moving parts. Such processes still involve a step of combustion or nuclear reaction in the generation of thermal energy and it is convenient to consider them at this stage.

2. Magnetohydrodynamics

Faraday's second law states that if a conductor moves in a magnetic field, a current will flow in the conductor in a direction at right angles to both the

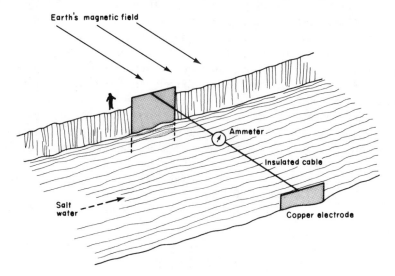

Fig. 63. *Kelvin's MHD generator.*

direction of its motion and the magnetic field. Lord Kelvin showed that tidal water (salty and therefore conducting) flowing in a river estuary in the Earth's magnetic field can act as a simple generator (Fig. 63). The modern concept of an MHD generator (Fig. 64) is not fundamentally different from Kelvin's experiments, except that an electrically conducting gas flowing at high speed past the electrodes is used as the working fluid instead of water, and the Earth's weak magnetic field is replaced by that of a powerful electromagnet. In general, gases are poor electrical conductors, though their conductivity can be increased to the levels necessary for MHD power generation by heating to, say, 3000 K and adding small concentrations of salts of metals with low ionization potentials—a process known as seeding. On ionization, the alkali metals produce free electrons which act as current-carriers in the gas stream.

In a typical generation unit (Fig. 65), air (or oxygen) is compressed to about 500 kN m^{-2} and preheated in a heat exchanger to 1700 K before passing to a combustion chamber. The mixture of air and flue gas leaving the furnace at around 3100 K is allowed to expand through a nozzle down to a pressure of 10 kN m^{-2}, thereby attaining a very high velocity as it passes between the electrodes from which current is drawn. Gases leave the generator at around 1800 K and can be used to preheat incoming air before passing to a conventional generator unit. The system as described is of the open cycle type and has the disadvantage of venting costly and corrosive seed material to the atmosphere. Closed cycle schemes have also

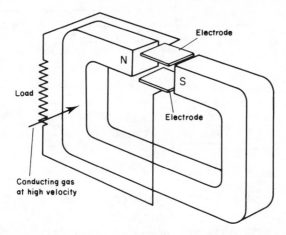

Fig. 64. *Schematic diagram showing the principle of MHD power generation.*

been investigated and, in order to reduce radioactive hazards, these would be used where the combustion chamber was replaced by a nuclear reactor.

Although the fundamental principles of MHD are well understood, the development of a practical generator poses enormous problems, mainly due to the lack of suitable materials capable of withstanding the very high temperatures involved. The electrodes, for example, become very hot and must therefore be made from a refractory material, at the same time possessing a reasonable electrical conductivity. Economics is the overriding factor in the design of a generator. For example, the lower the gas conductivity, the larger is the duct length required for slowing down the gas and converting its kinetic energy into electrical energy. In order to build a generator of realistic length (say 10 m for a 100 MV unit) a conductivity of at least $10 \, \text{A} \, \text{V}^{-1} \, \text{m}^{-1}$ is required. This can be achieved by heating the gases in the duct to above 2300 K when thermal ionization of the seed is sufficient, though this involves materials problems. Other methods investigated of attaining the required conductivity include the use of shock waves (high-velocity shock waves passed through a gas can increase the percentage of ionization to 20–30% compared with the fraction of a per cent obtained by high-temperature seeding), the addition of solid particles of

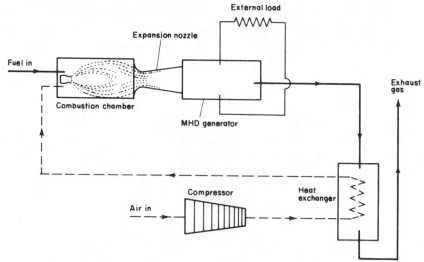

Fig. 65. *Open-cycle MHD power generator.*

thermionic emitters to the gases and utilization of non-equilibrium ionization existing in certain parts of flames. For example, the addition of halogens to flames can promote abnormally high ionization at gas temperatures easily contained in conventional furnace materials.

The output of MHD generators as described is direct current and, although this may be converted to alternating current relatively cheaply, suggestions have been made in which as oscillating shock wave or flame front passes between the electrodes, thus producing an alternating form directly.

Materials problems have so far limited the net output of an MHD generator, certainly for any length of time, though the field is an extremely active area of research (Rosa 1973) particularly in the USSR (Anon. 1978a). One very important advantage of the MHD generator is that the exhaust gases can still be used in a conventional generating station and in this way "top-up" the overall efficiency of generation from, say, 35% to possibly 65%. The outlook is generally hopeful, though the future depends on the development of acceptable materials with respect both to resistance to the extreme conditions demanded and to cost.

3. *Thermionics*

The phenomenon of electron emission from metals at high temperature was first investigated by Edison in his development of the conventional

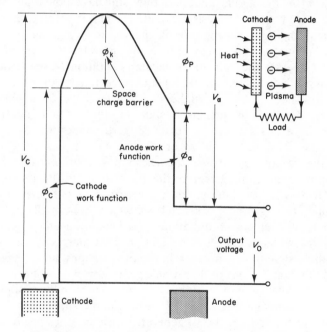

Fig. 66. *Principles of thermionic power generation.*

vacuum tube. In recent years considerable work has resulted in experimental devices with conversion efficiencies of around 15% with the possibility of considerable improvement. In a thermionic convertor, the cathode or electron emitter is not heated electrically as in a diode, but by combustion or fission processes. The electrons produced have enough energy to pass through an intervening space to a cooled collector, the anode, and the potential so created can be used to drive a current through an external load. In simple terms, an electron must receive enough energy at the cathode to overcome certain barriers (Fig. 66). Firstly, energy is required to raise the energy level of an electron in the cathode material to that corresponding to a point just outside its surface (this is known as the cathode work function, φ_c). In addition, emitted electrons set up a negative space-charge barrier φ_k outside the cathode which tends to repel the less energetic electrons as they try to emerge from the cathode and energy is also lost in the potential gradient φ_p due to the resistivity of the electron gas. As electrons fall into the anode, they lose as heat an amount of energy corresponding to the anode work function φ_a. Provided care is taken in obtaining suitable values of φ_c and φ_a and conditions are chosen to obtain a minimum value of $(\varphi_p - \varphi_k)$, then, as the electrons reach their energy level in the anode material, they still have potential energy V_0, available to do work in the resistive load. The major problem in producing an efficient thermionic generator is that of reducing the space-charge barrier φ_k. One solution is to reduce the interelectrode spacing to say $10 \,\mu m$ and operate the unit under vacuum conditions. Convertors of this type have produced about 0·6 W per square centimetre of cathode area at about 6% efficiency. Much higher efficiencies have been obtained by introducing positive ions such as caesium into the system to neutralize the negative space charge. This type of convertor is known as a "plasma diode" and 12 W cm^{-2} with an efficiency of 15% has been achieved, though the reactive nature of the caesium vapour tends to introduce corrosion problems, thus lowering the working life of the system.

One feature of the thermionic convertor is that it operates from a high-temperature source (1900–2500 K) which is normally beyond the range of fossil fuel powered stations and hence the unit is particularly suited for use with nuclear reactors and solar heat sources. Using solar heat permits the system to be employed in remote locations, and it is perhaps in this field that applications of thermionic generators will be most extensively developed. Silence of operation is an advantage in military applications, coupled with convenience, ease of transport and compactness. The latter quality is illustrated by a 200 W generator with an efficiency of 13% and mass of 4·5 kg and volume of 650 cm^3.

4. Thermoelectrics

Thermoelectric generation of electrical power from heat is based on the Seebeck effect discovered in 1822, when T. J. Seebeck produced potential differences by heating one of the junctions between two dissimilar conductors. The suitability of a particular material for thermoelectric generation is given by a factor Z, high values of which indicate good thermoelectric material. Z is given by:

$$Z = \frac{S^2}{pk}$$

where S is the Seebeck coefficient $(V (\deg K)^{-1})$, p is the electrical resistivity $(\Omega\ m)$ and k the thermal conductivity of the material $(W\ m^{-1} K^{-1})$. Thus a good thermoelectrical material should have a high value of S and relatively low values of p and k. The efficiency of conversion of heat into electrical power using metallic junctions is only about 1%, but certain junctions of n-type and p-type semiconductors have values of S approaching 170 V $(\deg K)^{-1}$ and a 10% conversion efficiency has been achieved, which can theoretically be improved. Bismuth telluride (Bi_2Te_3)

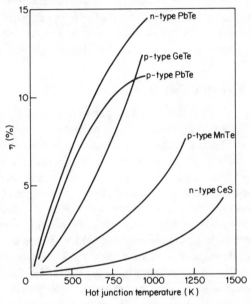

Fig. 67. *Direct conversion efficiencies of some semiconductors.*

doped with antimony or selenium has been investigated widely and values as high as 10^{-5} have been obtained for z, with theoretical conversions of 25% depending on the temperature range. Other materials which show promise include lead telluride (PbTe), zinc antimonide (ZnSb), cerium sulphide (CeS) (Fig. 67) and newer materials such as high atomic mass binary compounds of transition metals and oxygen, sulphur, selenium and polonium called chalcogenides.

Progress in the application of thermoelectric generators in Europe and the USA has been slow until fairly recently, though in the USSR, Joffe developed several simple methods of generation in the 1930s. Today a 250 W thermoelectric unit which utilizes an external heat source can be built into a 30 kg pack, and a 10 W radioisotope-heated unit is now in use in remote locations such as oil-wells and buoys. Absence of moving parts, simplicity of construction and lack of maintenance makes their use in space vehicles attractive and a SNAP generator powered the transmission of signals from the US Navy's satellite Transit 4A. This weighed only 2·1 kg and was 12·7 cm in diameter, but its plutonium-238 fuel pellet was capable of producing 2·7 W of steady power for longer than the 5 years the satellite was designed to operate. Compared with the best mercury batteries which yield up to 100 W kg^{-1}, this plant would produce the same output in 5 years as batteries weighing 1350 kg, illustrating that the high initial cost was more than offset by the low weight in this particular application.

Rowe (1978) has provided a survey of recent progress in the development of thermoelectric devices, where again cost must be balanced against performance in terms of output and reliability.

B. Chemical to Electrical Conversion

Chemical energy may be converted directly into electrical energy without producing heat in an intermediate stage by using an electrochemical cell. An example of such a cell is the dry battery which is a convenient portable generator, but cannot be used for large-scale power generation for two fairly obvious reasons. Firstly the "fuel", usually zinc, is fairly expensive and the cell is useless once the limited supply of fuel has been exhausted. In addition, the cost of power from the mains is about 4p per unit, whereas dry battery power works out at several pounds per unit. Nevertheless, the potentially high efficiency with which direct conversion can be achieved electrochemically (at least 50%) has presented a fascinating challenge to man's scientific ingenuity, and in 1839, Sir William Grove successfully demonstrated what he called a "gas battery" in which the energy of the oxidation of hydrogen appeared directly as electric current. Such a system, which is now known as a fuel cell, overcomes the disadvantages of the dry battery in that fuel is supplied continuously to the unit, and the use of cheap, and particularly gaseous, fuels such as hydrocarbons and natural gas permits the system to be used for comparatively large-scale power generation. Although the generation of heat is not a prerequisite of the system, the oxidation of the fuel may be thought of as a slow combustion process.

A fuel cell is an electrochemical device which converts conventional fuel continuously into electricity. The process is essentially one of reversed electrolysis, the energy of the chemical reaction being released in the form of electrical energy.

$$H_2 + \tfrac{1}{2}O_2 \rightarrow H_2O + \text{electrical energy}$$

Compared with a secondary cell, such as a lead accumulator, where one or both of the electrodes is consumed, the electrodes in a fuel cell are unchanged and merely localize and catalyse the cell reactions. In its simplest form, a fuel cell consists of two electrodes separated by an electrolyte, arranged so that fuel and oxidant can be supplied to the respective electrodes and waste products can be removed. Direct reaction between the fuel and oxidant is avoided and provision is made for controlling the temperature of the electrolyte. When the electrodes are connected externally, fuel at the anode ionizes, forming positive ions and electrons. At the cathode, the oxidant takes up electrons and forms negative ions, which react with the positive ions to give reaction products. Electrons flow through the external circuit producing a current between the fuel electrode and the oxidant electrode. The basic problem in fuel cell design is that of bringing about contact between the solid electrode, the liquid electrolyte and the gaseous fuel or oxidant and many designs of cell have been developed. A typical cell output is only about 1 V, so that a working power system would be a combination of several cells giving the desired current and voltage characteristics, and with a means of feeding in (and processing where necessary) the fuel and oxidant, removing the waste products and maintaining the required operating temperature. The operating temperature provides a convenient basis for classification of fuel cells:

(i) *Low-temperature (up to* 550 K) *cells.* In order to attain a reasonable reaction rate, low-temperature cells employ some form of electrode activation such as a catalyst with an aqueous electrolyte, often an alkaline solution. Corrosion is not usually a problem and plastic materials may be used for cell construction. Unfortunately, the catalysts used are expensive and sensitive to poisoning and this type of cell does not work with hydrocarbon fuels; special fuels such as hydrogen, methanol and hydrazine are required (Anon. 1972).

(ii) *Medium-temperature* (600–900 K) *cells.* These normally employ a molten alkali-metal carbonate electrolyte contained in a porous ceramic with cheap porous metal electrodes, which do not require additional catalysts (Marianowski 1978). This type of cell operates with hydrocarbon fuels, but although waste heat can be recovered, the cell is slow to start up and corrosion problems are severe.

(iii) *High-temperature* (1000–1500 K) *cells.* At present, cells in this range are mainly limited to those using ion-conducting ceramic electrolytes such as zirconia with calcium or yttrium oxide and, although hydrocarbon fuels may be used, carbon formation must be avoided. There are in addition constructional problems associated with the high temperatures.

The large supplies of natural gas presently available at relatively low costs and the increase in noise and pollution in urban areas have a significant bearing on possible applications of fuel cells, especially in the fields of power production and transportation (Gardner 1973).

Fuel cells fed with natural gas could supply the power requirements of a block of offices or flats and such a unit could replace transformer substations in the range 500–1000 kW. Small delivery vehicles and private cars seem to provide the greatest potential for electrical propulsion (Kordesch 1971, Anon. 1971c) and fuel cells with an output of 5 kW powered by hydrogen have been envisaged as suitable power units. Large 50 kW units for buses and small locomotives would alleviate the noise and pollution problem. Where the density of rail traffic does not warrant electrification of the track, larger units of 2000 kW fuelled by liquid hydrocarbons may be developed in the future. As with thermoelectric and thermionic devices, lighthouses and buoys in remote locations provide obvious applications for fuel cells with outputs of a few watts. A fuel cell with an output of 12 kW designed for domestic applications has been described (Anon. 1972e) and Fickett (1978) has discussed fuel cell power plants. An excellent bibliography on fuel cells has been prepared by ERDA (1977) and some recent work has been reported (Howe 1979) in which the electrolyte is replaced with a solid having a high proton conductivity.

VI. FURTHER READING

Baker, B. S. (1965). "Hydrocarbon Fuel Cell Technology". Academic Press, London and New York.

Blackmore, D. R. and Thomas, A. (1977). "Fuel Economy of the Gasoline Engine". Macmillan, London.

Bradley, J. N. (1969). "Flame and Combustion Phenomena". Butler and Tanner, London.

Chigier, N. A. (1978). "Synthetic Fuels and Combustion". Pergamon Press, Oxford.

Combe, R. A. (1964). "MHD Generation of Electrical Power". Chapman and Hall, London.

Dolezan, R. and Varcop, L. (1970). "Automatic Control of Steam Generating Plant". Elsevier, London.

Ducarme, J., Gerstein, M. and Lefebvre, A. H. (1960). "Progress in Combustion Science and Technology". Pergamon Press, London.

Edwards, J. B. (1974). "Combustion". Ann Arbor Science Publishing Co.

Field, M. A., Gill, D. W., Morgan, B. B. and Hawksley, F. G. W. (1967). "Combustion of Pulverized Coal". BCURA, Leatherhead.

Fischer, L. J. (1961). "Combustion Engineers' Handbook". Newnes, London.

Francis, W. (1965). "Boiler House and Power Station Chemistry". Edward Arnold, London.

Fristram, R. M. and Westenberg, A. A. (1965). "Flame Structure". McGraw-Hill, New York.

Gardner, J. W. (1973). "New Frontiers in Electricity". Foulis, London.

Gas Council (1967). "Burning Natural Gas in Industrial Burners". Ind. Gas Comm., London.

Gaydon, A. G. and Wolfhard, H. G. (1960). "Flames—Their Structure, Radiation and Temperature". Chapman and Hall. London.

Gilchrist, J. D. (1963). "Furnaces". Pergamon Press, Oxford.

Goodall, P. M. (1980). "The Efficient Use of Steam". IPC Science and Technology Press, Guildford.

Goodger, E. M. (1953). "Petroleum and Performance". Butterworth, London.

Gould, R. F. (ed.) (1969). "Fuel Cell Systems". Advances in Chemistry No. 90. American Chemical Society.

Griswold, J. (1946). "Fuels, Combustion and Furnaces". McGraw-Hill, New York.

Hatsopoulos, G. N. and Gyftopoulos, E. P. (1973). "Thermionic Energy Conversion", 1. MIT Press, Cambridge, Mass.

Kanbury, A. H. (1975). "Introduction to Combustion Phenomena". Gordan and Breach, New York.

Lewis, B. and von Elbe, G. (1961). "Combustion Flames and Explosions of Gases". Academic Press, New York and London.

Liebhafsky, H. A. and Cairns, E. J. (1968). "Fuel Cells and Fuel Batteries". Wiley, New York.

Lyle, O. (1947). "The Efficient Use of Steam". HMSO, London.

Palmer, H. B. and Beer, J. M. (1974). "Combustion Technology". Academic Press, New York and London.

Patterson, D. J. and Henein, N. A. (1972). "Emissions from Combustion Engines and their Control". Ann Arbor Science Publishing Co.

Reed, R. D. (1973). "Furnace Operations". Gulf Publishing Co., Houston.

Shaha, A. K. (1974). "Combustion Engineering and Fuel Technology". Oxford and IBH Publishing Co.

Shercuff, J. A. (1965). "A Textbook of MHD". Pergamon Press, Oxford.

Soo, S. L. (1968). "Direct Energy Conversion". Prentice-Hall, New York.

Spring, K. H. (1965). "Direct Generation of Electricity". Academic Press, London and New York.

Strehlow, R. A. (1968). "Fundamentals of Combustion". Int. Textbook Co., Pennsylvania.

Thring, M. W. (1962). "The Science of Flames and Furnaces". Chapman and Hall, London.

Townend, D. T. A. (1927). "Flame and Combustion in Gases". Longmans
    Green, London.
Trinks, W., Trinks, W. and Mawhinney, M. H. (1953). "Industrial
    Furnaces". John Wiley, New York.
Young, G. J. (1963). "Fuel Cells", 2. Reinhold, New York.

Energy Conversion without Combustion

8

I. INTRODUCTION

The delicate balance between energy supply and demand and the OPEC price rises of 1974 have stimulated work into the possibilities of obtaining energy from other sources. The years since 1974 have been marked by economic stagnation and the resulting over-production of oil led to complacency where there should have been concern. Various incidents have also stimulated the search for the so-called "clean" alternatives of wind, water, solar, tidal and geothermal energy and this chapter will consider the possibilities of these sources for future use and compare their likely development with that of nuclear power.

II. WIND POWER

It has been estimated by McMullen (1977) that 370×10^6 MW is available from wind and wave power of the earth's surface, although a substantial portion of this will be dissipated over the oceans or in inaccessible regions of the land mass. Thus there is power available in the wind capable of making a contribution to the world's energy requirements providing that it can be harnessed in an economic and environmentally acceptable way.

The power available from the wind, that is air in motion, is calculated on the basis that power is energy per unit time and the kinetic energy for any particle is $0.5\,mv^2$ where m is its mass and v is the velocity. The volume per unit time of wind moving with velocity v through an area A is Av and

195

the mass per unit time is $\varrho\, Av$ where ϱ is the density of air. Hence,

$$\begin{aligned}
\text{Available power} &= 0{\cdot}5mv^2 \\
&= 0{\cdot}5(\varrho Av)v^2 \\
&= 0{\cdot}5\varrho Av^3 \quad \text{W}
\end{aligned}$$

Substituting $\varrho = 1{\cdot}2\ \text{kg m}^{-3}$ for average ambient conditions and considering unit area gives the theoretical maximum power as

$$P = 0{\cdot}6v^3 \quad \text{W m}^{-2}$$

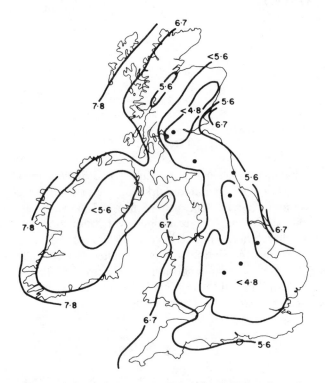

Fig. 68. *Annual isovent map for Great Britain* (m s^{-1}).

Betz (1927) showed that the theoretical maximum efficiency of a windmill was 59·3% though later work by Shepard (1976) raises this figure to 60%. Thus the normal maximum power is

$$P = 0{\cdot}36v^3 \quad \text{W m}^{-2}$$

Since the power available from the wind is proportional to the cube of its velocity, this velocity is of prime importance in considering the design of the rotors and in the selection of suitable sites. It is therefore important to consider where in the world is there sufficient wind to be economically useful, the annual available wind energy for a particular site, the distribution of that energy as a function of time, and the probability of very high and very low wind velocities during any given time period.

Average annual wind speeds vary from 0·5 to 18 m s⁻¹ with the lower figure quoted by Iyer (1948) for Dibrugarp in Assam, reputed to be the calmest place on earth. Putnam (1948) gives a five-year average of 15·2 m s⁻¹ at the summit of Mt. Washington at a height of 1920 m. Data for the UK are shown in Fig. 68. For economic generation the average wind speed should lie between about 6·5 and 11·5 m s⁻¹ giving an output of between 100 and 550 W m⁻². The largest windmill erected in the United

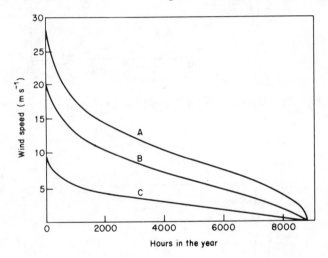

Fig. 69. *Velocity–duration curves for three UK sites: A, Rhossili Down; B, St. Annes Head; C, Leicester.*

States had a twin-bladed propeller 53·5 m in diameter mounted on a tower 33·5 m high and capable of an output of 1·25 MW, though it failed to withstand high winds shortly after it was constructed in 1941.

In order to determine the available energy from a particular site, meteorological data on wind speed are required so that hourly mean speeds throughout the year are available. These data are presented either as velocity–duration curves (Fig. 69) or as velocity–frequency curves (Fig. 70). Figures 69 and 70 show three sets of velocity data from sites in the UK quoted by Golding (1955). Curve A is taken from the summit of Rhossili Down in S. Wales at a height of 193 m, B is from St. Ann's Head (height

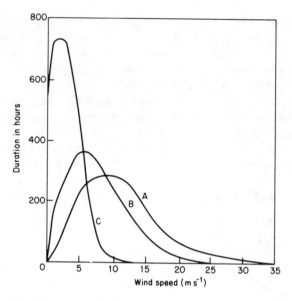

Fig. 70. *Velocity–frequency curves for the three sites of Fig. 69.*

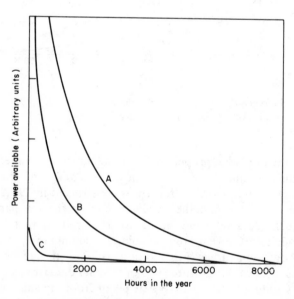

Fig. 71. *Potential power output for the three sites of Fig. 69.*

43 m), and curve C is data plotted from Leicester. The average wind speeds for the three sites are 10·7, 7·2 and 2·8 m s⁻¹. Figure 70 shows the number of hours in the year for which the speed equals or exceeds each particular value; Fig. 69 replots the same data to show the annual hours of duration of various wind speeds.

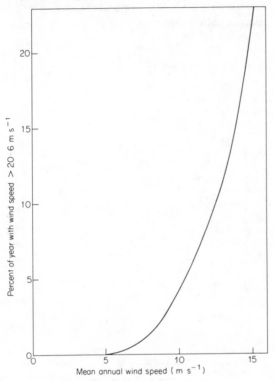

Fig. 72. *Duration of high-speed winds.*

The suitability of each site is illustrated in Fig. 71, where the velocities of Fig. 69 have been cubed to give the power on an arbitrary scale as the ordinate. The superiority of a site like Rhossili Down is apparent.

The load on a windmill structure increases with the square of the wind velocity, so that if advantage is to be taken of an exposed coastal site, for example, the support must be capable of withstanding that load. As the device must be able to generate power in calm conditions as well as when the wind is strong, these considerations must inevitably lead to a compromise in design.

To avoid wind damage, a windmill should not be used in winds greater than the upper limit of Beaufort force 8, i.e. 20·6 m s⁻¹. Figure 72 shows the proportion of the year with winds greater than this speed as a function of the mean annual speed. Thus for a good site in the UK with an average speed of 11·6 m s⁻¹, winds over 20·6 m s⁻¹ will persist for 8% of the year, at which times the device cannot be safely used.

Similarly, mechanical limitations impose a lower operating limit of 1·8 m s⁻¹, below which satisfactory operation is impossible and Fig. 73 shows the duration of calm periods as a function of the mean annual speed.

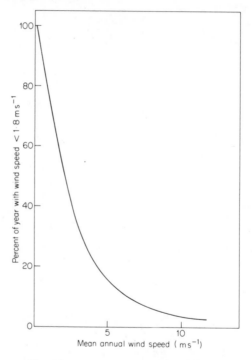

Fig. 73. *Duration of low-speed winds.*

The windmills of past centuries are far removed from the substantial concrete structure needed for modern power generation. Limitations of mechanical strength mean that sail diameter must be restricted and as electricity generation demands high rotational speeds compared with the low speed and high torque demands of flour milling, for example, redesign of the rotors becomes essential.

Mounting a single propeller on a horizontal axis offers an alternative with a maximum efficiency of 60% together with severe dynamic problems which can be overcome by using two- or three-bladed air screws. Unless the device is pointing directly into the wind, however, the efficiency falls further so that a vane assembly must be devised to ensure reaction to changing winds. The constructional difficulties are considerable and an alternative, illustrated in Fig. 74 shows two vertical-axis wind rotor designs in which the axes of the rotors and of the support structure coincide. The need for a steering device is obviated but the efficiency is not high as that of a well designed propeller.

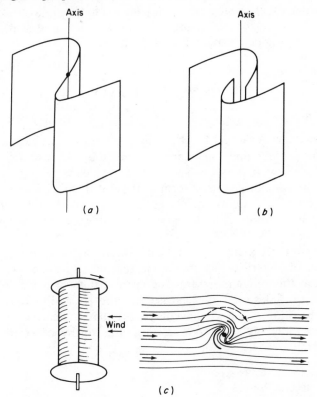

Fig. 74. *Wind rotor designs. (a) Simple S rotor. (b) Savonius rotor. (c) Principle of Savonius rotor.*

It has been seen that a very large windmill might be capable of generating 1 MW so that to replace one large conventional power station could require some 4000 windmills. The environmental impact of building these structures on suitable exposed positions is obvious and it is hard to imagine that any proposed scheme of this scale and nature would ever be built. In the early 1950s, the then Central Electricity Authority proposed to build an experimental 100 kW windmill in Wales though this was abandoned because of public feeling. Assuming that environmental problems could be overcome, the wind could only be employed to produce 5% of the UK electricity demand, which at a cost of £1000 kW^{-1} compares unfavourably with a nuclear installation.

It would appear that the logical conclusion is that wind power is not a viable alternative to conventional means of power generation at present or indeed in the near future. Small-scale use of windmills in isolated positions for provision of electricity where no mains supply is available or for pumping water to storage for use later are systems used at present and which will have added attraction in the future.

III. WATER POWER

A. Introduction

The use of the water wheel for the grinding of corn dates back 2000 years and at the present time there are a number of old installations being restored for this very purpose. These wheels, which were initially horizontal, took their familiar vertical form in the fourth century and, like their wind-powered equivalents, produced a low-speed, high-torque output ideal for the purpose, but in no way suitable for the generation of electricity.

There are three main areas in which water may be used for the direct production of electricity—hydroelectric schemes, tidal power and wave power—and this order represents the current state of technology in the field. The principles used in each case are different and there is no doubt that, for the future, each will have its part to play. As each is based on an indefinite supply of "free" power, they are worthy of examination in greater detail.

B. Hydroelectric Power

Hydroelectric power is generated by water flowing from a high level to a low level, at a high efficiency. The high-level water is usually dammed to provide a large storage lake, though in the first major installation at Niagara Falls, opened in 1895 with an output of 3·75 MW, there is no storage facility. In order to generate electricity, water is allowed to flow from the high level through a device which converts the kinetic energy of the water into rotational kinetic energy of a rotor which is linked to a generator to produce the required electricity.

A good example of hydroelectricity generation is the North of Scotland Hydroelectric Board station at Loch Awe where the power station is built inside the hills. The available head is 370 m and the scheme is illustrated in Fig. 75.

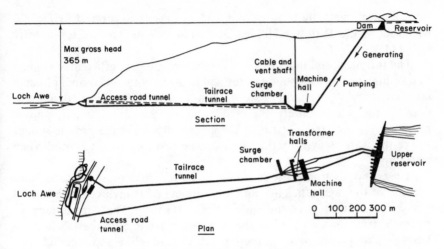

Fig. 75. *The Loch Awe scheme.*

The energy available as potential energy is given by:

$$E = mgh$$
$$= 1000 \times 9\cdot81 \times 370$$
$$= 3\cdot63 \times 10^6 \text{ J m}^{-3}$$
$$\equiv 3\cdot63 \text{ MJ m}^{-3}$$

This energy is converted to kinetic energy as it accelerates towards the turbines and if the entry velocity at the turbine is v, then

$$3\cdot63 \times 10^6 = 0\cdot5mv^2 = 0\cdot5 \times 1000v^2$$

or

$$v = 85\cdot2 \text{ m s}^{-1}$$

The output of the generators is 400 MW so that if x kg s^{-1} water passes through the turbines,

$$xgh = 400 \times 10^6$$

and

$$x = 1\cdot1 \times 10^5 \text{ kg s}^{-1}$$

As losses in the turbines, frictional losses and generating losses must also be considered, this mass flow rate is the minimum for the specified power output. The Loch Awe scheme has an overall efficiency of about 75% which is over twice that of a conventional power station. It has the added advantage that the process is reversible when power is not required, as the scheme can be used to pump water to the higher level. This storage facility is particularly useful when the catchment area of the reservoir is insufficient for continuous generation.

A typical cycle showing output and storage is illustrated in Fig. 76 which shows the Turlough Hill installation in Ireland. The output capacity is 292 MW.

The turbines used in hydroelectric schemes are very efficient, designed to take high velocity incoming water and to abstract the maximum possible kinetic energy by discharging the water at as low a velocity as possible. In Fig. 77 the water enters the wide end of the spiral casing and is progressively diverted inwards by the guide vanes on to the turbine runner where the water leaves by the tailrace. The reverse process is used when pumping.

The cost of hydroelectric schemes can be very high in capital terms, but because of the high efficiency and low running costs involved, the overall cost of generation is of the order of £1000 kW^{-1}. The contribution of hydroelectricity is about 5% of the total generated in both the UK and the USA and, despite its many attractions, this figure is likely to remain at this level due to the relatively small number of suitable sites.

C. Tidal Power

The essential difference between hydroelectric schemes described above and those designed to make use of the tides is that the latter will operate at a very low head of water with a very high volumetric throughput. Compared with conventional hydroelectric schemes which are numerous throughout the world, there are only two tidal power stations in operation—at La Rance in France and Kislaya Guba in Russia with outputs of 240 MW and 2 MW respectively.

It has been estimated that the rise and fall of the tides over the earth is capable of a potential power output of 3×10^6 MW, but in practice only the tides around coasts could be utilized to realize perhaps one third of this figure. The potential energy stored in an area A, height h above a datum is equal to $A\varrho gh$. If some of this water is discharged causing a small fall in level of dh, the energy released is dE and

$$dE = A\varrho gh \, dh$$

Integrating between limits $h = 0$, $E = 0$ and $h = h$, $E = E_{max}$ gives

$$E_{max} = \tfrac{1}{2}A\varrho gh^2$$

The height h is called the range, R, and is the difference in level between high and low tides. Thus the maximum energy release per tidal cycle of about 12 hours is

$$E_{max} = \tfrac{1}{2}A\varrho gR^2 \quad J$$

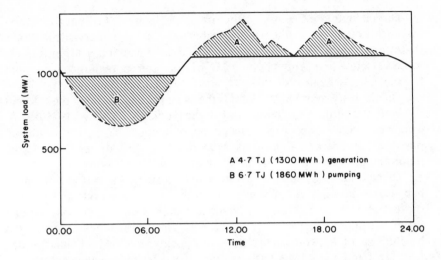

A 4·7 TJ (1300 MWh) generation
B 6·7 TJ (1860 MWh) pumping

Fig. 76. *Generation and storage cycle, illustrating the Turlough Hill installation in Ireland.*

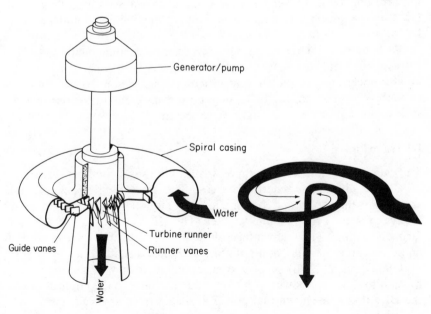

Fig. 77. *A hydroelectric turbine.*

The maximum efficiency of the process is likely to be about 25% and this fact, coupled with the small number of suitable estuary sites, means that the potential contribution to energy demand from tidal power is likely to be very low and probably only 1% of that from potential conventional hydroelectric schemes.

The Severn estuary in England is the most promising site in the UK and has been the subject of a number of studies, notably by Shaw (1974–1976). The mean tidal range is 9·8 m and by building a barrage it would be possible to generate about 4000 MW or about 2% of the UK energy requirement at an estimated (1976) cost of £1000–£2500 million.

The simple tidal scheme operating from a single basin is not favoured because of the variation in power output during the tide cycle and because the effective height through which the water would fall in passing the turbines would be less than the tidal range. These difficulties are overcome by the use of a two-basin scheme in which the area is divided into a high-level and a low-level basin by means of a barrage. Sluice gates allow the high-level basin to fill between mid and high tide and they are shut between mid and low tide. The gates of the low-level basin are opened to allow it to empty between mid and low tide but remain shut between mid and high tide. Electricity generation is by means of turbines between the high- and low-level basins. The output from this scheme is much more uniform but the low-level basin takes the appearance of mud flats at low tide, though this objection may be minimized depending upon the particular location.

Although the source of energy is free and environmentally ideal, the construction time for schemes on this scale is very long and this adds greater uncertainty to the already difficult considerations of cost. In terms of conservation of existing fuels, tidal power has great attractions, but the savings are not as great as might be expected.

D. Wave Power

The energy available in the form of waves in the sea is the least researched of all the alternative energy sources. The attractions are enormous: resulting as they do from a combination of solar and wind power, waves are always present, even in calm weather. The UK has 1500 km of Atlantic-facing coastline to take advantage of the most favourable wave conditions and the source is totally non-polluting and inexhaustible.

Glendenning (1976) presented an excellent review of the theory and possibilities of wave power with particular reference to the implications for the UK. It can be shown that power available from a wave is given by

$$P = 0.55 H_s^2 T_z \quad \text{kW m}^{-2}$$

where H_s and T_z are known as the significant wave height (metres) and zero crossing period (seconds) respectively. Data on these parameters are published for a particular sea area as a result of oceanographic surveys and a comprehensive set of data for the North Atlantic is available from the weather ship India (50°N 19°W) by Draper (1967). Use may be made of the distribution of H_s and T_z values to predict the available wave power for a particular time of year. Figure 78 shows the potential available for the

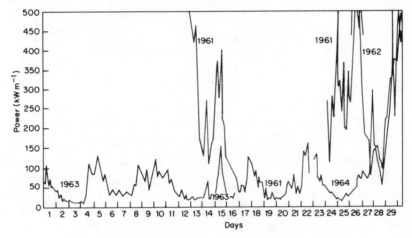

Fig. 78. *Wave power at Station India: January.*

month of January taken from the data for 1961 to 1964. It will be seen that the output varies by an order of magnitude, but a base load of 30–50 kW m⁻¹ is possible with an average of 80 kW m⁻¹. If the raw data is analysed in a different way to show a load factor (defined as the energy actually available over a given period up to a specified power level, divided by the

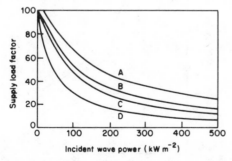

Incident wave power ($kW\,m^{-2}$)

Fig. 79. *Supply–load factor curves for Station India* (1955–1966). A, *Winter (Dec.–Jan.)*; B, *Autumn (Sept.–Nov.)*; C, *Spring (March–May)*; D, *Summer (June–Aug.)*.

energy which would be produced if the specified power output could be maintained during that period) as a function of the incident wave power, Fig. 79 results. As more energy is available in the winter than the summer, the output follows the same pattern as the demand and the greatest potential savings of fossil fuels occur at peak demand times.

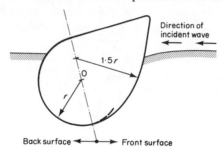

Fig. 80. *Geometry of the Salter Duck. The device is designed to rotate about* O, *with the waves incident from the right.*

The available wave energy along the Atlantic-facing coastline amounts to 120 GW which is more than twice the quantity of electricity now generated in the UK. The realization of the possibilities inherent in the waves is a difficult and expensive task on a commercial scale and, to date, most of the experimental work has been carried out using small scale-models.

The earliest devices tried consisted of an air bell whose lower open surface was located under the surface of the water, thus trapping air in the

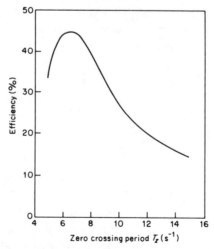

Fig. 81. *Notional performance of a Salter Duck of* 18 m *diameter.*

bell above. The motion of a wave caused a cyclic variation in the air pressure within the bell which could be harnessed through a valve and turbine to produce electrical power. While unsuitable for any large-scale generation of electricity, these air bells have found very successful application in the powering of self-sufficient navigation buoys.

Two of the most promising devices have been the so-called Salter duck first proposed by Salter (1974) and the system devised by Sir Christopher Cockerell and reported by Wooley (1975). Salter's duck, shown in section in Fig. 80, is capable of extracting 90% of the incident power in regular waves in a test tank, though this figure is expected to be halved for an 18 m diameter unit in the sea as shown in Fig. 81.

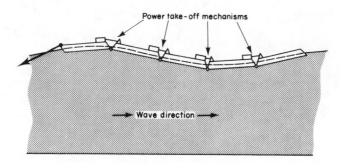

Fig. 82. *The Cockerel wave contouring raft.*

Cockerell's raft, shown in Fig. 82, consists of a series of flat rafts coupled together to contour the wave. It progressively extracts the energy from the wave as it progresses down the line. The floats are hinged together and power is extracted from the relative motion of adjacent elements. Clearly, the civil engineering problems associated with large offshore structures of these types are considerable, especially when it is realized that to match an output of 1000 MW from a conventional power station will require, after allowing for losses, a structure some 40 km long. Denton (1975) estimated the likely capital costs at £400–£800 kW^{-1}, but at this early stage this figure is likely to be highly suspect.

IV. SOLAR POWER

A. Introduction

The net energy flow from the sun to the earth is around 1360 W m^{-2} after allowing for the incident radiation which is immediately reflected (Chapter

1). A further loss is caused by the absorption of a further fraction into the atmosphere so that under the most favourable conditions in desert areas a maximum of 1000 W m^{-2} is available. It is this quantity which is usually referred to when considering solar power as the ultimate "free" and renewable energy source.

Unfortunately, the value of 1000 W m^{-2} is reduced considerably when averaged over the 24 hours of the day to allow for periods of darkness and also when averaged over the year to allow for the greatly reduced amounts available in winter. Figure 83 shows the combined average over the US and Fig. 84 shows the summer and winter averages for the UK.

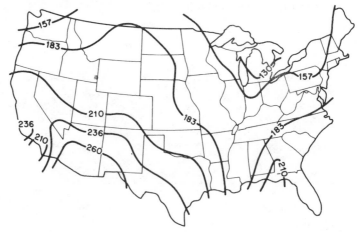

Fig. 83. *The distribution of average daily solar energy in the US* (W m^{-2}).

To translate the data into practical terms, an average of 208 W m^{-2} is equivalent to 5 kWh day^{-1} m^{-2} so that for a UK consumer, approximately 4 m^2 should be capable of making a significant reduction in the energy required from conventional sources—although in the summer more energy may be available from a solar collector than a household may be capable of using and vice versa in winter.

B. Solar Energy Collection

Before any solar energy can be used in a form capable of, say, generating electricity or providing hot water, it must first be collected. The Carnot efficiency, η, of a heat engine operating between high and low temperatures, T_H and T_L, is given by:

$$\eta = \frac{T_H - T_L}{T_H}$$

If high efficiencies are to be attained, T_H must be as high as possible and for radiation, the temperature T which can be reached for an incoming power density P is given by:

$$P = \sigma e T^4$$

where σ is the Stefan–Boltzmann constant ($5 \cdot 67 \times 10^{-8}$ W m^{-2} K^{-4}) and e is the emissivity of the absorbing material.

A body which re-emits all the radiation incident upon it is known as a black body and has $e = 1$. One which emits no radiation has an emissivity

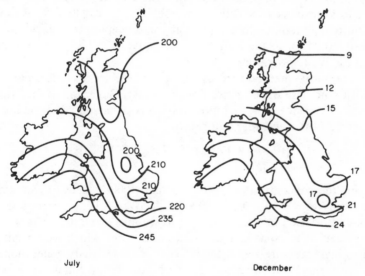

July   December

Fig. 84. *The distribution of average daily solar energy in the UK* (W m^{-2}).

of zero. Highly polished aluminium and powdered carbon have emissivities of $0 \cdot 04$ and $0 \cdot 9$ respectively. A black body also absorbs all radiant energy incident upon it and is said to have an absorptivity, α, of unity. A real body will only absorb a fraction of the incident radiation and so has a value of less than unity. Typically, α and e have values of about $0 \cdot 8$ to $0 \cdot 9$ and both depend upon the wavelength of the radiation.

If a solar collector is capable of absorbing 80% of the solar radiation in which it is placed, i.e. $\alpha = 0 \cdot 8$, and has an emissivity for these wavelengths of $0 \cdot 5$, then for favourable conditions, where the available daytime energy is 800 W m^{-2}:

$$\alpha P = \sigma e T^4$$

or

$$0 \cdot 8 \times 800 = 5 \cdot 67 \times 10^{-8} \times 0 \cdot 5 T^4$$

and

$$T = 388 \text{ K} \quad \text{or} \quad 115°C$$

which is only a little more than the normal boiling point of water. If this temperature is then used in a perfect heat engine at an ambient temperature of 293 K the efficiency will be

$$100(388 - 293)/388 = 24·5\%$$

There are two possible ways of increasing the temperature. It is possible to use collector material with a high value of α and a low value of e. This is known as a selective absorber and is capable of achieving significantly high temperatures, albeit at greater capital cost. If α becomes 0·9 and $e = 0·04$ for example, T becomes equal to 750 K which is a much more attractive temperature.

An alternative method is to use a focusing device such as a parabolic reflector to increase the effective power density. Reverting to the original example, if a concentration ratio of 10:1 is achieved, the equilibrium temperature of the absorber will rise to

$$T = [(0·8 \times 800 \times 10)/(5·67 \times 10^{-8} \times 0·5)]^{0·25}$$
$$= 690 \text{ K}$$

Increasing the concentration ratio to 100 and 1000:1 leads to equilibrium temperatures of 1225 K and 2180 K respectively. Temperatures in this range could be used in desert areas to heat tanks of molten salts through which passed heat exchanger pipes carrying water which would be converted to high pressure steam for conventional electricity generation. To be effective, the parabolic receiver must be tracked to follow the sun and the necessary steering mechanism is expensive.

The ultimate system proposed for the collection of solar energy has been described McMullan (1977) and involves placing two satellites in stationary orbit above the earth. The collector satellite would consist of a solar panel 8 km square connected to a second which would convert the electrical power to microwave power and beam it to earth from a 2 km square antenna. Such a scheme could provide 7000 MW with a collection area some six times that of a fossil fuel power station of the same output, though the cost could be quite prohibitive.

C. Utilization of Solar Power

1. Solar heating

In solar heating, cold water is passed through a suitable collector where it is warmed and removed either for direct or for storage heating. Figures 83 and 84 show that the surface area which could be available on a house roof would limit the scheme to the provision of hot water only and for this purpose about 4 m² would be required. A simple collector is shown in Fig. 85, and Fig. 86 illustrates three possible schemes for completing a satisfactory domestic installation. The cost of the collectors can vary from about £20 m⁻² for a home-made unit to £150 m⁻² for an installed commercial unit. Realistic savings in the UK might amount to £50 per year so the resulting economics are not favourable when compared with normal investment of the capital sum. There is no doubt, however, that many of these small units will be installed in the future and they will contribute in a very small way to the conservation needs of the country.

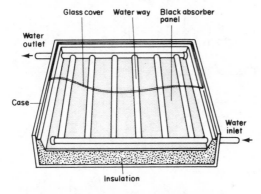

Fig. 85. *A typical solar collector.*

Space heating by solar means is possible in the more favoured States in America, for which the average household requirement is 420 MJ. One cubic metre of water, if raised through 20 deg K, is capable of storing 84 MJ, so that 5 m³ water storage would be needed for the average house. Crushed rock could be used for storage as part of the house foundations but the quantity would be massive and again the number of installations is likely to be very small.

Perhaps the ideal means of using solar energy is for the heating of swimming pools. The advantages in this situation are the low temperature rise required, large available storage in the pool itself, space around the pool available for the collecting system and the fact that the heat is at its most plentiful in the summer when use of the pool is required.

Solar energy may be used for air conditioning and refrigeration and has the advantage of the demand being matched by the availability of the energy source. Nice airport in France is air conditioned in this way and claims substantial conventional energy savings as a result. An absorption

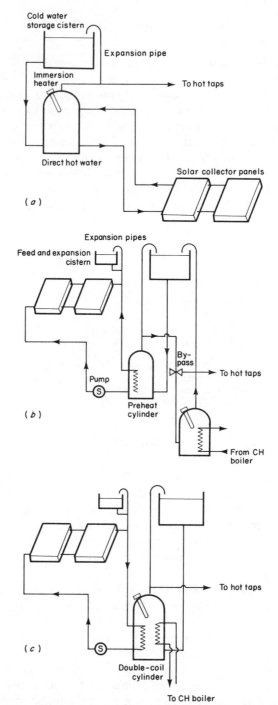

Fig. 86. *Three domestic solar water heating systems. (a) Direct system. (b) Indirect system wih pre-heat. (c) Indirect system with double-coil cylinder.*

refrigeration system is used and cool air may be produced directly or the energy may be stored in the form of ice.

2. *Solar distillation*

Solar stills for the production of fresh water from brackish or seawater have been used in very simple forms for hundreds of years. A plant of $4740 \, m^2$ has operated successfully for 113 years in Chile and a plant to supply $30 \, m^3 \, day^{-1}$ of fresh water from the sea was opened on the Greek island of Patmos in 1967 with an area of $8700 \, m^2$. A similar, but smaller plant on another Greek island built at about the same time involved capital costs of only £10 m^{-2} and very low operating costs.

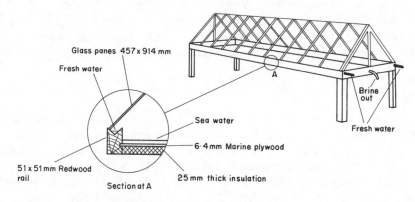

Fig. 87. *Scheme of the basic arrangement for solar-powered water distillation.*

The principle is illustrated in Fig. 87. Sheets of glass are placed at an angle over shallow black basins of salt water. The sunshine heats the inside of the structure but not the glass—the greenhouse effect—and is absorbed by the water which vaporizes and condenses on the glass. It runs down the inside of the glass surface where it is collected in wooden troughs. This application is ideal for situations where the climate and the need for fresh water at low capital cost combine to produce a perfect use for solar energy.

3. *Electricity production*

The generation of electricity via heat obtained from solar energy has been discussed earlier. The means of direct generation by means of photoelectric effects are well established and in use in the space programme. The efficiency is about 14% and the cost per kW about 100 times that of a conventional power station. Devices used at present are based on the use of semiconductors, typically p- and n-type silicon, in very thin layers. The photons of light energy incident on the semiconductors break bonds in the two layers and produce a voltage at the junction which can be used to produce current in an external circuit.

Higher efficiencies can be obtained with cells based on gallium arsenide and gallium aluminium arsenide and used in conjunction with a device for concentrating the intensity of solar energy incident upon them. With a two thousand fold increase in concentration, it is anticipated that outputs of $200 \, kW \, m^{-2}$ might be possible from the cells which would be very much smaller, and hence cheaper, than those without a focusing facility. This is clearly a very promising area for future research which offers the possibility of using the technology initially developed and proved in the space field. The cost of a research programme into suitable materials will be high, but, with ever increasing fuel costs, the incentive exists and the successful use of solar energy would have enormous potential (Benningta 1978).

4. *Fuel growth*

The combination of sunlight and a favourable climate can produce high rates of plant growth which, if harvested and dried, could then be burned to produce either heat directly or electricity. Wood was the primary fuel until the turn of this century and still is in many parts of the world. Peat is used on a very large scale for domestic heating and burning in power stations in Ireland. The concept of plant growth specifically for energy production is worth considering. Up to $10 \, kg \, m^{-2}$ of dry plant material could be produced from plant growth on land with up to $30 \, kg \, m^{-2}$ being possible by growing suitable plants on sewage enriched ponds. Whilst the overall efficiency of the process sunlight to stored energy is only about 3% and labour requirements might be high, this type of yield is attractive.

In the UK it is possible to grow trees at a rate of $0.3 \, m \, year^{-1}$ and it has been estimated that a power station based on wood could produce $0.8 \, MW \, km^{-2}$ of forest at a cost not dissimilar to a coal-fired station. Demands on land and labour could pose problems, but a solution exists here without the environmental, economic or technological difficulties associated with other forms of solar energy.

V. GEOTHERMAL POWER

The attraction of being able to obtain energy from the interior of the earth from which heat has been evolved for millions of years, and will carry on for millions more, is considerable. There are differing theories as to the origin of the heat, but the most likely explanation is that the bulk is produced by the slow decay of radioactive materials deep within the molten core of the planet. A meaningful estimate of the energy potential in this source is almost impossible. Twidell (1978) quoted a figure of 3×10^7 MW which, for a world population of about 3.5×10^9, would seem to offer a generous solution to the energy problem. The difficulty is of course to obtain at an economic cost even a minute fraction of this enormous figure.

The rate of heat flow of 0.063 W m^{-2} over the surface of the earth quoted by Shepard (1976) agrees well with the above figure and represents a level too low ever to be capable of exploitation. The rate at which temperature increases with depth into the earth's crust varies from 8 to 15 deg K km^{-1} and as present day technology is limited to drilling to a maximum of about 12 km, the drilling of convenient holes where required can be dismissed. It is fortunate, however, that sites of intense activity exist in the vicinity of volcanoes, hot springs and geyser fields where the distance from the surface to very hot rocks is of the order of a few hundred metres. These sites lie on the boundaries of the six major plates which cover the molten core of the earth and which extend to a depth of 2900 km below the surface. These plates move slowly with respect to each other and along the boundaries are formed the major earthquake and volcanic zones formed by the resulting stresses forcing molten rock up into the outer crust of the earth. This action may manifest itself as a volcano or an earthquake or, if the magma encounters water within 10 km of the surface, as steam or boiling water geysers.

Figure 88 shows the distribution of power station installations based on geothermal energy as presented by Koenig (1973); the familiar areas of activity around California and Japan are seen to have been exploited.

There are four main methods of extracting the available energy: dry steam, wet steam, hot water and the injection of water from the surface to hot rocks below.

Hot water may be used directly in district heating schemes; the most familiar example is in Iceland at Hveragerdi and provides 60% of the domestic heating in Reykjavik. This location is expected to have a thermal output of 32 MW by 1980, and a 3 MW electricity generation plant is located at Namafjall using the same source. Hot water sites are the most common throughout the world and even the UK has a number of warm water sites. Paris has buildings heated directly by water drawn from hot wells and there is clearly potential for small-scale schemes using this form of energy.

The ideal geothermal medium is dry steam and the first geothermal power station was opened in 1904 and now has a capacity of 370 MW with the potential of a further 15% increase in output. The largest operating station is at Geysers in California which had an output of 302 MW in 1972 with ultimate output of 1180 MW. Although dry steam is the ideal source for electricity generation, geothermal steam arises at low pressures ($0·75$–$11·3$ MN m^{-2}) which leads to low efficiency of generation. In addition, the low pressures and correspondingly low temperatures can cause problems with water droplets in the turbines.

Wet steam fields are more abundant than dry steam and may be utilized in wet steam turbines to produce electrical power. The disadvantages

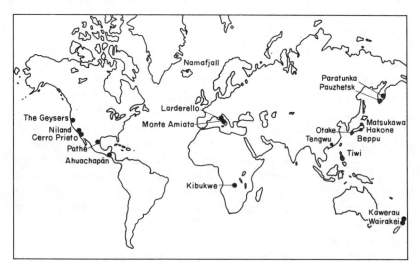

Fig. 88. *Distribution of geothermal electric power stations.*

inherent in this system may be overcome by the use of a heat exchanger in which a working fluid such as freon is vaporized and superheated and this vapour expanded through a turbine to produce power. The plant at Kamchatka in the USSR, which had an output of 31 MW in 1969, works on this principle.

The possibilities of utilizing the so-called "hot rocks" relatively near to the surface are currently being examined in the UK, where the granite areas in Cornwall could provide an energy source at 470–570 K. By drilling to the appropriate depth and pumping water down, the heat would generate steam which could then be used to generate electricity. The same technique is under test by the United States Atomic Energy Commission and the possibilities are clearly attractive.

The present figure of £3000 kW^{-1} is very high for the installed capital cost but this is partially offset by the nature of the "free" source which lowers the operating cost. The future use of geothermal energy would seem to be limited. Use is being made of the sites in geologically active areas now, but considerable expansion of output must be achieved if this source of energy is to provide any significant contribution to the world energy demand.

VI. NUCLEAR POWER

A. Introduction

Some of the alternatives to fossil fuels have been considered in this chapter and their limitations to large-scale exploitation have been discussed. There remains nuclear power; when it is realized that 1 kg of uranium-235 is capable at present of generating the same quantity of electricity as 2500 tonnes day^{-1} of coal in a conventional power station, the attractions are fairly obvious (Hunt *et al.* 1978). The cost of power produced from nuclear energy is a major factor and this has been discussed by Sweet (1978).

The mechanisms involved, the potential available, types of reactor and the possibilities for the future are considered briefly in the following sections.

B. The Nuclear Reaction

1. *Atomic structure*

The atom consists of a very small, massive, and positively charged nucleus surrounded by light negatively charged electrons. The nucleus itself is composed of positively charged heavy protons and electrically neutral neutrons which have a slightly larger mass than the protons. The mass of these particles is very small and is usually referred to in terms of the atomic mass unit, a.m.u., which is equal to one twelfth of the mass of a carbon-12 atom and has a value of 1.660531×10^{-24} g. On this basis, the atomic particles have the masses:

proton   1.007277 a.m.u.
neutron   1.008665 a.m.u.
electron 0.00548593 a.m.u.

The atomic number of an element represents the number of protons in the nucleus and is equal to the number of electrons surrounding the nucleus. It is possible for two nuclei to exist with the same number of protons but with a different number of neutrons and these are known as isotopes. These have a different atomic mass, but will be chemically similar, as they have the same number of electrons. The atomic mass number, A, is the sum of the number of protons and the number of neutrons contained in the nucleus. Uranium, with an atomic number of 92, has three naturally occurring isotopes with mass numbers of 234, 235, and 238, usually written as $^{234}_{92}U$, $^{235}_{92}U$ and $^{238}_{92}U$. The subscript 92 is frequently omitted since it is defined by the chemical symbol. The natural abundance of these three isotopes of uranium is 0·006%, 0·714% and 99·28% respectively; only ^{235}U is naturally fissile.

There is a difference between the experimentally determined mass of the nucleus and the mass of the number of neutrons and protons contained in the nucleus. This difference represents the energy which binds the protons and neutrons together and is known as the binding energy, ΔE, given by Einstein's equation:

$$\Delta E = \Delta mc^2$$

where Δm is the difference in mass or mass deficit and c is the speed of light. For one atomic mass unit,

$$E = (1·66 \times 10^{-24}\,g)(3 \times 10^{10}\,cm\,s^{-1})^2 = 14·918 \times 10^{-4}\,erg$$
$$\equiv 931\,MeV$$

This energy is expressed in millions of electron volts (MeV) where 1 eV is equivalent to $1·6 \times 10^{19}$ J. Each fission in ^{235}U releases 200 MeV or $3·2 \times 10^{-11}$ J so that $3·1 \times 10^{10}$ fissions per second would release 1 W of power. The complete fission of 1 kg of ^{235}U over 24 hr would produce energy in the form of heat at a rate of 1000 MW which, even allowing a low conversion efficiency of 30% to electrical power, makes the attractions of nuclear power very clear.

2. Nuclear fission

The nuclear fission reaction between a neutron and ^{235}U is illustrated in Fig. 89 and represented typically by the equation:

$$^{235}_{92}U + n \rightarrow ^{94}_{37}Rb + ^{140}_{55}Cs + 2n + 3·2 \times 10^{-11}\,J$$

The neutrons produced as a result of fission either escape or go on to collide with other nuclei to give more fissions and produce a chain reaction. As long as the chain reaction can be controlled by removing the heat as it is formed, this reaction may be used in a nuclear reactor where excess neutrons are absorbed to ensure that only one fission reaction results from the neutrons of each earlier reaction. The size of the uranium must be such that the neutrons do not escape before they can strike another nucleus and this lower limit is known as the critical mass. If on the other hand, more neutrons are released than can be controlled, the chain reaction proceeds exponentially and the kinetic energy of the fission products is released as an explosion—as in the nuclear bomb.

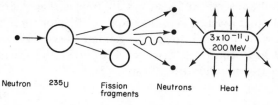

Neutron   235U   Fission   Neutrons   Heat
                   fragments

Fig. 89. *Schematic representation of nuclear fission.*

3. Nuclear fusion

The reverse process of fission is one in which two light nuclei combine to produce a stable nucleus with the release of energy and is known as fusion; this is illustrated in Fig. 90. Deuterium and tritium are two isotopes of

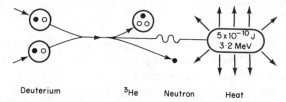

Deuterium   ³He   Neutron   Heat

Fig. 90. *Schematic representation of nuclear fusion.*

hydrogen containing respectively one and two neutrons and are capable of combining in different ways to produce helium as follows:

$$^2_1D + {^2_1}D \rightarrow {^3_2}He + n + \ 3 \cdot 2\,\text{MeV} \qquad \text{(Fig. 90)}$$

$$^2_1D + {^2_1}D \rightarrow {^3_1}T + {^1_1}H + \ 4 \cdot 0\,\text{MeV}$$

$$^2_1D + {^3_1}T \rightarrow {^4_2}He + n + 17 \cdot 6\,\text{MeV}$$

$$^2_1D + {^3_2}He \rightarrow {^4_2}He + {^1_1}H + 18 \cdot 3\,\text{MeV}$$

All of these reactions occur under extreme operating conditions and represent equations of the type which drive the sun. Temperatures involved are extremely high and well beyond the melting points of any possible material construction so that containment is likely to be achieved only within very powerful magnetic fields. The use of fusion reactions clearly lies in the future, and probably not less than 20 years ahead, but it is within this sort of time scale that these sources will have to be developed.

Of the four reactions above, it is likely that the third holds the most commercial promise. Deuterium is present is sea water at a concentration of 34 p.p.m. giving a potential source of some 3×10^{13} tonnes. Tritium will be produced from lithium in a reactor by neutron bombardment and recent estimates put the reserves of ^{6}Li at 7×10^5 tonnes. The energy potentially available from that reaction is of the order of 10^{35} J or some 10^{12} times the present reserves of fossil fuels. A general survey of fusion reactor development has been presented by Olds (1978) and Carruthers (1978) discusses power generation from fusion.

4. Breeder reactions

The reserves of naturally occurring^{235}U, 0.7% of the total uranium stock, are estimated at about 30 years, a comparable figure to that of oil. Most of the remaining uranium exists as ^{238}U which can be used in the following reaction to produce an isotope of plutonium ^{239}Pu:

$$^{238}_{92}\text{U} + \text{n} \rightarrow \,^{239}_{92}\text{U} \rightarrow \,^{239}_{93}\text{Np} + \beta$$
$$\downarrow$$
$$^{239}_{94}\text{Pu} + \beta$$

This isotope of plutonium is capable of undergoing fission when bombarded by slow neutrons, so that the above reaction produces fuel from a plentiful uranium source. The reaction is the basis for the breeder reactor which will be discussed later. The fact that it produces a nuclear fuel means that the resources of uranium when used in this way increase the known reserves by a factor of 140 or some 10 times that of the present coal reserves. The breeder reaction, ^{232}Th $\rightarrow \,^{233}$U offers further possibilities as world reserves of thorium are at least equal to those of uranium.

The breeder reactor, which is at an advanced stage of development, has its disadvantages. Plutonium is highly toxic and has a very low thermal conductivity which makes heat removal difficult (and it is the raw material for nuclear bombs). These problems will have to be overcome in the nuclear programme if fuel for reactors beyond the year 2000 is to be available.

C. Nuclear Reactors

In essence, a nuclear reactor is simple—the reaction provides a source of heat which is absorbed by a suitable coolant which in turn gives its heat to a secondary coolant which can then be used in a turbine or engine for power production. In practice, because of the hazardous nature of the nuclear process, the plant is of necessity more complex and must be built to very high safety standards (Southwood 1978). Before considering the main reactor types, the essential components of the reactor itself will be discussed.

1. Reactor components

(a) *Fuels*. The reactions of ^{235}U have been dealt with above. If the fuel is used in its naturally occurring concentration of $0 \cdot 7\%$, fuel processing costs are low but the reactor is very large. It can be concentrated to 1–2% and is then known as enriched, or to 90% and known as highly enriched, and used in suitable reactors of smaller size. The discarded ^{238}U can be converted to ^{239}Pu in the breeder reaction and ^{233}U can be produced from thorium.

(b) *Moderators*. The fission neutrons produced have about 80 times the energy required to trigger a further fission event so that the probability of further reaction with another ^{235}U atom is small. A moderator is a material which will slow down the neutron by collision with inert atoms and hence increase the desired reaction. Typical moderators are light water, heavy water and carbon.

(c) *Coolants*. The function of the coolant is to remove the heat released by fission from the core of the reactor. Ideally it should possess a high specific heat, high conductivity, stability and be easy to pump. Gases or liquids may be used, each with their own advantages and disadvantages and they include light and heavy water, liquid sodium, air and carbon dioxide. Light water has obvious cost advantages and can double in use as a moderator.

(d) *Control rods*. The need to ensure that the chain reaction proceeds at a controlled rate is achieved by means of rods of cadmium or boron which are capable of absorbing excess neutrons. They are inserted into the core of the reactor and may be raised or lowered, thus speeding up or slowing down the reaction and hence the output of the reactor.

(e) *Shielding*. The core of the reactor is highly radioactive as a result of reaction and gamma radiation produced by the reaction. The shield must prevent radiation from reaching the outside of the reactor. Water, steel and lead all form effective shields and massive quantities of concrete are used for reasons of economy.

2. Reactor types

Reactor types are a breeding ground for acronyms and abbreviations— Magnox, AGR, LWR, HTGR and Candu, for example. Each refers to a particular type of reactor and a brief description of some will serve to illustrate the combinations of fuel, coolant and moderator which have evolved in the past 20 years. All have the same essential construction summarized earlier and schematic illustrations will serve to provide a rudimentary idea of the various modes of operation.

(a) *The Magnox reactor.* The first British commercial stations derived their name from the magnesium oxide container of the natural uranium fuel. Illustrated in Fig. 91, the Magnox reactor uses carbon dioxide as the coolant gas with graphite as a moderator. The reactor is physically larger

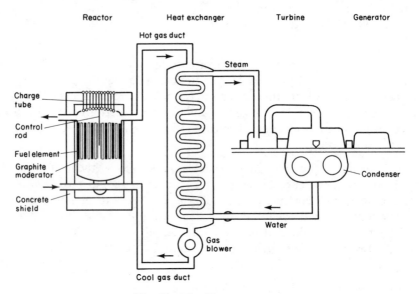

Fig. 91. *The Magnox reactor.*

than the water reactors described below and is believed by many to be safer (Anon. 1978b).

(b) *The light water reactor.* The LWR has found favour in the USA but has been the subject of some criticism. It uses water both as a coolant and as a moderator. The two different forms, the boiling water reactor (BWR) and the pressurized water reactor (PWR) are shown in Figs. 92 and 93 respectively.

The fuel used in a boiling water reactor is usually uranium dioxide enriched with 2·5–3·2% ^{235}U. The coolant water boils inside the reactor vessel and the steam generated at 6·9 MN m^{-2} and 560 K is used directly to drive a turbine. In the PWR, the conditions of temperature and pressure

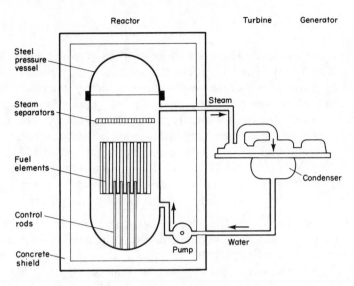

Fig. 92. *The boiling water reactor.*

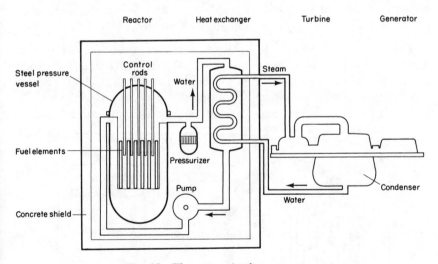

Fig. 93. *The pressurized water reactor.*

are more severe at 600 K and 15·5 MN m⁻², at which pressure the water is prevented from boiling. A heat exchanger within the core permits transfer of heat from the high-pressure water to a secondary water system which is converted to steam for power generation. The PWR overcomes the disadvantage of the BWR in which radioactive steam is passed directly through the turbines where serious hazards could arise as a result of leaks (Baumgarth 1978).

Light-water-moderated reactors are susceptible to two major criticisms with regard to safety. The strength of the containing steel pressure vessel depends upon the quality of the welding the very heavy sheets which must be employed. More important is the possibility of a failure in the supply of water to the core of the reactor for any reason. The water is serving both to cool and moderate the core and any interruption could cause a very rapid rise in temperature which could destroy the pressure vessel and cause a massive leak of radioactivity. This latter risk is lower in the BWR since the core is less tightly packed as the steam present is a less effective moderator and more time would be available in the event of water failure.

(c) *Gas cooled reactors.* The advanced gas cooled reactor (AGR) is the name given to the second generation of British reactors to succeed the Magnox. The gas cooling has the effect of making the reactor volume larger, giving inherently greater safety considerations. The high-temperature gas cooled reactor (HTGR) in the USA operates on a fuel consisting of 95% ^{232}Th and 5% ^{235}U. The coolant is helium which enters the reactor at 670 K and leaves at 1050 K and 4·8 MN m^{-2}. Steam is produced for electricity generation at 810 K and 17·2 MN m^{-2}.

(d) *The breeder reactor.* In the USA, there are three types of breeder, the liquid metal fast breeder reactor (LMFBR), the gas cooled fast breeder reactor (GCFBR) and the molten salt breeder reactor (MSBR). The first two operate on ^{238}U producing ^{239}Pu and the last converts ^{232}Th to ^{233}U. The LMFBR is shown schematically in Fig. 94. The fuel consists of 80%

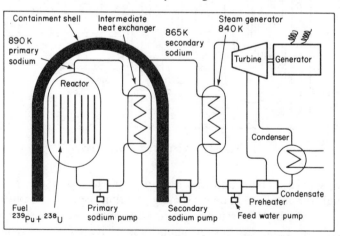

Fig. 94. *A liquid metal fast breeder reactor.*

UO_2 and 20% PuO_2 in stainless steel tubes and primary cooling is by liquid sodium at 890 K. A secondary liquid sodium stream enters the heat exchanger within the containing shell and it is that stream which raises the steam for electricity generation. This additional loop is necessitated by the intense radioactivity picked up by the sodium in the reactor—a problem which does not arise in the GCBR which is cooled with high-pressure ($8\cdot6$ MW m^{-2}) helium (Franklin 1979). The efficiency of these reactors is about 40%. The general safety of sodium-cooled fast reactors is discussed by Thornton and Brindley (1978).

D. Nuclear Reactor Safety

Since the late 1970s, there has been increasing opposition to the growth of the nuclear industry and in 1979, pressure groups succeeded in halting all construction work on nuclear sites in Germany; there have been similar activities in the USA. The 100 day enquiry into re-processing of nuclear waste at Windscale and interminable planning delays for new sites reflect a persistent opposition in the UK.

The consequences of a nuclear accident are potentially disastrous, though it should be noted that in the relatively few serious incidents, there has been no loss of life (Griffiths 1978). The nuclear industry operates to very high safety standards and problems with reactor safety and emissions represent the least worrying aspects of the potential hazards since these can be overcome with well established technology and the experience gained on many sites during the past 20 years of successful and safe operation. Safety from terrorist attacks is a totally different problem, but it is not a problem specific only to the nuclear industry. The real cause for concern lies in the area of nuclear waste where storage times are likely to be several thousands of years and certainly much longer than the present experience of the materials used for containment.

Spent fuel assemblies are highly radioactive and before any processing can take place they are allowed to "cool" to allow this radioactivity to decrease over a period of a few months. Reprocessing involves the recovery of uranium and plutonium after which the waste, which still contains many highly toxic elements, is stored in suitable containers (Keepin 1978, Koch 1978). As the nuclear industry expands, as it inevitably must, the waste problem will grow. The problem is long term with strontium-90 and caesium-137 typical of medium atomic mass fission products with half lives of up to about 30 years. To store these materials until the original activity has been reduced to one millionth involves storage for a few hundred years but thorium, uranium and plutonium have half lives of up to 25 000 years. This latter group presents problems for generations far into the future and no disposal method can carry confidence in its absolute safety on this sort of time scale. Encapsulation into massive concrete blocks for discharge to the deepest oceans is used at present as one possible means. It is one, however, which eliminates the possibility of future recovery should it ever be necessary and an alternative is to drill deep into mountains located away from any possibility of earthquake activity. While this seems a sensible and safe means, the search for suitable sites remote from areas of population is likely to be prolonged.

This chapter has tried to evaluate the possibilities for the future and it is apparent that there is no real alternative to an increasing nuclear programme, though that must have the confidence of the consumer and capturing that confidence may well pose problems as challenging as any of the technical difficulties (Lewis 1968).

VII. FURTHER READING

Benedict, M. and Pigford, T. H. (1957). "Nuclear Chemical Engineering". McGraw-Hill, New York.

Duffie, J. A. and Backman, W. A. (1974). "Solar Energy Thermal Processes". Wiley-Interscience, New York.

Flagg, J. F. (1961). "Chemical Processing of Reactor Fuels". Academic Press, London and New York.

Golding. E. W. (1955). "The Generation of Electricity by Wind Power". E. and F. N. Spon Ltd., London.

Gray, T. J. and Gashus, O. K. (eds.) (1972). "Tidal Power". Plenum Press, New York.

Guthrie-Brown, J. (ed.) (1970). "Hydroelectric Engineering Practice", Vol. II. Blackie, London.

Krenz, J. H. (1976). "Energy Conversion and Utilization". Alley and Bacon, New York.

Macrae, J. C. (1966). "An Introduction to the Study of Fuel". Elsevier, London.

McMullan, J. T., Morgan, R. and Murray, R. B. (1976). "Energy Resources". Edward Arnold, London.

McVeigh, J. C. (1977). "Sun Power". Pergamon Press, Oxford.

Montefiore, H. (1977). "Nuclear Crisis". Prism, London.

Patterson, W. (1976). "Nuclear Power". Penguin Books, Harmondsworth.

Putnam, P. C. (1948). "Power from the Wind". Van Nostrand, New York.

Thomas, P. H. (1945). "Electrical Power from the Wind". US Federal Power Commission.

Calculations in Fuel and Energy

9

I. INTRODUCTION

The production and processing of fuels may be largely qualitative in nature, but the application of fundamentals is of little value when considering, for example the performance of fuel plant without making calculations to assess the efficiency and, perhaps more important, the cost effectiveness of any operation. It must be stressed that the result of any calculation is only as good as the raw data used and the accuracy with which the calculation is made.

This chapter aims at presenting an introduction to the basic types of problems encountered in energy engineering, with special reference to mass and heat balances. Because of its considerable significance in calculations, the question of units will be considered at an early stage. Although engineers have been concerned with many systems of units in the past, indications are that future trends will be towards the SI (Système International d'Unités) system of units and this has been adopted throughout the book. Before considering the basic principles of mass and energy balances, the calculation of properties of fuels from raw experimental data will be considered, although it is beyond the scope of this chapter to consider the techniques involved. A significant part of this chapter is devoted to the question of stoichiometry, working from a fairly basic knowledge of chemistry, and this leads to an application of the fundamentals in considering problems concerned with evaluating the performance of combustion plant.

229

II. UNITS

Fuel engineers often find that the data they use are expressed in a variety of systems of units and it is important that one is able to express quantities in a common system.

Most of the physical properties determined in the laboratory relating to fuels are expressed in the c.g.s. system, while design data and operating conditions of fuel and boiler plant are expressed in engineering units, the lb.ft.hr. system, or special units which have their origin in a particular industry. For example, the c.g.s. unit of dynamic viscosity is the poise (P) where

$$1 \text{ P} = 1 \text{ g cm}^{-1} \text{ s}^{-1}$$

In engineering units, viscosity becomes lb/ft hr and the traditional unit in the petroleum industry is Redwood seconds, defined as the time taken for a fixed volume of oil to flow through a standard orifice under a specified set of conditions. This is but one example where a variety of units are used for the same property; a situation which it is hoped will be overcome by the introduction of a standardization system of units such as that adopted by the International Organization for Standardization—the SI system. This is based on the metric system and, although it has certain disadvantages, the merits are such that it is now being accepted by an ever increasing number of scientists and engineers. Some of the basic features of the SI system are now considered, though much more comprehensive treatments are available elsewhere (British Standards Institution 1967, Bigg 1964, Anderton and Bigg 1965, Ede 1966).

The basic units of the SI system are: length, the metre (m); mass, the kilogram (kg); time, the second (s); electric current, the ampere (A); and temperature, the Kelvin (K). In addition, certain derived units have been given special names and the more important of these, as applied to and energy, are shown in Table 32.

Certain values expressed in SI units may be of an inconvenient size, 1 year being about 31 500 000 s for example, though this may be overcome by the use of multiplying prefixes, some of which are shown in Table 32 (1 year is thus 31·5 Ms). The SI system is coherent in that, when unit quantities are multiplied or divided, no numerical values are involved. For example, the use of g is not involved as in a gravitational system of units, but only when the force of gravity is actually involved. Thus the weight of a mass of w kg is a force of wg N, where g is the acceleration due to gravity. One important feature of SI units, is that certain common physical properties are no longer unity. For example, the specific heat of water (1 BTU lb^{-1} °F^{-1} = 1 cal g^{-1} °C^{-1}) becomes 4·187 kJ kg^{-1} K^{-1}. As an aid

TABLE 32. *The SI system of units*

(a) Basic units

length	metre	m
mass	kilogram	kg
time	second	s
temperature	Kelvin	K
current	ampere	A

(b) Derived units

force	newton	N	($1\ N = 1\ kg\ m\ s^{-2}$)
work, energy, heat	joule	J	($1\ J = 1\ Nm = 1\ kg\ m^2\ s^{-2}$)
power	watt	W	($1\ W = 1\ J\ s^{-1} = 1\ kg\ m^2\ s^{-3}$)
electric potential	volt	V	($1\ V = 1\ W\ A^{-1} = 1\ kg\ m^2\ s^{-3}\ A^{-1}$)
frequency	hertz	Hz	($1\ Hz = 1\ cycle/s$)

(c) Prefixes for unit multiples and sub-multiples

10^{-6}	micro-	μ
10^{-3}	milli-	m
10^{-2}	centi-	c
10^{3}	kilo-	k
10^{6}	mega-	M
10^{9}	giga-	G
10^{12}	tera-	T
10^{15}	peta-	P
10^{18}	exa-	E

TABLE 33. *Physical constants and common properties*

(a) Physical constants

Boltzmann's constant, $k = 1\cdot381 \times 10^{-23}\ J\ K^{-1}$
Gravitational acceleration, $g = 9\cdot81\ m\ s^{-2}$
Universal gas constant, $R = 8\cdot314\ kJ\ kmol^{-1}\ K^{-1}$
Volume of 1 kmol ideal gas at s.t.p. = $22\cdot4\ m^3$
Standard temperature and pressure = $101\cdot3\ kN\ m^{-2}$ and $273\cdot15\ K$

(b) Common properties (approximate values)

Calorific value	carbon monoxide	$11\cdot9\ MJ\ m^{-3}$
	methane	$37\cdot1\ MJ\ m^{-3}$
	town gas	$18\cdot6\ MJ\ m^{-3}$
	coal	$37\cdot0\ MJ\ kg^{-1}$
	fuel oil	$45\cdot0\ MJ\ kg^{-1}$
Specific heat	water	$4\cdot18\ kJ\ kg^{-1}\ K^{-1}$
	flue gas	$1\cdot05\ kJ\ kg^{-1}\ K^{-1}$
	water vapour	$2\cdot0\ kJ\ kg^{-1}\ K^{-1}$
	air	$1\cdot0\ kJ\ kg^{-1}\ K^{-1}$
Density	water	$1000\ kg\ m^{-3}$
Viscosity	water	$0\cdot001\ N\ s\ m^{-2}$
	air	$170\ mN\ s\ m^{-2}$
Latent heat	water	$2\ MJ\ kg^{-1}$
Thermal conductivity	air	$0\cdot024\ W\ m^{-1}\ K^{-1}$

TABLE 34. *Conversion factors for some common units*

Length:	1 in.: 25·4 mm	Volume flow:	1 ft³/s: 0·028 m³ s⁻¹
	1 ft: 0·305 m		1 gal/h: 1·26 cm³ s⁻¹
Area	1 in.²: 645 mm²	Mass flow:	1 lb/h: 0·126 g s⁻¹
	1 ft²: 0·093 m²	Density:	1 lb/in.³: 27·7 g cm⁻³
Volume:	1 in.³: 16·39 cm³		1 lb/ft³: 16·0 kg m⁻³
	1 ft³: 0·028 m³	Pressure	1 lbf/in.²: 6·90 kN m⁻²
	1 gal: 4546 cm³		1 atm: 101·3 kN m⁻²
Mass	1 lb: 0·454 kg	Heat flow:	1 BTU/h: 0·293 W
	1 ton: 1·016 Mg	Viscosity:	1 poise: 0·1 N s m⁻²
Force:	1 lbf: 4·45 N		1 lb/ft h: 0·413 mN s m⁻²
			1 stokes: 0·0001 m² s⁻¹
Energy, work		Specific heat:	1 BTU/lb°F:
			4·187 kJ kg⁻¹ K⁻¹
heat:	1 cal:4·187 J	Temperature	
	1 BTU:1·055 kJ	difference	1°F = 0·556 deg K
	1 kWh: 3·6 MJ		
	1 therm: 105·5 MJ	Thermal	
		conductivity:	1 BTU ft hr⁻¹ ft⁻² °F⁻¹
			= 1·73 Wm⁻¹ deg K⁻¹
Calorific value:	1 BTU/ft³: 37·3 kJ m⁻³	Latent heat:	1 BTU/lb: 2·33 kJ kg⁻¹
	1 BTU/lb: 2·33 kJ kg⁻¹		

to gaining the "feel" of the SI system, selected properties encountered in fuel calculations are included together with physical constants in Table 33 and a list of common conversion factors in Table 34. The use of these conversion factors is illustrated in the following example.

Example 9.1

The criterion for the character of flow of a fluid in a duct or pipe, that is either streamline or turbulent, is the Reynold's number, $Re = d\,u\,\varrho/\mu$. A gas is flowing in a duct at a rate of 2000 ft³/min at a mean temperature and pressure of 200°F and 34 in. Hg, respectively. Calculate the volumetric flow at s.t.p. and the Reynolds number, if the duct is 9 in. in diameter, working in SI units. The density and viscosity of the gas at 200°F may be taken as 0·056 lb/ft³ and 218×10^{-6} poise.

(i) VOLUMETRIC FLOW

$$2000 \text{ ft}^3/\text{min} = 2000/60 = 33·33 \text{ ft}^3/\text{s}$$
$$= 33·33 \times 0·028 = 0·933 \text{ m}^3 \text{ s}^{-1}$$
$$200°F = 0·55 (200 - 32) + 273 = 366 \text{ K}$$
$$34 \text{ in. Hg} = 34 \times 3·386 = 115·1 \text{ kN m}^{-2}$$

Standard temperature and pressure $\equiv$ 273 K and 101·3 kN m^{-2}

Assuming ideal gas laws:

$$P_1V_1/T_1 = P_2V_2/T_2$$
$$\therefore (115·1 \times 0·933)/366 = (101·3 \times V_2)/273$$

from which
$$V_2 = \underline{\underline{0·791 \text{ m}^3 \text{ at s.t.p.}}}$$

(ii) REYNOLDS NUMBER

British units:

diameter of pipe, d = 9 in. = 0·75 ft

gas velocity, u = $2000/(\pi 0·75^2/4)$ = 4·526 × 10^3 ft/min

$\quad$ = 4·526 × 10^3 × 60 = 2·716 × 10^5 ft/min

density, ϱ = 0·056 lb/ft^3

viscosity, μ = 2·18 × 10^{-4} poise

$\quad$ = 2·18 × 10^{-4} × 242 = 0·0527 lb/ft hr

$\therefore$ Reynolds number = 0·75 × 2·716 × 10^5 × 0·056/0·0527

$\quad$ = $\underline{\underline{2·163 \times 10^5}}$

SI units:

$$d = 0·75 \text{ ft} = 0·75 \times 0·305 = 0·229 \text{ m}$$
$$u = 4·526 \times 10^3 \text{ ft/min} = 4·526 \times 10^3/60$$
$$= 75·43 \text{ ft/s}$$
$$= 75·43 \times 0·305 \text{ m s}^{-1}$$
$$= 23·01 \text{ m s}^{-1}$$
$$\varrho = 0·056 \times 16·02 = 0·897 \text{ kg m}^{-3}$$
$$\mu = 2·18 \times 10^{-4} \times 0·1 = 2·18 \times 10^{-5} \text{ N s m}^{-2}$$
$$\therefore \text{ Reynolds number} = 0·229 \times 23·01 \times 0·397/2·18 \times 10^{-5}$$
$$= \underline{\underline{2·168 \times 10^5}}$$

Check units:

$$\text{Re} = du\varrho/\mu = \frac{\text{m.m.kg.m}^2}{\text{s.m}^3\text{.N.s}}$$

$$= \frac{\text{kg.m}}{\text{s}^2\text{.N}} = \frac{\text{kg.m.s}^2}{\text{s}^2\text{.kg.m}}$$

i.e. dimensionless

Before proceeding to further calculations, a few general points may be noted. Firstly, the importance of working in consistent units; indeed, before tackling any problem, it is worthwhile converting all the given data to the same units. This procedure was carried out in Example 9.1, where the variety of units, ft³/min, in. Hg, °F, poise and so on were all converted to the SI equivalent. Even where SI units are not used, either consistent lb. ft. hr. or c.g.s. units should be employed. A related comment is that wherever an established equation or expression is used, it is well worthwhile checking the units on both sides of the equation to see that they are the same. In a simplified way, this was carried out in Example 9.1 when the Reynolds number was shown to be dimensionless.

III. ESTIMATION OF FUEL PROPERTIES FROM EXPERIMENTAL DATA

All design calculations and estimations of plant performance require a knowledge of the properties and compositions of the fuels and flue gases involved. These are determined by well established tests carried out in the laboratory, many of which involve significant calculation stages in obtaining the desired data from the experimental measurements. This section considers typical calculations associated with the more important tests which are described in Chapter 6.

A. Analysis of Solid Fuels

Solid fuels can be evaluated as regards gravimetric composition by well known analytical techniques providing data on the amounts of carbon, hydrogen, nitrogen, sulphur and so on in what is known as an ultimate analysis. This will not be considered here. Peculiar to solid fuels however, is proximate analysis in which constituents such as coke and volatile matter are determined (Himus 1946, British Standards Institution 1942). The method of obtaining such information from experimental measurements is illustrated in the following example.

Example 9.2

A sample of finely ground coal of mass 0·9945 g was placed in a crucible of 8·5506 g in an oven, maintained at 375 K for 4·0 ks. The sample was then removed, cooled in a dessicator and reweighed; the procedure being repeated until a constant total mass of 9·5340 g was attained. A second sample, of mass 1·0120 g in a crucible of mass 8·5685 g, was heated with a lid over a bunsen for 450 s. On cooling and reweighing, the total mass was 9·1921 g. This sample was then heated without a lid over a strong bunsen flame until a constant total mass of 8·6255 g was attained. Calculate the proximate analysis of the sample and express the results on "as sampled" and "dry, ash-free" bases.

(i) MOISTURE

$$\text{mass of sample} = 0·9945 \text{ g}$$
$$\text{mass of dry coal} = (9·5340 - 8·5506) = 0·9834 \text{ g}$$
$$\text{mass of moisture} = (0·9945 - 0·9334) = 0·0111 \text{ g}$$
$$\therefore \% \text{ moisture} = 0·0111 \times 100/0·9945$$
$$= 1·11\%$$

(ii) COKE

$$\text{mass of sample} = 1·0120 \text{ g}$$
$$\text{mass of coke} = (9·1921 - 8·5685) = 0·6236 \text{ g}$$
$$\therefore \% \text{ coke} = 0·6236 \times 100/1·0120$$
$$= 61·60\%$$

(iii) ASH

$$\text{mass of sample} = 1·0120 \text{ g}$$
$$\text{mass of ash} = (8·6255 - 8·5685) = 0·0560 \text{ g}$$
$$\therefore \% \text{ ash} = 0·0560 \times 100/1·0120$$
$$= 5·53\%$$

(iv) VOLATILE MATTER

$$\% \text{ VM} = 100 - (\% \text{ coke} + \% \text{ moisture}) = 100 - (61·60 + 1·11)$$
$$= 37·29\%$$

(v) FIXED CARBON

$$\% \text{ FC} = (\% \text{ coke} - \% \text{ ash}) = (61·60 - 5·53)$$
$$= 56·07\%$$

(vi) ANALYSIS

On an *"as sampled" basis*, the proximate analysis is:

total moisture 1·11%, ash 5·53%, volatile matter 37·29%, fixed carbon 56·07%

Thus the total moisture plus ash $= (5·53 + 1·11)\% = 6·64\%$ and hence, on a *"dry, ash-free" basis,*

$$\% \text{ volatile matter} = 37·29 \times 100/(100 - 6·64) = 39·9\%$$
$$\% \text{ fixed carbon} = (100 - 39·9) = 60·1\%$$

B. Analysis of Gaseous Fuels

Although modern methods of analysing fuel and flue gases such as gas chromatography are now used, as discussed in Chapter 6, the traditional Orsat chemical absorption and similar techniques still find wide application throughout the fuel industries, especially where data are required on site (Wheeler 1922, Himus 1946). The general principle is that various components of the gas mixture are selectively absorbed in chemical reagents and any remaining hydrocarbons together with hydrogen are then exploded in air. The method of computing the analysis from the experimental data is illustrated in the following example.

Example 9.3

In an Orsat analysis of a fuel gas, the volume of the sample was $50{\cdot}0\,cm^3$ at ambient temperature and pressure and the following results were noted:
volume remaining after absorption in potassium hydroxide solution $= 48{\cdot}9\,cm^3$
volume remaining after absorption in alkaline pyrogallol $= 48{\cdot}4\ cm^3$
volume remaining after absorption in acidified cuprous chloride $= 42{\cdot}2\ cm^3$
volume remaining after absorption in saturated bromine water $= 41{\cdot}8\ cm^3$
$10\ cm^3$ of the remaining gas was then exploded with $40\ cm^3$ air, after which the volume of gas was $36{\cdot}5\ cm^3$. This was reduced to $33{\cdot}6\,cm^3$ after absorption in potassium hydroxide solution. Calculate the volumetric analysis of the fuel gas.

Potassium hydroxide absorbs carbon dioxide

$$\therefore\ \%\ CO_2 = (50{\cdot}0 - 48{\cdot}9)100/50 = \underline{2{\cdot}2\%}$$

Pyrogallol absorbs oxygen

$$\therefore\ \%\ O_2 = (48{\cdot}9 - 48{\cdot}4)100/50 = \underline{1{\cdot}0\%}$$

Cuprous chloride removes the carbon monoxide

$$\therefore\ \%\ CO = (48{\cdot}4 - 42{\cdot}2)100/50 = \underline{12{\cdot}4\%}$$

Bromine water absorbs unsaturated hydrocarbons

$$\therefore\ \%C_nH_{2n} = (42{\cdot}2 - 41{\cdot}8)100/50 = \underline{0{\cdot}8\%}$$

During the explosion, the following reactions (discussed further in

Section V. A) take place:

$$CH_4 + 2O_2 \rightarrow CO_2 + 2H_2O$$
volumes: a $2a$ a $2a$

The water condenses out and hence the reduction in volume = $(a + 2a) - a = 2a$

$$H_2 + \tfrac{1}{2}O_2 \rightarrow H_2O$$
volumes: b $b/2$ b

Again the water condenses out and the reduction in volume = $(b + b/2) - 0 = 3b/2$. Now all the CO_2 formed during the explosion, $(36 \cdot 5 - 33 \cdot 6) = 2 \cdot 9$ cm^3, comes from the methane and hence volume of methane in the 10 cm^3 sample exploded, $a = 2 \cdot 9$ cm^3. The total reduction in volume, due to condensation of water and consumption of oxygen = $(50 \cdot 0 - 36 \cdot 5) = 13 \cdot 5$ cm^3.

$$\therefore 2a + 3b/2 = 13 \cdot 5$$
$$2 \times 2 \cdot 9 + 3b/2 = 13 \cdot 5$$
$$\text{or } b = 5 \cdot 1 \text{ cm}^3$$

Thus, in 10 cm^3 sample exploded,

volume of $CH_4 = 2 \cdot 9$ cm^3,
volume of $H_2 = 5 \cdot 1$ cm^3

Therefore in 41·8 cm^3 of gas mixture,

volume of $CH_4 = 2 \cdot 9 \times 41 \cdot 8/10 = 12 \cdot 1$ cm^3
volume of $H_2 = 5 \cdot 1 \times 41 \cdot 8/10 = 21 \cdot 3$ cm^3
$$\therefore \% CH_4 = 12 \cdot 1 \times 100/50 = \underline{24 \cdot 2\%}$$
$$\text{and } \% H_2 = 21 \cdot 3 \times 100/50 = \underline{42 \cdot 6\%}$$

The total percentage of the components computed so far = 83·2%

$$\therefore \% N_2 + \text{errors} = (100 - 83 \cdot 2) = \underline{16 \cdot 8\%}$$

C. Calorific Value

1. Gross and net values

The calorific value of a fuel is defined as the quantity of heat evolved when unit mass (or unit volume in the case of a gas) of the fuel is completely burned and the combustion products cooled to 288 K. This value is known as the "gross" calorific value. In practice, it is most undesirable that the flue gases should be cooled in this way and indeed, every effort is made to ensure that the flue gas leaves the plant at a temperature well above the dew point, thus avoiding condensation of water vapour and a whole host of corrosion problems. In this way, the flue gas carries away as vapour whose latent heat is not recovered the water produced by the combustion of hydrogen in the fuel. Thus the effective calorific value of the fuel is decreased by this amount and it is necessary to speak of a "net" calorific value as being the practical quantity of heat available.

Example 9.4

A coal, containing 5% hydrogen and 10% moisture as sampled, has a gross calorific of 33·5 MJ kg^{-1} on a dry basis. Calculate the gross calorific value on an "as sampled" basis and the net calorific values on "dry" and "as sampled" bases.

For the combustion of hydrogen,

$$H_2 \times \tfrac{1}{2}O_2 \rightarrow H_2O$$

molecular mass 2   16   18

Thus 2 kg hydrogen form 18 kg water.

In 1 kg coal, 0·05 kg hydrogen will thus form (0·05 × 18/2) kg = 0·45 kg water. In addition, the moisture in the coal, 0·10 kg/kg, passes into the flue gas and hence the weight of water in the flue gas = 0·55 kg.

Taking the latent heat of water vapour as 2·45 MJ kg^{-1}, and ignoring sensible heat losses, heat carried away in water vapour is 0·55 × 2·45 = 1·35 MJ kg^{-1} coal.

∴ Net calorific value on a dry basis = (33·5 − 1·35)
$$= 32 \cdot 15 \text{ MJ kg}^{-1}$$

On an "as sampled" basis, the fact that the moisture in the coal does not contribute to either of the calorific values must be taken into account, hence

gross CV = 33·5   (100 − 10)/100 = 30·2 MJ kg^{-1}

net CV = 32·15 (100 − 10)/100 = 28·9 MJ kg^{-1}

2. Calculation from experimental data

In experimental determinations of calorific value, a known mass (or volume) of the fuel is burned completely under carefully controlled conditions and the amount of heat transferred to water either flowing through or contained in a standardized calorimeter is measured. In such tests, the flue gases are cooled to ambient conditions and hence the values obtained represent gross calorific values. The method of calculating values from experimental data is illustrated in the following examples.

Example 9.5

In a test to evaluate the gross calorific value of a sample of coal using a Mahler bomb calorimeter, 0·5950 g coal together with 0·0075 g iron wire was exploded in an atmosphere of oxygen in a bomb calorimeter of water equivalent 0·375 kg containing 1·850 kg water. Before ignition, the temperature of the water fell 0·045 deg K in 0·30 ks and the measured temperature rise was 1·4931 deg K in 0·18 ks. After attaining its maximum value, the water temperature fell 0·060 deg K in 0·30 ks. Taking the calorific value of iron wire as 1·60 Mj kg^{-1}, calculate the gross calorific value of the coal sample.

Cooling correction = (length of firing period) × (mean of initial and final cooling rates)
$$= 0·18 \{0·5[(0·045/0·30) + (0·060/0·30)]\}$$
$$= 0·0315 \text{ deg K}$$
∴ Corrected temperature rise = 1·4931 + 0·0315 = 1·524 deg K

(This is the water temperature which would have been attained if no heat had been lost to the surroundings).

Heat transferred to the water and calorimeter
$$= (0·375 + 1·850) × 4·187 × 1·5246$$
$$= 14·19 \text{ kJ}$$

Heat supplied by iron wire = 0·0075 × 1·60 = 0·012 kJ
∴ Heat supplied by coal = (14·19 − 0·012) = 14·178 kJ
∴ Gross CV of coal sample = 14·178/0·5950 = 23·83 kJ g^{-1}
$$= \underline{\underline{23·83 \text{ MJ kg}^{-1}}}$$

Example 9.6

Using a Boys calorimeter under standardized conditions, 0·01 m^3 coal gas measured at 101·25 kN m^{-2} and 293 K, was burned giving a flue gas temperature of 296 K. During the test, 1·96 kg water was passed through the calorimeter, the mean inlet and outlet temperatures being 288·58 K and 309·91 K respectively, and 7·6 g condensate was collected from the combustion chamber. Calculate the gross and net calorific values of the sample.

Firstly, the volume of gas burned must be corrected to $101 \cdot 33$ kN m^{-2} and 288 K, thus,

volume $= 0 \cdot 01 \times (101 \cdot 25/101 \cdot 33)(288/293) = 0 \cdot 00983$ m^3
heat gained by the water $= 1 \cdot 96 \times 4 \cdot 187 (309 \cdot 91 - 288 \cdot 58)$
$$= 175 \cdot 0 \, kJ$$
or $175 \cdot 0/0 \cdot 00983 = 17810$ kJ/m^3 gas

The flue gas leaves the calorimeter at a temperature higher than 288 K and hence this is not the true gross CV. The gross CV is obtained by applying a correction $= 8 \cdot 27$ (flue gas temperature − room temperature) to this value. Thus,

$$gross \ CV = 17\,810 + 8 \cdot 27(296 - 293)$$
$$\underline{\underline{17\,835 \text{ kJ m}^{-3}}}$$

Taking the latent heat of water at 288 K $= 2 \cdot 45$ kJ g^{-1}

∴ heat in water produced by the combustion of hydrogen and hydrocarbons

$$= 7 \cdot 6 \times 2 \cdot 45 = 18 \cdot 6 \, kJ$$
or $18 \cdot 6/0 \cdot 00983 = 1895$ kJ m^{-3} gas
∴ $net \ CV = (17\,835 - 1895) = \underline{\underline{15\,930 \text{ kJ m}^{-3}}}$

3. *Calculation from fuel analysis*

In the case of solid and liquid fuels, various relationships are available for predicting the calorific values from the proximate and ultimate analyses. Such relationships are largely empirical in nature and are limited in their application. Bearing this in mind however, they may be used to provide a first-order estimate of the values required. With gases, the calculations are much more straightforward, providing the fuel may be regarded as a perfect mixture.

Example 9.7

A coal has the following analysis on an as-sampled basis:

C $80 \cdot 4\%$, H $5 \cdot 0\%$, O $4 \cdot 3\%$, N $1 \cdot 5\%$, S $0 \cdot 9\%$, moisture $2 \cdot 2\%$, ash $5 \cdot 7\%$, volatile matter $26 \cdot 9\%$, fixed carbon $65 \cdot 1\%$.

Estimate the gross calorific value of the sample from the results of both the ultimate and proximate analyses on a dry ash-free basis.

Considering the ultimate analysis, it is necessary to express the data on a dry, ash-free basis. As in Example 9.2, this is achieved by

multiplying each component by 100/(100 − (% ash + % moisture)),
or in this case, by 100/(100 − 7·9) = 1·085.

Thus the analysis becomes:

C 87·2%, H 5·4%, O 4·7%, N 1·6%, S 1·1%

The oldest relationship for CV is the Dulong Formula:

$$CV = 338·2C + 1442·8(H − O/8) + 94·2S \quad kJ\ kg^{-1}$$
$$= (338·2 \times 87·2) + 1442·8(5·4 − 4·7/8) + (94·2 \times 1·1)$$
$$= 36\,554\ kJ\ kg^{-1}$$

Perhaps a more reliable relationship is that due to Grumell and
Davies:

$$CV = (15·22H + 937)(C/3 + H − (O − S)/8) \quad kJ\ kg^{-1}$$
$$= [(15·22 \times 5·4) + 937][87·2/3 + 5·4 − (4·7 − 1·1)/8]$$
$$= 34\,620\ kJ\ kg^{-1}$$

(which gives some indication of the accuracy of the method).

The proximate analysis on a dry, ash-free basis becomes,

$$\% \text{ volatile matter} = 26·9 \times 1·085 = 29·2\%$$
$$\% \text{ fixed carbon} = 65·1 \times 1·085 = 71·8\%$$

The calorific value may now be calculated by the relationship
ascribed to Goutal (Taylor and Patterson 1929):

$$CV = 4·187((82FC) + (aVM))\ kJ\ kg^{-1}$$

where a is a variable and a function of V', the % volatile matter on a
dry, ash free basis, as shown in Fig. 95.

In this case $V' = 29·2\%$ and from Fig. 95, $a = 98·5$

$$\therefore CV = 4·187((82 \times 71·8) + (98·5 \times 29·2))$$
$$= 36\,620\ kJ\ kg^{-1}$$

Example 9.8

Estimate the gross and net calorific values of the gas sample given in
Example 9.3. The following calorific values may be assumed:

CO 12·71, CH_4 39·76, H_2 12·78, C_2H_4 62·41   MJ m^{-3} at s.t.p.

Hence *gross* CV of sample = (0·124 × 12·71) + (0·008 × 62·41) +
                                    (0·426 × 12·78) + (0·242 × 39·76)
                           = 16·69 MJ m^{-3}

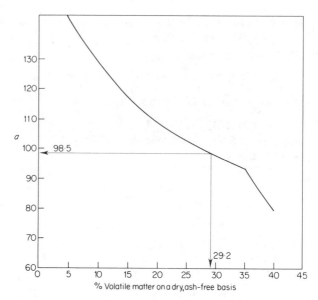

Fig. 95. *Determination of calorific value from proximate analysis (Example 9.7).*

In the combustion process,

$$CH_4 + 2O_2 \rightarrow CO_2 + 2H_2O$$
volumes: 1   2   1   2
∴ 0·242 m³ CH_4 form 0·484 m³ water

$$H_2 + \tfrac{1}{2}O_2 \rightarrow H_2O$$
volumes: 1 $\tfrac{1}{2}$ 1
∴ 0·426 m³ H_2 form 0·426 m³ water

$$C_2H_4 + 3O_2 \rightarrow 2CO_2 + 2H_2O$$
volumes: 1   3   2   2
∴ 0·008 m³ C_2H_4 form 0·016 m³ water

∴ In the combustion of 1 m³ gas (0·016 + 0·426 + 0·484) = 0·926 m³ water vapour is formed

$$= 0.926 \times 18/22.4 = 0.745 \text{ kg m}^{-3}$$

(see Section IV. A)

Taking the latent heat of steam as 2·45 MJ kg⁻¹ and ignoring sensible heat, heat lost due to water vapour in flue gas

$$= 0.745 \times 2.45 = 1.83 \text{ MJ m}^{-3}$$

∴ *Net* CV of sample = (16·69 − 1·83)

$$= 14.86 \text{ MJ m}^{-3}$$

D. Properties of Liquid Fuels

With the exception of calorific value, considered in Example 9.5, the great majority of tests on liquid fuels involve one or more direct readings, as for example in the determination of flash point or evaluation of a distillation curve. One test which involves calculation from raw data is the determination of viscosity as a function of temperature, and here, as with density, the main interest lies in the conversion from empirical units introduced in the distant past of the oil industry, into absolute values.

Example 9.9

A diesel fuel has a density of 37°API. Calculate the relative density at 288 K and estimate the gross calorific value of the fuel.

The density in degrees API (American Petroleum Institute) is given by:

$$°API = (141·5/d) - 131·5$$

where d = relative density at 288 K. In this case,

$$d = 141·5/(37 + 131·5) = \underline{\underline{0·84}}$$

The gross calorific value may be estimated from the relationship proposed by the US Bureau of Mines:

$$CV = 51·916 - 8·792d^2 \text{ MJ kg}^{-1}$$
$$= 51·916 - 8·792(0·84)^2 = \underline{\underline{45·73 \text{ MJ kg}^{-1}}}$$

Example 9.10

In a test using a Redwood viscometer No. 1, the following data were obtained for a lubricating oil:

Mean oil temperature (K) 370 335 310 295

Time to collect 50 cm³ (s) 52 122 350 560

Calculate the *viscosity index of the sample.*

The data are plotted in Fig. 96, from which

viscosity at 310 K = 350 s
viscosity at 373 K = 49 s

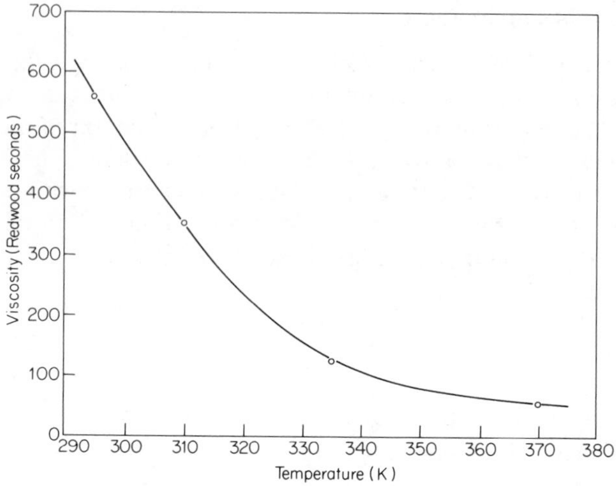

Fig. 96. *Viscosity as a function of temperature (Example 9.10).*

Converting Redwood seconds into stokes using data in Spiers (1945),
viscosity at 310 K = 0·85 stokes = 0·85 × 0·0001† = 35 × 10^{-6} m^2 s^{-1} = 85 m^2 Ms^{-1}
viscosity at 373 K = 0·093 stokes = 0·093 × 0·0001 = 9·3 × 10^{-6} m^2 s^{-1} = 9·3 m^2 Ms^{-1}

The viscosity index is calculated from two values L and H being the viscosities of two reference oils, having 0 VI and 100 VI respectively, at 310 K and both having the same viscosity at 373 K as the sample. Data on L and H are available in the literature (Institute of Petroleum 1964) or values may be estimated from the following approximate equations:

$$L = 2{\cdot}5\ \mu^{1{\cdot}85}\ \text{m}^2\ \text{Ms}^{-1}$$
$$H = 2{\cdot}5\ \mu^{1{\cdot}56}\ \text{m}^2\ \text{Ms}^{-1}$$

where μ m^2 Ms^{-1} is the viscosity of the sample at 373 K. Thus in this case,

$$L = 2{\cdot}5(9{\cdot}3)^{1{\cdot}85} = 150{\cdot}5\ \text{m}^2\ \text{Ms}^{-1}$$

and $$H = 2{\cdot}5(9{\cdot}3)^{1{\cdot}56} = 80{\cdot}6\ \text{m}^2\ \text{Ms}^{-1}$$

The viscosity index is then given by:

$$\text{VI} = 100(L - U)/(L - H)$$

† From Table 34.

where U = viscosity of sample at 310 K = 85 m^2 Ms^{-1}. Thus

$$VI = 100(150 \cdot 5 - 85)/(150 \cdot 5 - 80 \cdot 6)$$
$$= +93 \cdot 5$$

(This high value indicates a relatively low change in viscosity with temperature).

IV. MASS AND ENERGY BALANCES

A. Mass Balances

The law of conservation of mass states that in any process, mass is neither created nor destroyed; that is:

(mass in) = (mass out) + (accumulation (or depletion) within the system)

This statement applies both to physical operations and to those involving a chemical reaction and also to components within a system as well as the total mass.

Where all quantities are related to a fixed period of time, then the statement may also be applied to flowrates in and out of the process. It is important to differentiate between steady-state and non-steady-state operations at this stage. In the former, the accumulation in the system is zero and the amount or material within the unit does not enter into calculations. In addition, it may be assumed that physical and chemical changes take place instantaneously. This is not the case with non-steady-state, where calculations are more specialized and will receive but scant attention here. In general, fuel plant is operated continuously and it is reasonable to assume that steady-state conditions, as far as both mass and energy are concerned, have been attained.

In making a mass balance, it is usually necessary to carry out component balances in addition to an overall balance in order to completely specify the system. In the absence of chemical reaction, the number of components is the number of distinct chemical species which exist in all parts of the plant or unit. In this section, only systems involving physical processing will be considered; mass balances involving chemical reactions are dealt with after consideration of basic stoichiometry in Section V.

Example 9.11

An impure coal gas stream is to have its ammonia content reduced from 20% to 2% by weight by counter-current absorption in water

producing a solution containing 10% ammonia by mass. If the flow
of pure water to the column is 9 kg s^{-1} what mass of ammonia–coal
gas mixture can be handled?

BASIS: 1 s

Let the flow of ammonia-coal gas $= x$ kg s^{-1}.

Overall balance:

mass of coal gas in inlet stream $= (100 - 20)x/100 = 0.80x$ kg s^{-1}
    This is 98% of exit gas stream and hence,

mass of exit gas stream $= 100 \times 0.8x/98 = 0.817x$ kg s^{-1}
    mass of ammonia in exit gas stream $= 0.817x \times 2/100$
                                        $= 0.0163x$ kg/s

Ammonia balance:

ammonia in exit water stream $= 10\% = y$ kg s^{-1}
$\therefore 100y/(9 + y) = 10$
and $y = 1$ kg s^{-1}

balance

$$20x/100 = 1 + 0.0163x$$
$$\therefore x = 5.44 \text{ kg s}^{-1}$$

(It is a simple error to assume that $(20 - 2) = 18\%$ of the inlet gas is
absorbed. The true value is $(20 - 1.63) = 18.37\%$.)

Example 9.12

Air containing 0.005% carbon dioxide by volume is passed down a
pipe, 0.5 m in diamater to a junction where the pipe branches into
two lines 0.3 m and 0.4 m in diameter respectively. 0.001 m^3 s^{-1}
carbon dioxide is fed into the 0.5 m line as a tracer and analysis of
the gas well downstream in the 0.3 m line gives a CO_2 concentration
of 0.2% v/v. What are the mean air velocities in the 0.5 m and the
0.3 m lines?

Let the air flow in the 0.5 m line be A m^3 s^{-1}.

cross sectional area of 0.5 m line $= \pi \times 0.5^2/4 = 0.196$ m^2
cross sectional area of 0.4 m line $= \pi \times 0.4^2/4 = 0.126$ m^2
cross sectional area of 0.3 m line $= \pi \times 0.3^2/4 = 0.071$ m^2

Thus the ratio of the two branches is $0.126:0.071 = 0.64:0.36$, and hence it may be assumed that the gas flow is split into the branches in this ratio.

$$\text{total flow in } 0\cdot5\text{ m line} = A + 0\cdot001 \text{ m}^3 \text{ s}^{-1}$$
$$\therefore \text{ flow in } 0\cdot3 \text{ m line} = 0\cdot36(A + 0\cdot001) \text{ m}^3 \text{ s}^{-1}$$
$$\therefore \text{ flow in } 0\cdot4 \text{ m line} = 0\cdot64(A + 0\cdot001) \text{ m}^3 \text{ s}^{-1}$$

CO_2 BALANCE

It may be assumed that the concentrations of carbon dioxide in the $0\cdot3$ m and the $0\cdot4$ m lines are the same $= 0\cdot2\%$.

$$\therefore 0\cdot001 + 0\cdot005A/100 = 0\cdot36(A + 0\cdot001)0\cdot2/100$$
$$+ 0\cdot64\,(A + 0\cdot001)0\cdot2/100$$
$$= 0\cdot2(A + 0\cdot001)/100$$
$$\therefore A = 0\cdot512 \text{ m}^3 \text{ s}^{-1}$$
$$\therefore \text{ mean velocity in } 0\cdot5 \text{ m line} = 0\cdot512/0\cdot196 = \underline{\underline{2\cdot61 \text{ m s}^{-1}}}$$

$$\text{mean velocity in } 0\cdot3 \text{ m line} = 0\cdot36 \times 0\cdot512/0\cdot071 = \underline{\underline{2\cdot596 \text{ m s}^{-1}}}$$

These two problems illustrate mass balances and the topic is given further attention in Section V where the much more usual case of mass balance with chemical reaction is considered.

B. Energy Balances

As with mass, energy is conserved in any plant or unit, though the additional complication of conversion between forms of energy may be important. In fuel and combustion, heat is the most important form of energy and the heat content or enthalpy forms a basis for balance:

(heat added or removed from a process) = (enthalpy of products) − (enthalpy of feed streams)

This statement applies to physical systems and processes involving a chemical reaction, such as combustion of a fuel and includes all enthalpies and enthalpy changes such as those accompanying physical operations such as dilution and absorption. In calculating enthalpies, it is important that these should all be based on the same reference state and base temperature. For example, steam tables are based on liquid water at 273 K rather than solid ice, say, though for most combustion calculations, it is sensible to use ambient temperature as a datum in which case the enthalpies of streams entering at this temperature are zero, thus simplifying calculation.

Example 9.13

Before entering a furnace, $1 \, \text{kg s}^{-1}$ air has to be heated from 297 K to 320 K by steam, saturated at 136 kN m^{-2} in a shell and tube unit. If the condensate is at 361 K and the mean specific heat of air may be taken as $1 \cdot 005 \, \text{kJ kg}^{-1} \, \text{K}^{-1}$, what flow of steam is required? What would be the outlet air temperature if the steam were injected directly into the air? Neglect heat losses in both cases.

(i) SHELL AND TUBE UNIT

(Datum: inlet air temperature = 297 K)
$$\therefore \text{ enthalpy of inlet air} = 0$$
$$\text{enthalpy of outlet air} = 1 \cdot 005(320 - 297) = 23 \cdot 12 \, \text{kJ kg}^{-1}$$
$$\therefore \text{ heat gained by air} = (1 \times 23 \cdot 12) \, \text{kJ s}^{-1} = \underline{\underline{23 \cdot 12 \, \text{kW}}}$$

From steam tables,
$$\text{enthalpy of saturated steam at 136 kN m}^{-2} = 2689 \, \text{kJ kg}^{-1}$$
$$\text{enthalpy of water at 361 K} = 368 \, \text{kJ kg}^{-1}$$
$$\therefore \text{ heat lost by steam} = (2689 - 368) = 2321 \, \text{kJ kg}^{-1}$$

Taking mass flow of steam as $w \, \text{kg s}^{-1}$,
$$\text{heat lost by steam} = \underline{\underline{2321w \, \text{kW}}}$$

Balance:
$$\text{heat lost by steam} = \text{heat gained by air} + \text{losses}$$
$$\therefore 2321w = 23 \cdot 12 + 0$$
$$\therefore w = \underline{\underline{0 \cdot 01 \, \text{kg s}^{-1}}}$$

(ii) DIRECT INJECTION

(Datum: 273 K)
Heat in:
$$\left. \begin{array}{l} \text{air} = 1 \times 1 \cdot 005(297 - 273) = 24 \cdot 1 \, \text{kW} \\ \text{steam} = (0 \cdot 01 \times 2689) = 26 \cdot 9 \, \text{kW} \end{array} \right\} 51 \cdot 0 \, \text{kW}$$

heat out: assuming the air-steam mixture leaves at T K and 101·3 kN m^{-2}, it will contain 0·01 kg steam and 1·0 kg air dividing by the molecular mass (Section V),

$$\left. \begin{array}{l} 0 \cdot 01 \, \text{kg steam} = 0 \cdot 01/18 = 0 \cdot 00056 \, \text{kmol} \\ 1 \cdot 0 \, \text{kg air} = 1 \cdot 0/28 \cdot 9 = 0 \cdot 0346 \, \text{kmol} \end{array} \right\} 0 \cdot 03516 \, \text{kmol}$$

(28·9 being the mean molecular mass of air)
$$\therefore \text{ concentration of water vapour} = 0 \cdot 00056 \times 100/0 \cdot 03516$$
$$= 1 \cdot 59\% \text{ by volume}$$

$\therefore$ vapour pressure of water vapour $= 101\cdot3 \times 1\cdot59/100$
$$= 1\cdot61 \text{ kN m}^{-2}$$

From tables, water has a vapour pressure of $1\cdot61$ kN m^{-2} at 287 K at which the latent heat $= 2466$ kJ kg^{-1}. (This is the dew point and being less than ambient temperature is unsuitable as a datum; 273 K being a wiser choice).

$\therefore$ heat in steam $=$ sensible heat in water $+$ latent heat $+$ sensible
heat in vapour
$$= 4\cdot187(287 - 273) + 2466 + 1\cdot88(T - 287)$$
$$= 1\cdot88T + 1985 \text{ kJ kg}^{-1}$$
(taking the mean specific heat of water vapour as $1\cdot88$ kJ kg^{-1} K^{-1})
$$= 0\cdot01(1\cdot88T + 1985) \text{ kJ s}^{-1} = 0\cdot0188T + 19\cdot85 \text{ kW}$$
heat in air $= 1\cdot005(T - 273) \text{ kJ kg}^{-1}$
$$= 1\cdot0(1\cdot005T - 274\cdot4) \text{ kJ s}^{-1}$$
$$= (1\cdot005T - 274\cdot4) \text{ kW}$$

Balance:
heat in air $+$ steam $=$ heat in air-steam mixture $+$ losses
$$51\cdot0 = (1\cdot005T - 274\cdot4) + 0\cdot0188T + 19\cdot85 + 0$$
$$\therefore \ T = \underline{\underline{298\cdot5K}}$$

(In this case, the temperature rise, $1\cdot5$ deg K compared with the previous 23 deg K, is much lower because the latent heat of the steam is not recovered).

C. Mass and Energy Balances

The problems considered previously have been concerned with mass and energy balances in physical systems only, that is in the absence of chemical reaction and at steady state. In addition, mass and energy balances have been made independently. In fuel and combustion, the vast majority of problems involve chemical reaction, that is the combustion process, and it is usually necessary to carry out simultaneous mass and energy balances. These types of problem will be considered in the next section, which forms the major part of the present chapter. For a general introduction to mass and energy balances reference should be made to Whitwell (1969).

V. STOICHIOMETRY

A. Basic Concepts of Chemical Reaction

Almost all combustion problems involve a chemical reaction and an understanding of the basic chemistry is of considerable significance. To take perhaps the simplest reaction involved:

$$C + O_2 \rightarrow CO_2$$

the combination of 1 atom of carbon with 1 molecule of oxygen to form 1 molecule of carbon dioxide. At the outset it will be seen that 1 molecule of oxygen contains 2 atoms of oxygen and 1 molecule of carbon dioxide contains 1 atom of carbon and 2 atoms of oxygen. Thus a basis for balance exists in that the numbers of atoms of any component are the same on both sides of the equation. In addition, the law of conservation of mass dictates that the mass of 1 carbon atom plus the mass of 1 oxygen molecule must equal the mass of 1 molecule of carbon dioxide. The mass of 1 carbon atom would prove impracticable to handle in calculations and the atomic masses are scaled up, such that the atomic mass of hydrogen, the lightest element is approximately unity. One atom of carbon is twelve times as massive as the hydrogen atom and hence its atomic mass is 12. Similarly the atomic mass of oxygen is 16 and since 1 molecule of oxygen contains two atoms, the molecular mass of oxygen is 32; 1 molecule of oxygen being 32 times

TABLE 35. *Atomic and molecular weights*

	Symbol	Molecular formula	Atomic mass	Molecular mass
Elements				
carbon	C	C	12	12
hydrogen	H	H_2	1	2
oxygen	O	O_2	16	32
sulphur	S	S	32	32
nitrogen	N	N_2	14	28
Compounds				
carbon dioxide		CO_2	–	44
carbon monoxide		CO	–	28
sulphur dioxide		SO_2	–	64
water		H_2O	–	18
methane		CH_4	–	16
propane		C_3H_8	–	44
ethane		C_2H_6	–	30
butane		C_4H_{10}	–	58
ethylene		C_2H_4	–	28
propylene		C_3H_6	–	42
butylene		C_4H_8	–	56
acetylene		C_2H_2	–	26
benzene		C_6H_6	–	78
toluene		$C_6H_5 \cdot CH_3$	–	92

as massive as the hydrogen atom. The atomic and molecular masses of the elements and compounds (a compound contains more than one element) commonly encountered in combustion calculations are shown in Table 35. Thus in the equation, conservation of mass states that 12 lb carbon react with 32 lb oxygen to form 44 lb carbon dioxide or 12 kg carbon react with 32 kg oxygen to form 44 kg carbon dioxide, this being the basis of all mass balances involving chemical reaction. When the molecular mass (or atomic mass) of any compound (or element) is expressed in kg, this is known as 1 kilogram–molecule or 1 kmol. Thus 1 kmol C = 12 kg C, 1 kmol CH_4 = 16 kg methane and so on. The equation states therefore that:

1 kmol carbon reacts with 1 kmol oxygen to form 1 kmol carbon dioxide.

It is important to notice that the numbers of kmol on both sides of an equation unlike mass, do not balance and yet, as will be seen later, the "kmol" provides an extremely convenient basis for calculation.

One further feature of the kmol is that it enables ready conversion between mass and volume. This stems from the fact that 1 kmol of any gas occupies the same volume ($22\cdot4$ m³) at standard temperature and pressure ($101\cdot33$ kN m⁻² and 273 K). This is known as the kilogram–molecular volume and values in other units are:

1 gmol occupies 22 400 cm³ at 760 mm Hg and 0°C
1 lb mol occupies 359 ft³ at $14\cdot7$ lb in.⁻² and 32°F
1 kmol occupies $22\cdot4$ m³ at $101\cdot33$ kN m⁻² and 273 K

In this way, the basic chemical equation provides information on the mechanism involved, the mass balance and volumes of gases taking part. To summarize by considering the combustion of hydrogen:

$$H_2 + \tfrac{1}{2}O_2 \rightarrow H_2O$$

Thus,

2 kg hydrogen react with 16 kg oxygen to form 18 kg water
1 kmol hydrogen reacts with $\tfrac{1}{2}$ kmol oxygen to form 1 kmol water
$22\cdot4$ m³ hydrogen react with $11\cdot2$ m³ oxygen to form 18 kg water,
which as vapour occupy $22\cdot4$ m³ at s.t.p.

These two reactions are the most important in combustion, though further equations are involved some of which are shown in Table 36. In all these equations, combustion with oxygen only is considered. It is worth noting that, where air is the oxidant, the nitrogen takes no part in the reaction and, although it does not have any effect on mass balance, its effect on heat balance cannot be discounted.

TABLE 36. *Combustion equation*

$$C + O_2 \rightarrow CO_2$$
$$C + \tfrac{1}{2}O_2 \rightarrow CO \text{ (incomplete combustion)}$$
$$CO + \tfrac{1}{2}O_2 \rightarrow CO_2$$
$$S + O_2 \rightarrow SO_2$$
$$H_2 + \tfrac{1}{2}O_2 \rightarrow H_2O$$
$$CH_4 + 2O_2 \rightarrow CO_2 + 2H_2O$$
$$C_2H_6 + \tfrac{7}{2}O_2 \rightarrow 2CO_2 + 3H_2O$$
$$C_3H_8 + 5O_2 \rightarrow 3CO_2 + 4H_2O$$
$$C_2H_4 + 3O_2 \rightarrow 2CO_2 + 2H_2O$$
$$C_3H_6 + \tfrac{9}{2}O_2 \rightarrow 3CO_2 + 3H_2O$$
$$C_2H_2 + \tfrac{3}{2}O_2 \rightarrow 2CO_2 + H_2O$$
$$C_6H_6 + \tfrac{15}{2}O_2 \rightarrow 6CO_2 + 3H_2O$$

Example 9.14

What are the densities at s.t.p. of methane–air mixtures containing (i) 10% methane by weight, (ii) 10% methane by volume?

(i) Air contains 21% oxygen by volume, 23% oxygen by weight. Mean molecular mass of air (hypothetical, as air is a mixture not a compound):

100 kg air contain 23 kg oxygen = (23/32) = 0·719 kmol
and 77 kg nitrogen = (77/28) = 2·750 kmol
∴ total kmol = 3·469/100 kg
∴ molecular mass = 100/3·469 = 28·9 kg kmol⁻¹

In 100 kg methane–air mixture,

10 kg methane = (10/16) = 0·625 kmol which occupy
(0·625 × 22·4) = 14·0 m³ at s.t.p.
90 kg air = (90/28·9) = 3·11 kmol which occupy
(3·11 × 22·4) = 69·76 m³ at s.t.p.
∴ total volume = 83·76 m³
and density = (100/83·76) = 1·194 kg m⁻³ at s.t.p.

(ii) In 100 m³ methane–air mixture:
10 m³ methane = (10/22·4) = 0·446 kmol which have mass
(0·446 × 16) = 7·14 kg
90 m³ air = (90/22·4) = 4·018 kmol which have mass
(4·018 × 28·9) = 116·12 kg
∴ total mass = 123·26 kg
and density = (123·26/100) = 1·233 kg m⁻³ at s.t.p.

Example 9.15

For the complete combustion of carbon, the heat of reaction is 33·89 MJ /kg C. Neglecting dissociation of combustion products, what is the effect of flame temperature of ignoring the presence of nitrogen in the air?
(Mean specific heats: CO_2 =0·905, N_2 = 1·02 kJ kg^{-1} K^{-1})

(i) For combustion with oxygen only, the equation is:
    12 kg C + 32 kg O_2 → 44 kg CO_2 + (12 × 33·89) = 406·7 MJ
The flame temperature is approximated by
        (heat released)/(heat content of flue gas)
        = (406·7 × 10³)/(44 × 0·905)
        = 10213 K

(ii) 32 kg O_2 us associated with 32 × 77/23† = 107 kg N_2 For combustion with air, the equation becomes:
12 kg C + 32 kg O_2 + 107 kg N_2 → 44 kg CO_2 + 107 kg N_2 + 406·7 MJ
∴ flame temperature = (406·7 × 10³)/((44 × 0·905) + (107 × 1·02))
        = 2730 K

(Due to the dissociation of CO_2 (29%) and N_2 (11%), the actual flame temperature is 2600 K. A general discussion of dissociation in flame gases and the calculation of equilibrium flame temperatures has been presented by Harker (1967) and Harker and Allen (1969).)

B. Theoretical Air Requirements

Forgetting for the moment complications such as incomplete combustion and dissociation, a simple mass balance states that for complete combustion,

(mass of fuel) + (mass of air) = (mass of dry flue gas) + (mass of water produced)

Proceeding from this, there are in essence only three types of problem to be considered:

(i) Given a fuel analysis, to calculate the theoretical air required, that is the amount of air which will just ensure complete combustion of the fuel.

(ii) Given the fuel analysis and the actual air supplied, to calculate the composition and possibly the mass of flue gas produced.

(iii) Given the fuel analysis and the composition of the flue gas, to

† Air is 23% O_2 by mass

calculate the actual air supplied. (In the case of simple fuels, it is also possible to calculate the composition of the fuel from the flue gas analysis).

These three types of problem will be considered before proceeding to more complex situations.

In making calculations, it is possible to work throughout in mass (kg) or kmol. The latter will be used in this section as this makes for simpler calculation and facilitates conversion into volume terms, though the calculation of theoretical air will be illustrated by both methods.

1. Stoichiometric method

Example 9.16(a)

What are the theoretical air requirements for the following fuels?

(i) coal: C 74%, H 5%, N 1·5%, O 10%, S 1%, moisture 5%, ash 3·5%

(ii) gas: CH_4 25%, H_2 45%, CO_2 3%, CO 10%, O_2 1%, C_2H_4 1%, N_2 15%

(i) The reactions involved are:

$$C + O_2 \rightarrow CO_2$$
$$12 \quad 32 \quad 44$$

$$H_2 + \tfrac{1}{2}O_2 \rightarrow H_2O$$
$$2 \quad 16 \quad 18$$

$$S + O_2 \rightarrow SO_2$$
$$32 \quad 32 \quad 64$$

BASIS: 100 kg COAL

oxygen required to burn 74 kg C= $(74 \times 32)/12 = 197$ kg
oxygen required to burn 5 kg H= $(5 \times 16)/2 = 40$ kg
oxygen required to burn 1 kg S= $(1 \times 32)/32 = 1$ kg
i.e. total oxygen = 238 kg/100 kg coal

Oxygen in the coal = 10 kg,

∴ oxygen to be supplied = $(238 - 10) = 228$ kg/100 kg coal

Air is 23% oxygen by mass,

∴ air to be supplied = $(228 \times 100/23) = 991\cdot3$ kg/100 kg coal
                     = 9·91 kg/kg coal

density of air $= (28\cdot9/22\cdot4) = 1\cdot290\,\mathrm{kg\,m^{-3}}$ at s.t.p.

$\therefore$ theoretical air requirements $= (9\cdot91/1\cdot29) = \underline{7\cdot64\,\mathrm{m^3/kg\ coal}}$

(ii) The reactions involved are:

$$CH_4 + 2O_2 \;\rightarrow\; CO_2 + 2H_2O \qquad\qquad CO + \tfrac{1}{2}O_2 \;\rightarrow\; CO_2$$
$$16 \quad 64 \qquad\quad 44 \quad\; 36 \qquad\qquad\quad 28 \quad 16 \qquad\quad 44$$
$$H_2 + \tfrac{1}{2}O_2 \;\rightarrow\; H_2O \qquad\qquad\quad C_2H_4 + 3O_2 \;\rightarrow\; 2CO_2 + 2H_2O$$
$$2 \quad 16 \qquad\quad 18 \qquad\qquad\qquad 28 \quad 96 \qquad\qquad 88 \quad\; 36$$

BASIS: $100\,\mathrm{m^3}$ GAS

$$25\,\mathrm{m^3\,CH_4} \; = (25 \times 16/22\cdot4) = 17\cdot86\,\mathrm{kg}\ \text{require}\ (17\cdot86 \times 64/16)$$
$$= 71\cdot4\,\mathrm{kg\,O_2}$$
$$45\,\mathrm{m^3\,H_2} \; = \; (45 \times 2/22\cdot4) = \; 4\cdot02\,\mathrm{kg}\ \text{require}\ \; (4\cdot02 \times 16/2)$$
$$= 32\cdot2\,\mathrm{kg\,O_2}$$
$$10\,\mathrm{m^3\,CO} \; = (10 \times 28/22\cdot4) = 12\cdot50\,\mathrm{kg}\ \text{require}\ (12\cdot50 \times 16/23)$$
$$= \; 7\cdot1\,\mathrm{kg\,O_2}$$
$$1\,\mathrm{m^3\,C_2H_4} = \; (1 \times 28/22\cdot4) = \; 1\cdot25\,\mathrm{kg}\ \text{require}\ \; (1\cdot25 \times 96/28)$$
$$= \; 4\cdot3\,\mathrm{kg\,O_2}$$
$$\text{total oxygen } 115\,\mathrm{kg/100\,m^3}\ \text{gas}$$

Oxygen in the gas $= 1\,\mathrm{m^3}$ or $(1 \times 32/22\cdot4) = 1\cdot43\,\mathrm{kg}$

$\therefore$ oxygen to be supplied$= (115\cdot0 - 1\cdot4) = 113\cdot6\,\mathrm{kg/100\,m^3}$ gas

$\therefore$ air to be supplied$= (113\cdot6 \times 100/23) = 493\cdot9\,\mathrm{kg/100\,m^3}$ gas

$$= 4\cdot94\,\mathrm{kg\,m^{-3}}\ \text{gas}$$

$\therefore$ theoretical air requirements $= (4\cdot94/1\cdot29) = \underline{3\cdot78\,\mathrm{m^3/m^3}\ \text{gas}}$

2. "Mol" method

In working in kmol, it is necessary in the case of solid and liquid fuels to convert the mass of each component into kmol (by dividing by the molecular mass) as the analysis is always expressed by mass. This step is not required for gaseous fuels, where the composition is in volume terms, since equal numbers of kmol occupy the same volume.

Example 9.16(b)

Repeat example 9.16(a), working in terms of kmol.

(i) The reactions involved are:

$$1\,\mathrm{kmol\,C} + 1\,\mathrm{kmol\,O_2} \rightarrow 1\,\mathrm{kmol\,CO_2}$$
$$1\,\mathrm{kmol\,H_2} + \tfrac{1}{2}\,\mathrm{kmol\,O_2} \rightarrow 1\,\mathrm{kmol\,H_2O}$$
$$1\,\mathrm{kmol\,S} + 1\,\mathrm{kmol\,O_2} \rightarrow 1\,\mathrm{kmol\,SO_2}$$

BASIS: 100 kg COAL

The working may be laid out in tabular form:

% wt.	÷ by MW	= kmol	kmol O_2 required
C 74	12	6·17	6·17
H 5	2	2·50	1·25
N 1·5	28	0·05	–
O 10	32	0·31	−0·31
S 1	32	0·03	0·03
moisture 5	18	0·28	–
ash 3·5	–	–	–
100·0			7·14 kmol/100 kg coal

Air is 21% oxygen by volume,

$\therefore$ air to be supplied $= (7\cdot14 \times 100/21)$ $\quad = 34\cdot0$ kmol/100 kg coal

$\qquad\qquad\qquad\qquad = (34\cdot0 \times 22\cdot4/100) = \underline{7\cdot64\ \text{m}^3/\text{kg coal}}$

(mass of air $= 34\cdot0 \times 28\cdot9/100 = 9\cdot90$ kg/kg coal)

(ii) The reactions involved are:

1 kmol CH_4 + 2 kmol $O_2 \rightarrow$ 1 kmol CO_2 + 2 kmol H_2O

1 kmol H_2 + $\frac{1}{2}$ kmol $O_2 \rightarrow$ 1 kmol H_2O

1 kmol CO + $\frac{1}{2}$ kmol $O_2 \rightarrow$ 1 kmol CO_2

1 kmol C_2H_4 + 3 kmol $O_2 \rightarrow$ 2 kmol CO_2 + 2 kmol H_2O

BASIS: 100 kmol GAS

% vol	kmol	kmol O_2 required
CH_4 25	25	50·0
H_2 45	45	22·5
CO_2 3	3	–
CO 10	10	5·0
O_2 1	1	−1·0
C_2H_4 1	1	3·0
N_2 15	15	–
100	100	79·5 kmol/100 kmol gas

$\therefore$ air to be supplied $= (79\cdot5 \times 100/21) = 378\cdot6$ kmol/100 kmol gas

$\qquad\qquad\qquad\qquad = 3\cdot79$ kmol/kmol gas

$\qquad\qquad\qquad\quad$ or $\underline{3\cdot79\ \text{m}^3/\text{m}^3\ \text{gas}}$

C. Flue Gas Produced

1. *Volumetric analysis of dry flue gas*

This type of calculation requires a knowledge of the amount of excess air supplied, where:

$$\% \text{ excess} = 100 \text{ (actual} - \text{theoretical)/(theoretical)}$$

and is an extension of the calculation of theoretical air. In sampling flue gases, the water condenses out on cooling and only the dry flue gas is analysed. This is adequate in assessing conditions in the furnace and the amount of water is usually only of importance in heat balances.

Example 9.17

What is the composition of the dry flue gas produced on burning the gas in Example 9.16 with (i) the theoretical, and (ii) 50% excess air?

' (i) Using the data in Example 9.16(b)

BASIS: 100 kmol GAS

Air supplied $= 3\cdot79 \text{ m}^3/\text{m}^3$ gas
$= 379 \text{ kmol/100 kmol gas containing } (379 \times 21/100)$
$= 79\cdot5 \text{ kmol O}_2$
and $(379 - 79\cdot5) = 299\cdot5 \text{ kmol N}_2$

Therefore dry flue gas contains:

$CO_2 = 25 \text{ (from CH}_4) + 3 \text{ (from fuel)} + 10 \text{ (from CO)}$
$+ 2 \text{ (from C}_2\text{H}_4) = 40 \text{ kmol}$

$O_2 = \text{zero}$
$N_2 = 15 \text{ (from fuel)} + 299\cdot5 \text{ (from air)} = 314\cdot5 \text{ kmol}$
$\therefore$ total dry flue gas $= 354\cdot5 \text{ kmol/100 kmol gas}$
$\therefore \% \text{ CO}_2 = 40 \times 100/354\cdot5 = \underline{11\cdot28\%};$

$\% \text{ N}_2 = 314\cdot5 \times 100/354\cdot5 = \underline{88\cdot72\%}$

(ii) Air supplied, 50% excess $= (379 \times 1\cdot50) = 568\cdot5 \text{ kmol/100 kmol}$
gas containing

$$(568\cdot5 \times 21/100) = 119\cdot4 \text{ kmol O}_2$$
$$\text{and } (568\cdot5 + 119\cdot4) = 449\cdot1 \text{ kmol N}_2$$

dry flue gas contains:

$$CO_2 = 40 \text{ kmol (as above)}$$
$$O_2 = (119{\cdot}4 + 79{\cdot}5) = 39{\cdot}9 \text{ kmol}$$
$$N_2 = 15 \text{ (from fuel)} + 449{\cdot}1 \text{ (from air)} = 464{\cdot}1 \text{ kmol}$$
$$\therefore \text{ total dry flue gas} = 544 \text{ kmol}$$

$\% \ CO_2 = 40 \times 100/544 = \underline{\underline{7{\cdot}35\%}}; \qquad \% \ O_2 = 39{\cdot}9 \times 100/544 = \underline{\underline{7{\cdot}33\%}};$

$\% \ N_2 = 464{\cdot}1 \times 100/544 = \underline{\underline{85{\cdot}3\%}}$

The calculation may be repeated for other amounts of excess air with results as shown in Fig. 97.

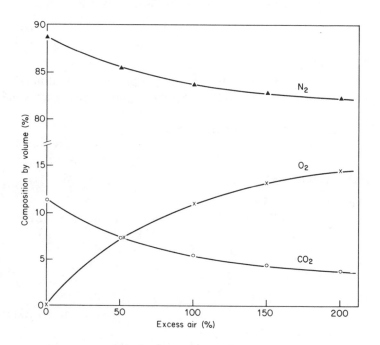

Fig. 97. *Composition of dry flue gas (Example 9.17).*

2. *Mass of flue gas produced*

If the mean molecular weight of the dry flue gas was known, it would be a simple matter to convert the kmol of flue gas into mass. Unfortunately this is not the case and it is necessary to consider each component in the flue gas in turn, as illustrated in the following example.

Example 9.18

What is the total mass of flue gas produced when the gas in Example 9.16 is burned with 75% excess air?

BASIS: 100 kmol GAS

Using the data in Example 9.16(b):

kmol		kmol CO_2 formed	kmol H_2O formed
CH_4	25	25	50
H_2	45	–	45
CO_2	3	3	–
CO	10	10	–
O_2	1	–	–
C_2H_4	1	2	2
N_2	15	–	–
	100	40	97

Theoretical air = 379 kmol/100 kmol gas
∴ actual air = (379 × 1·75) = 663 kmol/100 kmol gas
containing (663 × 21/100) = 139 kmol O_2
and (663 − 139) = 524 kmol N_2
∴ Flue gas contains: CO_2 = 40 kmol; O_2 = (139 − 79·5) = 59·5 kmol;
H_2O = 97 kmol; N_2 = (524 + 15) = 539 kmol;
∴ mass of flue gas: CO_2 = (40 × 44) = 1760 kg ⎫
O_2 = (59·5 × 32) = 1904 kg ⎬ 18 764 kg/100 kmol gas
N_2 = (539 × 28) = 15 100 kg ⎭
H_2O = (97 × 18) = 1745 kg/100 kmol gas
∴ mass of dry flue gas = 18 764/(100 × 22·4) = 8·38 kg/m³ gas
mass of water = 1745/(100 × 22·4) = 0·78 kg/m³ gas
∴ total mass of flue gas = 9·16 kg/m³ gas

In Example 9.18, the amount and mass of flue gas produced was calculated from a knowledge of the actual air used in the combustion process. In a practical situation, this information is not available and one must usually work from an analysis of the dry flue gas. It is here that two points must be stressed:

(i) Although the total kmol on each side of an equation rarely balance (for example: $CO + \frac{1}{2}O_2 \rightarrow CO_2$ kmol reactants = $1\frac{1}{2}$, kmol products = 1) the number of kmol of each element do and this is an important basis for making a balance. For example:

$$CH_4 + 2O_2 \rightarrow CO_2 + 2H_2O$$

	kmol		
	C	H_2	O_2
reactants: 1 kmol CH_4 contains 1 kmol C + 2 kmol H_2 2 kmol O_2	1	2	2
products: 1 kmol CO_2 contains 1 kmol C + 1 kmol O_2 2 kmol H_2O contains 2 kmol H_2 + 1 kmol O_2	1	2	2

(ii) In order to make use of this fact, it is important to choose a suitable component in making a balance. Consider the combustion of a fuel containing C and H, possibly combined as in a hydrocarbon gas. Thus, in general:

$$\text{fuel} \quad + \quad \text{air} \quad \rightarrow \text{dry flue gas} \quad + \quad \text{water}$$
$$\text{(C, H)} \quad \text{(O, N)} \quad \text{(C, O, N)} \quad \text{(H, O)}$$

where the elements contained in each stream are shown. Thus, the only element common to the flue gas and the fuel is C and hence a carbon balance may be used to calculate the amount of flue gas produced per unit of fuel consumed (Example 9.19). Similarly from the flue gas analysis, the air supplied can be calculated from a nitrogen balance, this being the only element appearing in these two streams and no other (Example 9.20). Finally having got this far, an oxygen balance will give the amount of water formed, as this does not appear in the fuel, and hence a hydrogen balance will give the composition of the fuel (Example 9.22). These points are now illustrated in the following examples.

Example 9.19

The gas in Example 9.16 is burned to give a flue gas of the following composition (dry basis):

$$CO_2 \ 7 \cdot 35\%, \ O_2 \ 7 \cdot 33\%, \ N_2 \ 85 \cdot 3\%$$

What is the volume of dry flue gas and the total mass of flue gas produced?

BASIS: 100 kmol GAS

C BALANCE: In 100 kmol gas, kmol C = 25 (in CH_4) + 3 (in CO_2) + 10 (in CO) + 2 (in C_2H_4) = 40 kmol

In 100 kmol dry flue gas, there are $7 \cdot 35$ kmol CO_2, which contain $7 \cdot 35$ kmol C. It is obvious, therefore that if 100 kmol gas is burned, more than 100 kmol dry flue gas are produced as 100 kmol contain only $7 \cdot 35$ kmol C.

In fact, dry flue gas produced = $(100 \times 40/7\cdot35)$ = 543 kmol/100 kmol gas

$$\text{or } \underline{5\cdot43 \text{ m}^3/\text{m}^3 \text{ gas}}$$

Mass of dry flue gas, considering each component in turn,

$$
\left.
\begin{array}{l}
CO_2 = (543 \times 7\cdot35/100) = 40\,\text{kmol} = (40 \times 44) = 1760\text{ kg} \\
O_2 = (543 \times 7\cdot33/100) = 39\cdot9\text{ kmol} = (39\cdot9 \times 32) = 1318\text{ kg} \\
N_2 = (543 \times 85\cdot3/100) = 464\text{ kmol} = (464 \times 28) = 13\,010\text{ kg}
\end{array}
\right\} 16\,088\text{ kg}
$$

From Example 9.18, water produced = 97 kmol = (97×18) =
1745 kg

$$
\begin{aligned}
\therefore \text{ total mass of flue gas} &= 17\,833 \text{ kg/100 kmol} \\
&= 17\,833/(100 \times 22\cdot4) \\
&= \underline{7\cdot97 \text{ kg/m}^3 \text{ gas}}
\end{aligned}
$$

D. Actual Air Used

Example 9.20(a)

The gas in Example 9.16 is again burned to give the dry flue gas given in Example 9.19. What is the actual air and excess air used? (From Example 9.17, the answer is obviously 50% excess. This may be shown as follows).

BASIS: 100 kmol GAS

From Example 9.19, dry flue gas produced = 543 kmol/100 kmol gas.

N_2 BALANCE. Let x kmol air be supplied/100 kmol gas, then,

$$
\begin{aligned}
(N_2 \text{ in air}) + (N_2 \text{ in fuel}) &= (N_2 \text{ in flue gas}) \\
(79x/100) + 15 &= (543 \times 85\cdot3/100) \\
\therefore x &= 569 \text{ kmol/100 kmol gas}
\end{aligned}
$$

and air supplied = $5\cdot69 \text{ m}^3/\text{m}^3$ gas

$$
\begin{aligned}
\text{(mass of air} &= (569 \times 28\cdot9/100) = 64\cdot2 \text{ kg/kmol gas or } (64\cdot2/22\cdot4) \\
&= 2\cdot87 \text{ kg/m}^3 \text{ gas)}
\end{aligned}
$$

From Example 3.16, theoretical air = $3\cdot79 \text{ m}^3/\text{m}^3$ gas

$$
\therefore \% \text{ excess} = 100(5\cdot69 - 3\cdot79)/3\cdot79 = \underline{50\cdot2\%}
$$

In practice, a full analysis of the dry flue gas is not always available rather the amount of one component, say oxygen, indicated by a meter. In this case, one approach is to construct curves such as shown in Fig. 97, which are then used as a calibration. For example, a dry flue gas containing 10·8% oxygen would correspond to 100% excess air. Alternatively the value may be calculated thus:

Example 9.20(b)

How much excess air is supplied if the dry flue gas produced by burning the gas in Example 9.16 contains 7·33% oxygen?

BASIS: 100 kmol GAS

Theoretical air = 379 kmol/100 kmol
Let (actual + theoretical air) = excess air, be y kmol/100 kmol gas.
Thus in dry flue gas:

$$N_2 = (379 \times 79/100) = 299 \text{ kmol from theoretical air} \left.\begin{array}{c} \\ \\ \end{array}\right\} 314 \text{ kmol}$$
$$\text{and} \quad 15 \text{ kmol from fuel}$$
$$CO_2 = 40 \text{ kmol (Example 9.18)}$$
$$O_2 = (21y/100) \text{ in excess air}$$

Excess air = y kmol

$$\therefore \% \text{ oxygen, } 7\cdot33 = (21y/100)100/(314 + 40 + y)$$
$$\text{from which, } y = 189 \text{ kmol/100 kmol gas}$$
$$\therefore \% \text{ excess} = 100 \text{ (excess)/(theoretical)}$$
$$= (100 \times 189/379) = \underline{\underline{50\%}}$$

A similar calculation may be carried out where any other component is known. Again, based on a nitrogen balance, it is possible to estimate the excess air from the dry flue gas analysis, even without the composition of the fuel, providing the nitrogen in the fuel is less than 2–3%. Thus the gas in Example 9.16, which we have laboured so much, would be ruled out on this basis, although the coal in the same problem would be suitable.

Example 9.21

A solid fuel containing less than 2% nitrogen is burned to give the following dry flue gas:

$$CO_2 \ 14\cdot5\%, \ O_2 \ 4\cdot5\%, \ N_2 \ 81\cdot0\%$$

How much excess air is supplied?

BASIS: 100 kmol DRY FLUE GAS

Excess $O_2 = 4 \cdot 5$ kmol

$$\therefore \text{ excess air} = (4 \cdot 5 \times 100/21) = 21 \cdot 2 \text{ kmol}$$

and

$$\text{excess } N_2 = (21 \cdot 2 \times 79/100) = 16 \cdot 9 \text{ kmol}$$
$\therefore N_2$ associated with the oxygen used in the combustion $= (81 \cdot 0 - 16 \cdot 9)$
(i.e. "theoretical" N_2) $= 64 \cdot 1$ kmol/100 dry flue gas
$\therefore$ % excess air $= 100$ (excess)/(theoretical)
$\qquad\qquad\quad = $ (excess N_2)/(theoretical N_2)
$\qquad\qquad\quad = (100 \times 16.9/64 \cdot 1)$
$\qquad\qquad\quad = \underline{\underline{26 \cdot 4\%}}$

In this Example, 100 kmol dry flue gas is used as a basis for the first time. There is no other choice as these are the only data available.

E. Composition of Fuel from Flue Gas Analysis

This represents the third type of basic problem, as outlined in Section V. B and is an extension of the methods adopted in Example 9.21. The method used is only applicable to the simpler fuels, which are again low in nitrogen.

Example 9.22

An oil fuel, containing carbon and hydrogen only, is burned to produce the following flue gas (dry basis):

$$CO_2 \ 10 \cdot 5\%; \ O_2 \ 7 \cdot 5\%; \ N_2 \ 82 \cdot 0\%$$

Estimate the gravimetric analysis of the fuel and the excess air supplied.

BASIS: 100 kmol DRY FLUE GAS

O_2 BALANCE: let z kmol O_2 be in the water produced by combustion of hydrogen.
In flue gas, kmol $O_2 = 10 \cdot 5$ (in CO_2) $+ 7 \cdot 5$ (excess)
$\qquad\qquad\qquad\quad = 18 \cdot 0$

Actual air $= (82 \cdot 0 \times 100/79) = 103 \cdot 9$ kmol/100 kmol flue gas

$$\therefore \text{ In air, kmol } O_2 = (103 \cdot 9 \times 21/100) = 21 \cdot 8 \text{ kmol}$$

Thus, (O_2 in air) = (O_2 in flue gas) + (O_2 in water)

$$21 \cdot 8 = 18 \cdot 0 + z$$
$$\therefore z = 3 \cdot 8 \text{ kmol}/100 \text{ kmol dry flue gas}$$

In water, 1 kmol oxygen is associated with 2 kmol hydrogen

$$\therefore \text{ water formed} = (2 \times 3 \cdot 8) = 7 \cdot 6 \text{ kmol}$$

1 kmol water contains, 1 kmol hydrogen

$$\therefore H_2 \text{ burned} = 7 \cdot 6 \text{ kmol} = (7 \cdot 6 \times 2) = 15 \cdot 2 \text{ kg}$$

In 100 kmol flue gas, kmol C = $10 \cdot 5$ (in CO_2) $\qquad\qquad$ 141·2 kg

$$\therefore \text{ C burned} = 10 \cdot 5 \text{ kmol or } (10 \cdot 5 \times 12) = 126 \cdot 0 \text{ kg}$$

The analysis of the oil is therefore:

$$C \ (126 \cdot 0 \times 100/141 \cdot 2) = 89 \cdot 2\%$$
$$H \ (15 \cdot 2 \times 100/141 \cdot 2) = \underline{\underline{10 \cdot 8\%}}$$

Theoretical oxygen:

oxygen required to produce $10 \cdot 5$ kmol $CO_2 = 10 \cdot 5$ kmol $\Big\}$ 14·3 kmol
oxygen required to produce $7 \cdot 6$ kmol $H_2O = \ \ 3 \cdot 8$ kmol

$$\therefore \% \text{ excess air} = 100 \text{ (excess } O_2)/(\text{theoretical } O_2)$$
$$= (100 \times 7 \cdot 5/14 \cdot 3) = \underline{\underline{52 \cdot 5\%}}$$

F. Incomplete Combustion

In the previous examples, it has been assumed that enough air has been supplied to convert all the carbon in the fuel to carbon dioxide, that is, actual air is greater than theoretical. In practice, it may be that either insufficient air is supplied or the conditions in the combustion chamber are such that poor mixing of fuel and oxygen is achieved resulting in the formation of carbon monoxide. Since the heat of formation of carbon monoxide is less than that of carbon dioxide, this incomplete combustion results in loss of heat recovery in the furnace and is generally avoided where possible. In the case of solid fuels, some carbon is lost in the ash; and with all fuels, the formation of smoke results in loss of heat recovery. Examples involving incomplete combustion of this type are considered in this section.

1. *Formation of carbon monoxide*

This is the result of either poor mixing of fuel and oxidant or an inadequate air supply. It is important to note that oxygen and carbon monoxide can exist in the same flue gas as the equilibrium set up at high temperatures between carbon monoxide and these gases (Section V. F.4) is effectively quenched on sampling.

Example 9.23

A coal containing 84% C, is burned to produce a flue gas of the following composition (dry basis):

$$CO_2 \ 12\cdot5\%; \ CO \ 1\cdot5\%; \ O_2 \ 5\cdot5\%; \ N_2 \ 80\cdot5\%$$

Estimate the mass of carbon converted to carbon monoxide per kg coal burned.

BASIS: 1 kg COAL

The ratio of carbon forming carbon monoxide to the total carbon burned:

$$\% \ CO/(\% \ CO + \% \ CO_2) = 1\cdot5/(12\cdot5 + 1\cdot5) = 0\cdot107 \ kg/kg \ C \ burned$$

In burning 1 kg coal, mass C burned $= 0\cdot84$ kg

$$\therefore \ \text{mass of C forming CO} = (0\cdot84 \times 0\cdot107)$$
$$= 0\cdot0899 = \underline{0\cdot09 \ kg/kg \ coal}$$

Example 9.24

An endothermic gas generator burns coal gas with less than the stoichiometric air requirements to produce a purge gas to be used as a furnace atmosphere in an annealing operation. If the gases have the following analysis:

coal gas: $CO_2 \ 2\%; \ O_2 \ 1\%; \ N_2 \ 12\%; \ CO \ 7\%; \ H_2 \ 46\%;$
              $CH_4 \ 30\%; \ C_2H_6 \ 2\%$

purge gas: $H_2 \ 18\%; \ CO \ 10\%; \ N_2 \ 63\%; \ CO_2 \ 3\%; \ H_2O \ 6\%$

estimate (i) the volume of purge gas produced per m³ town gas
              burned,
          (ii) the percentage air deficiency.
(This is an extension of the type of problem considered in Sections V.C and D).

BASIS: 100 kmol TOWN GAS

(i)

	kmol	kmol C	kmol O_2 required
CO_2	2	2	–
O_2	1	–	–1
N_2	12	–	–
CO	7	7	3·5
H_2	46	–	23·0
CH_4	30	30	60·0
C_2H_6	3	4	7·0
	100	43	92·5

∴ theoretical air $= (100 \times 92\cdot5/21) = 441$ kmol/100 kmol gas
or $4\cdot41$ m^3/m^3 gas

C BALANCE:

100 kmol coal gas contains 43 kmol C
100 kmol purge gas contains 10 (from CO) + 3 (from CO_2) = 13 kmol C
∴ purge gas produced $= (100 \times 43/13) = 331$ kmol/100 kmol coal gas
or $\underline{3\cdot31 \text{ m}^3/\text{m}^3 \text{ gas}}$

(ii) N_2 BALANCE:

$(N_2$ in coal gas$) + (N_2$ in air$) = (N_2$ in purge gas$)$

Let a kmol air be supplied per 100 kmol coal gas:

∴ $12 + (79a/100) = (331 \times 63/100)$
∴ $a = 249$ kmol/100 kmol coal gas
or $2\cdot49$ m^3/m^3 coal gas
air deficiency $= (4\cdot41 - 2\cdot49) = 1\cdot92$ m^3/m^3 gas
which as a percentage of the theoretical air
$= (1\cdot92 \times 100)/4\cdot41 = \underline{43\cdot5\%}$

2. Loss of carbon in ash

In carrying out an ultimate analysis of a solid fuel, the percentage carbon reported is the total carbon, which includes any carbon combined for example as carbonates in the mineral matter in the fuel. This will be left on combustion of the fuel and will appear in the ash. In calculating such a loss, it is necessary to make the not unreasonable assumption that the ratio:

(carbon associated with ash)/ash

is the same in both fuel and the final ash.

Example 9.25

A coal containing 84% C and 10% ash is burned in a furnace leaving an ash which contains 25% C. Estimate:
  (i) the mass of carbon lost in the ash per kg coal burned,
  (ii) the percentage of the carbon burned.

BASIS: 100 kg COAL

(i) Let c kg C be associated with the ash in 100 kg coal. In 100 kg final ash residue,

$$\text{mass of carbon} = 25 \text{ kg}$$
$$\text{mass of ash} = (100 - 25) = 75 \text{ kg}$$
$$\therefore c/10 = (25/75)$$
$$\therefore c = 3 \cdot 33 \text{ kg C}/100 \text{ kg coal burned}$$
$$\text{or} \quad \underline{0 \cdot 033 \text{ kg/kg coal burned}}$$

(ii) In 100 kg coal, mass of C = 84·0 kg
$$\therefore \text{mass of C burned} = (84 \cdot 0 - 3 \cdot 33) = 80 \cdot 67 \text{ kg}$$
$$\therefore \text{percentage C burned} = (80 \cdot 67 \times 100)/84$$
$$= \underline{96 \cdot 0\%}$$

3. Heat losses due to incomplete combustion

The heat evolved when 1 kg C is completely combusted is given by:

$$C + O_2 \rightarrow CO_2 \qquad \Delta H = 33 \cdot 96 \text{ MJ/kg C}$$

When the combustion is incomplete however, the heat evolved on formation of carbon monoxide is:

$$C + \tfrac{1}{2}O_2 \rightarrow CO \qquad \Delta H = 10 \cdot 23 \text{ MJ/kg C}$$

Thus, for every kg of carbon which forms carbon monoxide rather than carbon dioxide, $(33 \cdot 96 - 10 \cdot 23) = 23 \cdot 73$ MJ are lost, which is often a significant proportion of the calorific value of the fuel. Where carbon is completely unburned as in the formation of smoke or in loss of carbon in ash, then all of the 33·96 MJ are lost.

Example 9.26

Assuming the coal in Examples 9.23 and 9.25 has a gross calorific value of $31\cdot4$ MJ kg^{-1}, estimate the heat lost by the incomplete combustion,
    (i) due to the formation of carbon monoxide in Example 9.23,
    (ii) due to loss of carbon in the ash in Example 9.25.

(i) $0\cdot09$ kg C/kg coal form CO rather than CO_2.
Heat lost due to formation of CO = $23\cdot73$ MJ/kg C
$$= (23\cdot73 \times 0\cdot09) = 2\cdot136 \text{ MJ/kg coal}$$
or as a percentage of gross CV,
$$\text{heat lost} = (2\cdot136 \times 100)/31\cdot4$$
$$\underline{\underline{6\cdot8\%}}$$

(ii) $0\cdot033$ kg C/kg coal remains unburned.
Heat lost due to non-combustion of carbon = $33\cdot96$ MJ/kg C
$$= (33\cdot96 \times 0\cdot033)$$
$$= 1\cdot121 \text{ MJ/kg coal}$$
or as a percentage of gross CV,
$$\text{heat lost} = (1\cdot121 \times 100)/31\cdot4$$
$$= \underline{\underline{3\cdot57\%}}$$

4. *Dissociation*

So far, in considering the combustion of a hydrocarbon fuel with air, for example, it has been assumed that, providing at least the theoretical air is available, the combustion products contain only CO_2, H_2O, N_2 and any excess oxygen. At high temperatures, however, such as are encountered in flame gases, the molecules of these gases split up or dissociate, into simpler species. For example:

$$CO_2 \rightleftharpoons CO + \tfrac{1}{2} O_2$$
$$H_2O \rightleftharpoons H_2 + \tfrac{1}{2} O_2$$
$$\text{or } H_2O \rightleftharpoons \tfrac{1}{2} H_2 + OH$$

At even higher temperatures, atomic hydrogen and oxygen may be formed:

$$\tfrac{1}{2}H_2 \rightleftharpoons H$$
$$\tfrac{1}{2}O_2 \rightleftharpoons O$$

All these dissociation reactions are endothermic, that is they require heat to shift the equilibrium to the right and hence they reduce the amount of available heat in the flame and therefore the flame temperature. Indeed, the equilibrium flame temperature of any fuel–oxidant mixture is limited by the degree of dissociation taking place and this explains why a stoichiometric mixture of cyanogen (C_4N_2) and ozone (O_3) has a very high flame temperature (5516 K) due to formation of stable species CO and N_2. All dissociation reactions are reversible and on cooling a flame the equilibrium moves to the left with consequent evolution of heat. It is possible however to quench the gases, say on sampling (Example 9.23), and this may result in CO and O_2, for example, being in the same flue gas, with consequent loss of heat.

Example 9.27

A stoichiometric mixture of hydrogen and oxygen is burned at 101.3 kN m^{-2} and 3000 K. Analysis of the flame gases shows that 40% of the water formed has dissociated to hydrogen and oxygen at this temperature. Estimate the percentage dissociation if the combustion is carried out at 500 kN m^{-2} and 3000 K.

BASIS: 1 kmol H_2O INITIALLY PRESENT

The reaction is:

$$H_2O \rightleftharpoons H_2 + \tfrac{1}{2}O_2$$
or 1 kmol H_2O forms 1 kmol H_2 + $\tfrac{1}{2}$ kmol O_2

Of the initial 1 kmol H_2O, 0.4 kmol dissociate to form 0.4 kmol H_2 and 0.2 kmol O_2 leaving $(1 - 0.4) = 0.6$ kmol water. Thus at equilibrium, the mixture contains:

$$\left. \begin{array}{l} 0.6 \text{ kmol } H_2O \\ 0.4 \text{ kmol } H_2 \\ 0.2 \text{ kmol } O_2 \end{array} \right\} \begin{array}{l} \text{total } 1.2 \text{ kmol,} \\ \text{hence mol fraction} = \end{array} \left\{ \begin{array}{l} H_2O(0.6/1.2) = 0.50 \\ H_2(0.4/1.2) = 0.33 \\ O_2(0.2/1.2) = 0.17 \end{array} \right.$$

The partial pressure of each component, $p = $ (mol fraction $\times$ total pressure)

$$\therefore p_{H_2O} = (0.50 \times 101.3) = 50.7 \text{ kN m}^{-2}$$
$$\therefore p_{H_2} = (0.33 \times 101.3) = 33.4 \text{ kN m}^{-2}$$
$$\therefore p_{O_2} = (0.17 \times 101.3) = 17.2 \text{ kN m}^{-2}$$

The equilibrium constant K for the reversible reaction, is given by:

$$K = p_{H_2O}/[p_{H_2}(p_{O_2})^{0.5}]$$

For the reaction, $aA + bB \rightarrow cC + dD$, $K = p_A{}^a.p_B{}^b/(p_C{}^c.p_D{}^d)$

$$\therefore K = 50.7/(33.4(17.2)^{0.5}) = \underline{\underline{0.365}}$$

The equilibrium constant is a function of temperature only and independent of pressure. If x kmol H_2O, dissociate,

$(1 - x)$ kmol H_2O remain and x kmol H_2 and $x/2$ kmol O_2 are formed.

Total products $= (1 + x/2)$ kmol and hence:

$$p_{H_2O} = (1-x)p/(1 + x/2), \qquad p_{H_2} = xP/(1+x/2), \qquad p_{O_2} = (xP/2)/(1+x$$

where P kN m^{-2} is the total pressure.

Thus, in general,

$$K = [(1-x)P(1+x/2)(1+x/2)^{0.5}]/[(1+x/2)xP(xP/2)^{0.5}]$$
$$= (1-x)(2+x)^{0.5}/(x^{1.5}P^{0.5})$$

When the total pressure, $P = 500$ kN m^{-2}

$$0.365 = (1 + x)(2 + x)^{0.5}/(x^{1.5} \, 500)^{0.5}$$
$$\therefore 32.8x^3 + 1.5x = 1$$

Letting $\phi = 32.8x^3 + 1.5x$, this is calculated and plotted against x in Fig. 98, from which $\Phi = 1$, when $x = 0.265$. Thus,

dissociation at 500 kN m^{-2} = 26.5%

In this section, the use of the chemical equation as a way of carrying out mass balances has been considered, with little attention to heat balances in the presence of chemical reaction. This forms the major part of the next

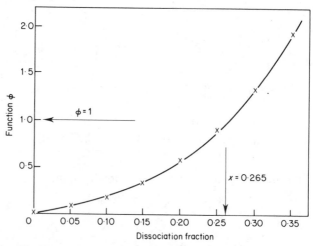

Fig. 98. *Determination of degree of dissociation (Example 9.27).*

section. One final point worthy of mention is that, throughout Section IV, mention has only been made of "flue gas" in referring to combustion in furnaces and boilers. The basic equations used here also apply to combustion in engines with the qualification that "flue gas" should read "exhaust" and the obvious restriction on the use of solid fuels.

VI. APPLICATION TO COMBUSTION PLANT

A. Heat Recovery

In this section, the concepts of Section IV are extended to include the question of heat balance in the presence of chemical reaction, restricting problems to those where the heat evolved may be taken as the calorific value of the fuel and where the mean specific heats may be assumed constant over the temperature range involved. It is convenient to group these problems under the heading "combustion plant" as, in the industrial sphere, heat means money and the most economic and profitable operation of plant is of prime importance. To this end, every attempt is made to recover as much of the available heat in the fuel as possible, in addition to that released on the boiler or furnace, which to some extent is limited by process conditions. This is done by using the hot flue gas to preheat the combustion air in a preheater, or the feed water in an economizer or possibly to raise low-grade steam in a waste-heat boiler. Examples involving such plant are considered in this section before dealing with boiler and furnace efficiency. General reference may be made in relation to the application to combustion plant to Davies (1970) and Thring (1962).

1. *Heat losses in flue gas*

Before considering heat recovery, it is worthwhile assessing the amount of heat which is available for recovery in ancilliary plant, that is, the heat carried away in the flue gas. The important point here is that the water vapour in the flue gas is of prime importance since it carries away the latent heat of vaporization in addition to its sensible heat.

Example 9.28

Calculate the percentage heat loss in the flue gas when methane, CH_4, is burned with its theoretical air. The flue gas temperature is 530 K and ambient temperature, 288 K. (CV of methane = 44·6 MJ m^{-3}; mean specific heats are, CO_2 1·516, H_2O 1·409, N_2 1·245, air 1·316 kJ m^{-3} K^{-1}).

BASIS: 100 kmol CH_4

$$CH_4 + 2O_2 \rightarrow CO_2 + 2H_2O$$

100 kmol CH_4 require 200 kmol O_2 or $(200 \times 100/21) = 952$ kmol air

$$\therefore \text{ theoretical air} = 952 \text{ kmol}/100 \text{ kmol } CH_4$$
$$\text{or } 9\cdot52 \text{ m}^3/\text{m}^3 \text{ } CH_4$$

In the combustion, 200 kmol H_2O and 100 kmol CO_2 are produced. Nitrogen in air supplied $= (952 \times 79/100) = 752$ kmol.
Thus, on the basis of 1 m³ CH_4 burned, the flue gas contains:

$1\cdot0$ m³ CO_2, $2\cdot0$ m³ H_2O and $7\cdot52$ m³ N_2 (total $10\cdot52$ m³)

SENSIBLE HEAT IN FLUE GAS

$$= ((1\cdot0 \times 1\cdot516) + (2\cdot0 \times 1\cdot409) + (7\cdot52 \times 1\cdot245)) \times (530 - 273)$$
$$= (13\cdot70 \times 257) = 3520 \text{ kJ/m}^3 \text{ } CH_4$$

Heat in air $= 9\cdot52 \times 1\cdot316(288 - 273) = 31$ kJ/m³ CH_4

$$\text{sensible heat lost in flue gas} = (3520 - 313) = 3207 \text{ kJ/m}^3$$
$$= 3\cdot21 \text{ MJ/m}^3 \text{ methane}$$
$$= (3\cdot21 \times 100)/44\cdot6$$
$$= \underline{7\cdot20\%}$$

Taking the *latent heat* of water vapour into account:
% by volume of water vapour $= (2\cdot0 \times 100)/10\cdot52 = 19\cdot0\%$
$\therefore$ partial pressure of water vapour
$$= (19\cdot0 \times 101\cdot3/100) = 19\cdot3 \text{ kN m}^{-2}$$

From tables, the vapour pressure of water vapour is $19\cdot3$ kN m^{-2} at 333 K at which temperature the latent heat $= 2353$ kJ kg^{-1}
For 1 m³ CH_4 burned, 2 m³ H_2O is formed or $(2 \times 18/22\cdot4)$
$$= 1\cdot61 \text{ kg/m}^3 \text{ } CH_4$$

$\therefore$ Heat in water vapour $=$ (sensible in water)+(latent)
$$+(\text{sensible in vapour})$$
$$= 1\cdot61[4\cdot187(333 - 273) + 2353$$
$$+ 2\cdot09\dagger \text{ } (530 - 333)$$
$$= 4856 \text{ kJ/m}^3 \text{ } CH_4$$

Heat in CO_2 and $N_2 =$
$$[(1\cdot0 \times 1\cdot516) + (7\cdot52 \times 1\cdot245)](530 - 273) = 2796 \text{ kJ/m}^3 \text{ } CH_4$$

$\therefore$ total heat in flue gas $= (4856 + 2796) = 7652$ kJ/m³

† Assumed specific heat of water vapour (kJ kg^{-1} K^{-1})

Heat in air (as before) $= 313 \text{ kJ m}^{-3}$

$\therefore$ sensible and latent heat in flue gas
$$= (7652 - 313) = 7339 \text{ kJ/m}^3 \text{ methane}$$
$$= 7\cdot34 \text{ MJ/m}^3$$
$$\text{or } (7\cdot34 \times 100)/44\cdot6$$
$$= \underline{16\cdot5\%}$$

2. *Air heater*

One important way of recovering heat from flue gases is in the preheating of the primary air used for combustion. In this case, only the sensible heat of the flue gas needs to be considered as it is vital that the gases should not be cooled below the dew-point, thus avoiding condensation and hence corrosion problems. This type of problem is therefore a simple heat balance, once the flows of air and flue gas have been evaluated. Indeed the heat balance is merely an added step to the fundamental problems discussed in Sections V. C and D. In the following problem, the combustion of an oil fuel is considered.

Example 9.29

An oil fuel, containing 82% C and 15% H, is burned with 20% excess air. The flue gas passes to a preheater in which the air for combustion is heated from 288 K to 623 K. If flue gases leave the preheater at 483 K, at what temperature do they enter?

(Mean specific heats: air $1\cdot006$, water vapour $2\cdot032$, dry flue gas $1\cdot048 \text{ kJ kg}^{-1}\text{ K}^{-1}$).

BASIS: 100 kg OIL

% mass	÷ by	= kmol	kmol O_2 required	kmol CO_2	kmol H_2O
C 82	12	6·83	6·83	6·83	–
H 15	2	7·50	3·75	–	7·50
			10·58	6·83	7·50

$\therefore$ theoretical air $= (10\cdot58 \times 100/21) = 50\cdot4 \text{ kmol/100 kg oil}$
$\therefore$ actual air $= (50\cdot4 \times 120/100) = 60\cdot5 \text{ kmol}$
  containing $(60\cdot5 \times 21/100) = 12\cdot7 \text{ kmol } O_2$
    and $(60\cdot5 - 12\cdot7) = 47\cdot8 \text{ kmol } N_2$
  Mass of air supplied $= (60\cdot5 \times 28\cdot9) = 1749 \text{ kg/100 kg oil}$
    or $\underline{\underline{17\cdot49 \text{ kg/kg of oil}}}$

In flue gas,

CO_2 = 6·83 kmol or (6·83 × 44) = 300 kg
O_2 = (12·7 − 10·58) = 2·12 kmol or (2·12 × 32) = 68 kg
N_2 = 47·8 kmol or (47·8 = 28) = 1338 kg
Total 1706 kg or <u>17·06 kg/kg oil</u>
H_2O = 7·50 kmol or (7·50 × 18) = 135 kg or <u>1·35 kg/kg oil</u>

BASIS: 1 kg OIL

Heat balance:

(heat gained by air) = (heat lost by dry flue gas) + water vapour)

Assuming flue gas enters the preheater at t K,

$$17\cdot49 \times 1\cdot006(623 - 288) = (17\cdot06 \times 1\cdot048) + (1\cdot35 \times 2\cdot032)$$
$$(t - 483)$$
from which <u>t = 769 K</u>

3. Waste heat boiler

A fairly common way of recovering heat from a hot gas stream, whether flue gases or a process stream, is by generating low-grade steam in a waste heat boiler. Such operations are employed for example in oil gasification plants. The following problem introduces the concept of boiler efficiency and the minor point of steam requirements for oil atomization.

Example 9.30

Flue gas from an oil-fired furnace passes to a waste heat boiler in which saturated steam is generated at 459 K and 1170 kN m⁻². During a trial, lasting 2·88 ks, 18·59 Mg oil was consumed and the following data were noted:

CO_2 in flue gas = 9·35%
temperatures: flue gas in = 1050 K, out = 575 K, feed water = 339 K
steam for atomization = 0·3 kg/kg oil
overall efficiency of boiler = 87%
composition of oil fuel = C 85%, H 15%

What was the rate of steam generation?
(Mean specific heat of wet flue gas = 1·27 kJ m⁻³ K⁻¹; latent heat of steam at 459 K = 1·99 MJ kg⁻¹.)

BASIS: 100 kg OIL

C balance:

100 kmol flue gas (dry) contain 9·35 kmol C
100 kg oil contain 85 kg C or (85/12) = 7·08 kmol C
Thus, dry flue gas produced = (7·08 × 100)/9·35 = 75·7 kmol/100 kg oil.

H_2O balance:

100 kg oil contain 15 kg H_2 or (1572)'= 7·5 kmol H_2
1 kmol H_2 produces 1 kmol water
∴ 7·5 kmol H_2 produce 7·5 kmol water

In addition

0·3 kg steam/kg oil
or 30 kg steam/100 kg oil
is used for atomizing the oil and this appears in the flue gas. 30 kg is equivalent to (30/18) = 1·7 kmol water vapour.
  Therefore, total water in flue gas = (1·7 + 7·5) = 9·2 kmol
      total wet flue gas = (75·7 + 9·2) = 84·9 kmol/100 kg fuel
      1 kmol of flue gas occupies 22·4 m³ at 273 K
      or (22·4 × 812/273) = 66·6 m³ at 812 K
(mean flue gas temperature = 0·5 (1050 + 575) = 812 K)
      ∴ volume of wet flue gas = (66·6 × 84·9/100)
                    = 56·5 m³/kg fuel.

(This step assumes the mean specific heat refers to 1 m³ at the flue gas temperature. If it is referred to 273 K, then the molecular volume is 22·4 m³ kmol⁻¹ as usual.)

Heat lost by flue gas = 56·5 × 1·27 (1050 − 573) = 34 086 kJ/kg oil

The overall efficiency of the waste heat boiler is 87%, therefore heat transferred to steam

= (34 086 × 87/100) = 29 655 kJ/kg oil
or 29·7 MJ/kg oil.

The steam is saturated, not superheated and hence heat content = (latent) + (sensible in water). For m kg steam/kg oil.

1·99m + 4·187m(459 − 339) = 29·7
∴ m = 11·9 kg/kg oil

0·3 kg steam/kg oil is used for atomization and hence, net output =
11·6 kg/kg oil.

Consumption of oil = $(18·59/2·88) = 6·46$ Mg ks^{-1}

or $6·46$ kg s^{-1}

∴ Rate of steam generation = $(6·46 \times 11·6) = \underline{\underline{74·9 \text{ kg s}^{-1}}}$

(Taking the molecular volume as $22·4$ m^3 kmol^{-1}, that is, specific
heats referring to 1 m^3 at 273 K, the rate of steam generation is
$23·9$ kg s^{-1})

4. Effect of preheat

There is a considerable advantage to be gained in preheating the air, as in
Example 9.29, or the fuel or indeed both, from the point of view of the
heat available in a furnace, as illustrated in the following example. In
addition, the question of water vapour entering in the air and the fuel is
considered.

Example 9.31

The following producer gas (CV = $6·19$ MJ m^{-3}):

CO_2 2·5%,   CO 30%, CH_4 3·0%, H_2 12·0%, N_2 52·5%,

saturated with water vapour at 293 K (vapour pressure = $2·33$ kN
m^{-2}), is burned with 10% excess air (60% saturated at 293 K) in a
furnace at 1900 K.

What is the effect on the available heat in the furnace of:

(i) no preheat,
(ii) preheating the air to 1300 K,
(iii) preheating the gas to 1300 K,
(iv) preheating both the gas and the air to 1300 K.

ENTHALPIES (MJ kmol^{-1})

	CO_2	CO	CH_4	H_2O	H_2	N_2	O_2	air
1300 K	49·83	31·32	59·63	38·0	29·43	30·97	–	13·42
1900 K	84·40	–	–	66·35	–	52·01	54·83	–

BASIS: 100 kmol GAS

(i) NO PREHEAT

	kmol	kmol O_2 required	kmol H_2O	kmol CO_2	kmol N_2
CO_2	2·5	–	–	2·5	–
CO	30·0	13·0	–	30·0	–
CH_4	3·0	6·0	6·0	3·0	–
H_2	12·0	6·0	12·0	–	–
N_2	52·5	–	–	–	52·5
	100·0	27·0	18·0	35·5	52·5

Theoretical air = $(27·0 \times 100/12) = 129·2$ kmol/100 kmol gas.
Actual air = $(129·2 \times 110/100) = 142·0$ kmol/100 kmol gas containing

$$(142·0 \times 79/100) = 112·2 \text{ kmol } N_2$$
$$(142·0 - 112·2) = 29·8 \text{ kmol } O_2$$

Mol. fraction of water in fuel = partial pressure of water/partial pressure of fuel = $2·33/(101·33 - 2·33) = 0·0236$

∴ water in fuel = $(0·0236 \times 100) = 2·36$ kmol/100 kmol gas

Mol. fraction of water in air = $(0·0236 \times 60/100) = 0·0142$

∴ water in air = $(0·0142 \times 142·0) = 2·02$ kmol/100 kmol gas.

Hence in flue gas:

$$CO_2 \quad 35·5 \text{ kmol}$$
$$O_2 \quad (29·8 - 27·0) = 2·8 \text{ kmol}$$
$$N_2 \quad (52·5 + 112·2) = 164·7 \text{ kmol}$$
$$H_2O \quad (18·0 + 2·36 + 2·02) = 22·4 \text{ kmol}$$

Sensible heat in flue gas at 1900 K
= $(35·5 \times 84·4) + (2·8 \times 54·8) + (164·7 \times 52·0) + (22·4 \times 66·35)$
= 13 201 MJ

Heat in fuel = $6·19 \times 22·4 = 13854$ MJ

∴ heat available in furnace = $(13854 - 13201)100/13854 =$
4·71%

(ii) AIR PREHEATED TO 1300 K

Sensible heat in air and water at 1300 K = $(142 \cdot 0 \times 31 \cdot 27) + (2 \cdot 02 \times 38 \cdot 0) = 4517$ MJ

$$\text{Total heat in:} \quad \left. \begin{array}{l} \text{air} = 4517 \\ \text{fuel} = 13\,854 \end{array} \right\} 18\,371 \text{ MJ}$$

Total heat out: flue gas = $13\,201$ MJ

∴ heat available in furnace = $(18\,371 - 13\,201)100/13\,854$
$$= 37 \cdot 3\%$$

(N.B. Throughout this problem, the heat available is expressed as a percentage of the calorific value of the fuel for the purposes of comparison.)

(iii) GAS PREHEATED TO 1300 K

Sensible heat in 100 kmol producer gas at 1300 K

$$= (2 \cdot 5 \times 49 \cdot 83) + (30 \cdot 0 \times 31 \cdot 32) + (3 \cdot 0 \times 59 \cdot 63) + (12 \cdot 0 \times 29 \cdot 43) + (52 \cdot 5 \times 30 \cdot 97) + (2 \cdot 36 \times 38 \cdot 0)$$
$$= 3309 \text{ MJ}$$

$$\text{Total heat in:} \quad \left. \begin{array}{l} \text{fuel (sensible)} = 3309 \\ \text{fuel (CV)} = 13\,859 \end{array} \right\} 17\,168 \text{ MJ}$$

Total heat out: flue gas = $13\,201$ MJ

∴ heat available in furnace = $(17\,168 - 13\,201)100/13\,854 =$
$$\underline{\underline{28 \cdot 6\%}}$$

(iv) GAS AND AIR PREHEATED TO 1300 K

$$\text{Total heat in:} \quad \left. \begin{array}{l} \text{air} = 4517 \\ \text{fuel (sensible)} = 3309 \\ \text{fuel (CV)} = 13\,854 \end{array} \right\} 21\,680 \text{ MJ}$$

Total heat out: flue gas = $13\,201$ MJ

∴ heat available in furnace = $(21\,680 - 13\,201)100/13\,854 =$
$$\underline{\underline{61 \cdot 2\%}}$$

B. Boiler and Furnace Efficiency

In Example 9.31, the amount of heat usefully available in the furnace was calculated as a percentage of the heat available as calorific value in the fuel. In essence, this was a calculation of the furnace efficiency which may be expressed as (heat usefully recovered)100/(calorific value of fuel). Example 9.32 illustrates this concept and provides a useful summary of many of the points considered previously.

Example 9.32

A boiler plant consisting of a water-tube boiler, a superheater, economizer and air heater was the subject of a trial during which the following data were obtained:

    duration of trial $= 3\cdot0$ ks
    coal used $= 29\cdot0$ Mg   water evaporated $= 229$ Mg
    boiler steam pressure $= 1\cdot46$ MN m^{-2} (saturated at 470 K)
    superheat temperature $= 605$ K
    temperatures:
        economizer: water inlet $= 345$ K
                   water outlet $= 400$ K (boiler feed temperature)
        air heater: air inlet $= 320$ K   flue gas inlet $= 500$ K
                   air outlet $= 385$ K   flue gas outlet $= 405$ K
        boiler house $= 295$ K

analyses:
    flue gas: CO_2 $13\cdot0\%$, O_2 $6\cdot5\%$, N_3 $80\cdot5\%$
    coal (dry basis): C 73%, H 5%, O 8%, N $1\cdot5\%$, S $1\cdot0\%$, ash $11\cdot5\%$
    moisture as fired $= 15\%$ gross CV (dry) $= 29\cdot6$ MJ kg^{-1}

Estimate the thermal efficiency of each component and hence the overall efficiency of the plant.
    (Mean specific heats: (kJ kg^{-1} K^{-1}) dry flue gas $= 1\cdot005$, water vapour $= 2\cdot094$, water $= 4\cdot187$, air $= 1\cdot005$)

BASIS: 100 kg COAL

(i) THEORETICAL AIR

The first stage is to express the coal analysis on an "as fired" basis by multiplying each component by $(100 - \%$ moisture)/100. For example, $\%$ C on an as-fired basis $= 73(100 - 15)/100 = 62\cdot1\%$

	% wt.	÷by	=kmol	kmol O_2 required
C	62·1	12	5·18	5·18
H	4·3	2	2·15	1·08
O	6·8	32	0·21	−0·21
N	1·3	28	0·05	–
S	0·9	32	0·03	0·03
ash	9·8	–	–	–
moisture	15·0	–	–	–
	100·2			6·08

∴ theoretical air = $(6·08 \times 100/21) = 28·95$ kmol/100 kg coal
or 0·29 kmol/kg coal = $(0·29 \times 28·9) = $ <u>8·37 kg/kg coal</u>

(ii) ACTUAL AIR

C BALANCE

100 kg coal contain 5·18 kmol C
100 kmol dry flue gas contain 13·0 kmol C
∴ dry flue gas produced = $(5·18 \times 100/13·0)$
= 39·8 kmol/100 kg coal

N_2 BALANCE:
(N_2 in coal) + (N_2 in air) = (N_2 in flue gas)
Let a kmol air be supplied per 100 kg coal
$0·05 + (79a/100) = (39·8 \times 80·5/100)$
$a = 40·5$ kmol air/100 kg coal
∴ mass of air = $(40·5 \times 28·9/100) = $ <u>11·72 kg/kg coal</u>

(iii) WEIGHT OF WET FLUE GAS

Dry flue gas contains:

$CO_2 = 39·8 \times 13·0/100 = 5·18$ kmol or $(5·18 \times 4) = 227$ kg
$O_2 = 39·8 \times 6·5/100 = 2·59$ kmol or $(2·59x \times 32) = 83$ kg
$N_2 = 39·8 \times 80·5/100 = 32·03$ kmol or $(32·03 \times 28) = 897$ kg
total = 1207 kg

Water from combustion of hydrogen = 2·15 kmol

or $(2·15 \times 18) = 39$ kg }
Moisture in coal = 15 kg } total = 54 kg

∴ total mass of wet flue gas = 1261 kg/100 kg coal
or <u>12·61 kg/kg coal</u>

(iv) FLUE GAS ANALYSIS AND DEW POINT

In flue gas,

$$CO_2 = 5·18 \text{ kmol} \qquad O_2 = 2·59 \text{ kmol} \qquad N_2 = 32·03 \text{ kmol}$$
$$H_2O = (54/18) = 3·0 \text{ kmol}$$
$$\text{total} = 42·8 \text{ kmol}$$

Hence volumetric analysis of wet flue gas becomes:

$$CO_2 = 5·18 \times 100/42·8 = 12·1\%$$
$$O_2 = 2·59 \times 100/42·8 = 6·1\%$$
$$N_2 = 32·03 \times 100/42·8 = 74·8\%$$
$$H_2O = 3·0 \times 100/42·8 = 7·0\%$$

$\therefore$ partial pressure of water vapour $= (101·3 \times 7·0/100) = 7·09 \text{ kN m}^{-2}$

Water has a vapour pressure of $7·09 \text{ kN m}^{-2}$ at 313 K and hence this is the dew point.

$$\text{Latent heat of water at 313 K} = \underline{\underline{2·4 \text{ MJ kg}^{-1}}}$$

(v) HEAT LOST IN FLUE GAS

Sensible heat in dry flue gas $= 12·07 \times 1·005(405 - 295) = 1334 \text{ kJ/kg}$ coal or $1·33 \text{ MJ/kg coal}$

Heat in water vapour $= $ (sensible heat in water) $+$ (latent) $+$
$$\qquad \text{(sensible heat in vapour)}$$
$$= 0·54(4·187(313 - 295) + 2400 +$$
$$2·094(405 - 313)) = 1441 \text{ kJ}$$
$$\text{or } 1·44 \text{ MJ/kg coal}$$

$\therefore$ total heat lost in flue gas $= \underline{\underline{2·77 \text{ MJ/kg coal}}}$

(vi) THERMAL EFFICIENCIES (BASIS: 1 kg COAL)

(a) BOILER

enthalpy of steam at $1·46 \text{ MN m}^{-3} = 2·79 \text{ MJ kg}^{-1}$
enthalpy of feed water $= 4·187(400 - 273) = 532 \text{ kJ kg}^{-1}$
$$\text{or } 0·53 \text{ MJ kg}^{-1}$$

$\therefore$ heat transferred to steam $= (2·79 - 0·53) = 2·26 \text{ MJ kg}^{-1}$

water evaporated $= 229/29·0 = 7·90 \text{ kg/kg coal}$
$\therefore$ heat transferred to steam $= 2·26 \times 7·90 = 17·85 \text{ MJ/kg coal}$

Gross calorific value of coal as fired $= 29·6(100 + 15)/100$
$$= 25·16 \text{ MJ kg}^{-1}$$

$\therefore$ boiler efficiency $= (17·85 \times 100/25·16) = \underline{\underline{71·2\%}}$

(b) SUPERHEATER

Heat transferred to steam in superheater $= 7 \cdot 90 \times 2 \cdot 094(605 - 470)$
$$= 2233 \text{ kJ/kg coal}$$
$$\text{or } 2 \cdot 23 \text{ MJ/kg coal}$$

∴ superheater efficiency $= 2 \cdot 23 \times 100/25 \cdot 16 = \underline{\underline{8 \cdot 9\%}}$

(c) AIR HEATER

Heat transferred to combustion air $= 11 \cdot 72 \times 1 \cdot 005(385 - 320)$
$$= 766 \text{ kJ/kg coal}$$
$$\text{or } 0 \cdot 77 \text{ MJ/kg coal}$$

∴ air heat efficiency $= (0 \cdot 77 \times 100/25 \cdot 16) = \underline{\underline{3 \cdot 1\%}}$

(This amount of heat is already accounted for in the boiler efficiency)

(d) ECONOMIZER

Heat transferred to water in economizer $= 7 \cdot 90 \times 4 \cdot 187(400 - 345)$
$$= 1819 \text{ kJ/kg coal}$$
$$\text{or } 1 \cdot 82 \text{ MJ/kg coal}$$

∴ economizer efficiency $= (1 \cdot 82 \times 100/25 \cdot 16) = \underline{\underline{7 \cdot 2\%}}$

(vii) SUMMARY OF RESULTS (BASIS: 1 kg COAL)

Unit	Heat recovered (MJ)	% gross CV of wet coal	
boiler	17·13	68·1	
air heater	0·77	3·1	87·3%
superheater	2·23	8·9	
economizer	1·82	7·2	
heat in flue gas	2·77	11·00	12·7%
unaccounted for	0·43	1·70	

C. Gasification Problems

The most significant change in plants for the production of synthetic gaseous fuels over the past decade has been the introduction of processes in which the feedstock is a light oil or a hydrocarbon gas as distinct from traditional carbonization processes starting from coal and coke in the production of coal gas, producer gas and so on. Problems involving such processes introduce no new concepts and can be handled using the basic methods considered in previous sections. In many ways, the simplest approach is to consider the feedstock as the fuel, any solid residue (in the case of carbonization processes) as the ash, and the product gas at its various processing stages as the flue gas. This approach is illustrated in the following problems.

1. *Producer gas plant*

Example 9.33

The following producer gas:

$$CO\ 25\%,\ CO_2\ 5\%,\ H_2\ 12\%.\ CH_4\ 4\%,\ N_2\ 5\%$$
$$(CV\ 5{\cdot}9\ MJ\ m^{-3})$$

is manufactured from coke, containing 84% C and 12% ash on a producer gas plant. If the ash leaving the plant contains 13% C, estimate on the basis of 1 kg coke fired,

   (i) the weight of carbon gasified,
   (ii) the make of gas,
   (iii) the heat available in the gas.

(i) (The first part of this problem is merely an extension of the concept of loss of carbon in ash as dealt with in Section V.F.2. The working is the same).
   Let w kg C be associated with the ash in 100 kg coke

$$(w/12) = 13/(100 - 13)$$
$$w = 1{\cdot}79\ kg\ C/100\ kg\ coke$$

For every 100 kg coke processed $(84{\cdot}0 - 1{\cdot}79) = 82{\cdot}21$ kg C pass into the gas

$$\therefore\ \text{mass of carbon gasified} = (82{\cdot}31/100)$$
$$= \underline{\underline{0{\cdot}822\ kg/kg\ coke}}$$

(ii) The "make" of gas is simply the amount of gas produced, usually expressed in volumetric terms. This is calculated by treating the product gas as flue gas.

C BALANCE

In 100 kg coke, 32·21 kg C is gasified or (82·21/12) = 6·85 kmol
In 100 kmol gas, kmol C = 25(in CO) + 5(in CO_2) + 4(in CH_4)
                       = 34 kmol/100 kmol gas

∴ Amount of gas produced = (6·85 × 100/34·0)
                         = 20·15 kmol/100 kg coke
   Volume of gas produced = (20·15 × 22·4/100)
                          = 4·513 m³/kg coke at s.t.p.

(iii) Calorific value of product = 5·9 MJ/m⁻³

        ∴ heat in the gas = (5·9 × 4·513)
                          = 26·63 MJ/kg coke

2. Gasification of liquid fuels

The following two typical problems illustrate the way in which a product
gas may be considered as flue gas in calculation and how thermal efficiency
may be related to oil gasification processes.

Example 9.34

A light distillate containing 83·7% C and 16·3% H by weight is
gasified in two stages. Firstly a reaction with steam is carried out
and then a second stage reaction takes place after the addition of
air. The carbon monoxide in the product is then converted to
carbon dioxide which is removed and the gas is dried. Based on the
analyses shown, estimate:

    (i) the steam-feed ratio used in the first stage reaction,
    (ii) the air added before the second stage,
    (iii) the final volume of dry gas produced.

ANALYSES

	%CO_2	%CO	%H_2	%CH_4	%N_2	%H_2O
A. after first stage reaction	13·5	1·2	12·8	26·5	–	36·0
B. after second stage reaction	11·6	6·2	24·1	22·5	9·8	25·8
C. final dry product	0·8	2·7	44·5	32·6	19·4	–

(i) C BALANCE

In 100 kg feed, 83·7 kg C or (83·7/12) = 6·38 kmol C
In 100 kmol gas A, kmol C = 13·5 (in CO_2) + 1·2 (in CO)
    + 36·5 (in CH_4) = 51·2 kmol

∴ amount of gas A produced = (5·98 × 100/51·2)
                             = 13·63 kmol/ 100 kg distillate.

H_2 BALANCE

In 100 kg feed, 16·3 kg H or (16·3/2) = 8·15 kmol H_2
In 100 kmol gas A, kmol H_2 = 12·8 (as H_2) + 73·0 (in CH_4) + 36·0
(in H_2O) = 121·8 kmol.

∴ In 13·63 kmol gas A, kmol H_2 = (121·8 × 13·63/100) = 16·6
                   kmol/100 kg distillate

H_2 from steam + H_2 from distillate = H_2 in gas A

$$h + 8·15 = 16·6$$
∴ h = 8·45 kmol/100 kg distillate
∴ mass of steam added = (8·45 × 18) = 152 kg/100 kg distillate
∴ steam/feed ratio = 1·52 kg/kg distillate

(ii) C BALANCE

In 100 kg feed, there are 6·98 kmol C
In 100 kmol gas B, kmol C = 11·6 (in CO_2) + 6·2 (in CO)
        + 22·5 (in CH_4) = 40·3 kmol

∴ amount of gas B produced = (6·98 × 100/40·3)
                             = 17·32 kmol/ 100 kg distillate

N_2 BALANCE

Let a kmol air be added per 100 kg distillate before the second stage reaction.

$$N_2 \text{ in air} = N_2 \text{ in gas } B$$
$$(79a/100) = (17·32 × 9·8/100)$$
∴ a = 2·14 kmol/100 kg feed

∴ mass of air added = (2·14 × 28·9) = 62·1 kg/100 kg feed
        or 0·62 kg air/kg feed

(iii) N_2 BALANCE

Amount of gas B produced   = 17·32 kmol/100 kg distillate,
                                    containing (17·32 × 9·8/100)
                                    = 1·70 kmol N_2/100 kg distillate
∴ amount of gas C produced = (1·70 × 100/19·4)
                                    = 8·75 kmol/100 kg distillate
       or (8·75 × 22·4/100) = 1·96 m³/kg distillate at STP

Example 9.35

In a cyclic catalytic oil gasification plant, the mean production of gas is 200 m³ ks⁻¹, whilst the consumption of oil is 0·13 m³ ks⁻¹. 4·6% of the make gas is used for heating the catalyst during the "blow" and the average composition of the product is:

CO_2 11·5%,   CO 14·5%, O_2 0·5%, H_2 49·3%, CH_4 14·5%, C_2H_6 0·5%, C_nH_m 6·5%, N_2 2·7%

Neglecting the value of any by-products, estimate:
   (i) the net thermal yield in the product per m³ oil,
   (ii) the thermal efficiency of the process.
(Oil: relative density = 0·97, gross calorific value = 2·5 MJ kg⁻¹. Calorific values (MJ m⁻³):   CO = 11·92, H_2 = 11·92, C_nH_m = 85·2, C_2H_6 = 63·2, CH_4 = 37·05.)

(i) BASIS: 100 m³ PRODUCT GAS

Calorific value of product = (14·5 × 11·92) + (49·3 × 11·92) +
                                     (1·5 × 37·05) + (0·5 × 63·2) +
                                     (6·5 × 85·2)
                               = 1883 MJ/100 m³
                               or 18·83 MJ/m³ gas.
Production of gas = (200/0·13) = 1539 m³/m³ oil. But, 4·6% is used in heating the catalyst.

∴ net output = 1539(100 − 4·6)/100 = 1·68 m³/m³ oil
∴ thermal output = (18·83 × 1468)
                        = 27 646 MJ/m³ oil

(ii) RELATIVE DENSITY OF OIL = 0·97

∴ density = 970 kg m⁻³

Gross calorific value $= 42{\cdot}5\,\text{MJ}\,\text{kg}^{-1}$

or $\quad(42{\cdot}5 \times 970) = 41\ 225\,\text{MJ}\,\text{m}^{-3}$

$\therefore$ thermal efficiency $= (27\ 646 \times 100/41\ 225)$

$\qquad\qquad\qquad = \underline{\underline{67{\cdot}1\%}}$

D. Problems Associated With Conversion to Natural Gas

Recent trends in the fuel industries indicate considerable expansion in the combustion of gaseous fuels, particularly, for example with the advent of natural gas in the UK. This latest development has involved the conversion of burners in the UK to accommodate natural gas, which, being mainly methane, has about twice the calorific value, half the burning velocity and requires some two and a half times as much combustion air as compared with coal gas. It is beyond the scope of this chapter to consider anything other than the simple heat balances involved, though these introduce several interesting problems.

Example 9.36

A central heating installation, rated at $17{\cdot}5\,\text{kW}$, is to be converted from coal gas to natural gas. At maximum output, the fan supplies 15% more air than is required when burning coal gas with 75% excess air. Will the fan be adequate when burning natural gas with 75% excess air? Calculate the Wobbé Number for the two fuels.

Coal gas: CO_2 2·6%, O_2 1·0%, CO 13·2%, C_2H_4 0·4%, CH_4 21·6%, H_2 46·4%, N_2 14·8%.

Natural gas: CH_4 89·5%, CO_2 5·3%, O_2 0·2%, N_2 5·0%.

Calorific values $(\text{MJ}\,\text{m}^{-3})$: CO 12·71, CH_4 39·75, C_2H_4 62·4, H_2 12·78.

MEAN CALORIFIC VALUES

Coal gas $= (0{\cdot}132 \times 12{\cdot}71) + (0{\cdot}004 \times 62{\cdot}4) +$
$\qquad\qquad\quad (0{\cdot}216 \times 39{\cdot}75) + (0.64 \times 12{\cdot}78) = 16{\cdot}43\,\text{MJ}\,\text{m}^{-3}$
Natural gas $= (39{\cdot}75 \times 89{\cdot}5/100) = 35{\cdot}5\,\text{MJ}\,\text{m}^{-3}$

CONSUMPTION OF FUEL

Rating $= 17{\cdot}5\,\text{kW} = 17{\cdot}5\,\text{kJ}\,\text{s}^{-1}$ or $17{\cdot}5\,\text{MJ}\,\text{ks}^{-1}$

$\therefore$ consumption of coal gas $= (17{\cdot}5/16{\cdot}43) = 1{\cdot}065\,\text{m}^3\,\text{ks}^{-1}$
$\qquad$ consumption of natural gas $= (17{\cdot}5/35{\cdot}5) = 0{\cdot}494\,\text{m}^3\,\text{ks}^{-1}$

THEORETICAL AIR

Coal gas:

	kmol	kmol O_2 required
CO_2	2·6	–
O_2	1·0	−1·0
CO	13·2	6·6
C_2H_4	0·4	1·2
CH_4	21·6	43·2
H_2	46·4	23·2
N_2	14·8	–

73·2 kmol/100 kmol gas

$\therefore$ theoretical air = (73·2 × 100/21) = 349 kmol/100 kmol
or 3·49 m^3/m^3 gas

Natural gas:

	kmol	kmol O_2 required
CH_4	89·5	179·0
CO_2	5·3	–
O_2	0·2	−0·2
N_2	5·0	–

178·8 kmol/100 kmol gas

$\therefore$ theoretical air = (178·8 × 100/21) = 851 kmol/100 kmol
or 8·51 m^3/m^3 gas

FAN RATING

Actual air with coal gas = (3·49 × 1·75) = 6·10 m^3/m^3 gas
or (6·10 × 1·065) = 6·50 m^3 ks^{-1}

$\therefore$ maximum capacity of air fan = (6·50 × 1·15) = 7·47 m^3 ks^{-1}

Air required to burn natural gas with 75% excess
= (8·51 × 1·75)
= 14·9 m^3/m^3 gas
or (14·9 × 0·494)
= 7·35 m^3 ks^{-1}
$\therefore$ *The fan will therefore cope with the new duty.*

WOBBÉ NUMBER

Coal gas

Mean molecular mass = (0·026 × 44) + (0·01 × 32) +
(0·132 × 28) + (0·004 × 28) +

$$(0{\cdot}216 \times 16) + (0{\cdot}464 \times 2) +$$
$$(0{\cdot}148 \times 28)$$
$$= 13{\cdot}80 \text{ kg kmol}^{-1}$$

Mean molecular mass of air $= 28{\cdot}9$ kg kmol^{-1}

$\therefore$ specific gravity of gas relative to air $= (13{\cdot}80/28{\cdot}9) = 0{\cdot}478$

Wobbé number $=$ (calorific value)/$\sqrt{}$ (SG relative to air)
$$= (16{\cdot}43/\sqrt{0{\cdot}478})$$
$$= \underline{\underline{23{\cdot}76 \text{ MJ m}^{-3}}}$$

Natural gas

Mean molecular weight $= (0{\cdot}895 \times 16) + (0{\cdot}053 \times 44) +$
$$(0{\cdot}002 \times 32) + (0{\cdot}05 \times 28)$$
$$= 18{\cdot}11 \text{ kg kmol}^{-1}$$

$\therefore$ specific gravity relative to air $= (18{\cdot}11/28{\cdot}9) = 0.627$
$\therefore$ Wobbé number $= (35{\cdot}5/\sqrt{0{\cdot}627})$
$$= \underline{\underline{44{\cdot}82 \text{ MJ m}^{-3}}}$$

VII. FURTHER READING

Anderton, P. and Bigg, P. H. (1965). "Changing to the Metric System". HMSO, London.

British Standards Institution (1967). "The Use of SI Units". Publication PD 5686 1967.

Davies, C. (1970). "Calculations in Furnace Technology". Pergamon Press, London.

Institute of Petroleum (1978). "Methods for Analysis and Testing". Heyden, London.

Lewis and Radasch (1961). "Industrial Stoichiometry". McGraw-Hill, New York.

Peck, W. J. and Richmond, A. J. (1957). "Applied Thermodynamics Problems for Engineers". Edward Arnold, London.

Rogers, G. F. C. and Mayhew, Y. R. (1957). "Engineering Thermodynamics, Work and Heat Transfer". Longmans Green, London.

Schmidt, A. Z. and List, H. L. (1962). "Material and Energy Balances". Prentice-Hall, New York.

Whitwell, J. C. and Toner, R. K. (1969). "Conservation of Mass and Energy". Blaisdell Pub. Co., Boston, Mass.

Energy Economics

10

I. INTRODUCTION

This book has been concerned so far with the production and properties of fuels and their conversion into useful and convenient forms of energy. The choice of a particular energy source and conversion route depends on many factors including convenience, reliability and availability, environmental considerations, the political situation, manpower. Yet the overriding factor is cost. This chapter is an attempt to introduce some of the concepts involved in assessing the economics of a given operation and to deal briefly with one or two relatively new developments in which energy is produced in operations such as combined heat and power and total energy, for example.

To underline the importance of cost, consider the problem of domestic heating. In past centuries wood from the surrounding forest was burned providing an efficient and effectively inexhaustible supply of energy. Forests are now no longer available to urban society, which therefore has to depend on coal and, more recently, oil and electricity for its energy, and although availability and pollution are of importance, cost is the dominating consideration. As the cost of oil has increased, the trend has been gas-fired central heating and now, certainly in the UK, coal is again becoming increasingly attractive. Indeed, in densely populated areas, there is little choice in the source of energy for this purpose, though it may be noted that the costs of coal, oil and gas and electricity are usually varied to ensure that no particular energy source has more than a modest cost advantage. There are, of course, situations in which other factors are important and there may be only one way of achieving a particular task. A

290

simple example is the convenience of the dry cell in which 1 kJ of energy costs many times that of power from the grid. A similar case is that of bottled gas which is used in caravans and remote locations. Savings could be made by burning domestic refuse in the home, though here pollution would be a problem and people prefer to pay for the convenience of instant energy by way of gas and electricity and for cleanliness in the operation.

In supplying energy in convenient and acceptable forms, there are essentially two costs involved both in the industrial and domestic situation: capital and running costs. Capital cost is the cost of buying the equipment, usually spread over a number of years and running costs would include fuel, maintenance, manpower and so on. To take two extreme examples— the capital cost of an open fire is very modest, with high running costs, that is, in fuel and manpower. Against this, the running cost of solar devices and indeed any system operating by a renewable energy source are very low, though sadly the capital costs are often prohibitive. Whatever the system, the capital and running costs must be combined to give the cost per unit of energy in order to make useful and meaningful comparisons between alternatives. Similar considerations apply in the case of heat recovery, for which the capital cost of the equipment involved, expressed on an annual basis, must be compared with the value of the energy recovered. This leads to the concept of "pay-back time" which is the period over which the value of the energy saved is equivalent to the capital cost involved. Simple examples of this concept are provided by domestic insulation, where roof insulation is very attractive, cavity wall insulation has a rather longer pay-back time and double glazing longer still. For heat recovery, there are cases in which recovery is just not worthwhile. This is particularly so with with low-grade heat where the temperature gradients are such that the heat exchangers involved would be very large with correspondingly high capital costs. However, as the cost of energy escalates, more and more energy recovery systems are becoming viable and some recent proposals are quite novel, especially where the energy is used in quite a new application—using bath water to heat a greenhouse, for example. In the days of cheap energy, the energy usage in manufacturing a product often received modest attention compared with, say, manpower when the introduction of automation often seemed all important at the neglect of the 70 year old coal-fired boiler for example. At the present time, with high energy costs, detailed energy audits are carried out for most commercial operations. Many such calculations involve the total energy invested in a given operation and, indeed, it has been suggested that the cumulative output of a nuclear power station never exceeds the energy invested in its construction and in the preparation and transport of fuel. Some energy costs for a variety of common materials are given in

Table 37. Such calculations emphasize the rapid depletion of the world's
energy store and the need to conserve at all stages.

TABLE 37. *World energy costs of producing some common materials (1970)†*

Material	Production (10⁶ Mg)	Energy cost (MWh Mg⁻¹)	Energy cost (10⁹ kWh)
Crude steel	592·6	10·5	6222
Cement	567	2·2	1247
Aluminium	9·63	91	876
Copper	7·58	20	152
Lead	3·2	15	48
Plastics	30·35	45	1366
Glass	1·62	6·25	10
Paper	127·4	7·5	955

† World Energy Conference (1978).

II. ENERGY COSTING

A. Introduction

As explained, for any conversion route, there are essentially two costs
involved—the capital cost of the equipment, to achieve the conversion,
and the running costs, of which the fuel is usually the dominating factor. It
is convenient to consider the cost of fuels and equipment separately before
combining these in a further section: costs of energy. It is important to
appreciate that detailed costing procedures are beyond the scope of this
text and yet the approach should be adequate in permitting the preparation
of first-order cost estimates and certainly the evaluation of alternative
systems.

A vital consideration in any costing operation is the purchasing power
of the currency quoted at any particular time. This varies from year to year
and it is necessary to use a cost index to update prices, particularly of
equipment, from a given datum to the present time. In making calculations, current fuel prices should obviously be used. Such cost indices are
published as tables or graphs in the *Economist* in the UK and the
Engineering News Record Magazine in the US, in addition to various
periodicals concerned with the oil industry which publish indexes relevant
to plant and equipment. These include *Nelson's Refinery Index*, *Chemical
Engineering Cost Index* and *Marshall and Stevens Cost Index*. Some
indication of the increase in costs in the UK since 1956 is shown in Table 38
which is based on data published by the Electricity Council (1979). It will

TABLE 38. *Domestic and industrial price indexes* (*Basis*: 1955–56 = 100)†

Year	Price index		Delivered cost of fossil fuel	Price of electricity/kWh	
	Retail	Wholesale		Domestic	Industrial
1955–56	100	100	100	100	100
1956–57	100	100	110	105	105
1957–58	105	95	115	110	105
1958–59	110	95	120	105	105
1959–60	108	95	115	101	100
1960–61	110	95	120	105	100
1961–62	115	95	120	110	105
1962–63	125	95	122	115	105
1963–64	130	100	120	120	110
1964–65	135	110	120	120	115
1965–66	140	115	120	130	120
1966–67	145	115	140	130	120
1967–68	147	120	140	134	118
1968–69	160	120	140	140	125
1969–70	170	122	145	140	120
1970–71	175	125	180	140	127
1971–72	185	130	205	145	130
1972–73	200	135	215	155	130
1973–74	225	210	240	160	140
1974–75	275	275	400	208	220
1975–76	325	320	510	300	280
1976–77	375	375	580	360	325
1977–78	425	420	700	410	350
1978–79	455	450	725	450	405

† Electricity Council (1979).

be noted that retail and wholesale costs have increased by a factor of 4·5 since 1956 which is the same as the increase in electricity costs. The cost of fossil fuels was very similar until 1973–74, though in 1978–79 the equivalent factor was 7·25. A further comparison between fuel and plant costs is shown in Fig. 99 which is from a paper by Ryder (1976) and which takes 1970 as the datum. Again the rapid increase in fuel costs compared with plant costs is apparent. In quoting plant and energy costs, it is important, therefore, to quote the year to which the cost refers, £(1976) or $(1962) for example.

Few would have predicted the massive increase in fuel costs in recent years and it is equally difficult to estimate future costs of plant and energy. In assessing the cost of a given system, possibly the only reasonable approach is to base the calculations on present day costs on the assumption that the rise in the cost of plant and energy will not be dissimilar.

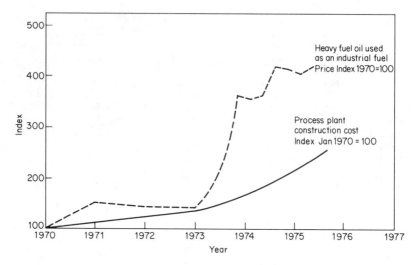

Fig. 99. *Comparison of energy prices with cost of process plant (Ryder 1976).*

B. Costs of Fuels

There are two problems associated with any discussion of the costs of fuels: the wide variation due to quantities involved, rebates and locality; and even more significant, the high escalation in prices which increase almost daily in the UK. Some indication of the variation in the price of fossil fuels is shown in Table 38 and a guide to the price of heavy fuel oil in recent years is shown in Fig. 99. Since the massive increase in fuel costs, particularly that of crude oil in 1973–74, there has been considerable discussion and prediction of fuel costs in coming years. One example of such a paper is that by White (1977) in which forecasts prepared by the Henley Centre for Forecasting in 1976 are reported. These are summarized in Table 39.

Recent data have been published on UK prices by the National Industrial Fuel Efficiency Service (1979) and these are shown in Table 40 from which it will be noted that the forecasts in Table 39 have already been exceeded by a considerable margin. Towards the end of 1979, crude oil was approaching $30/barrel and finished oil products were around £100/Mg. In Table 40, the average price in pence/therm (1 therm = 105·5 MJ) provides an interesting comparison between fuels; the prices are for supplies in excess of 100 000 therm/year. This variation between the forecasts made only two years previously and actual fuel costs highlights the very real problems in making such predictions.

TABLE 39. *UK industrial fuel price forecasts*†

	Crude oil ($/barrel)	Coal (£/ton)	Heavy fuel oil (£/ton)	Gas (p/therm)‡	Electricity (p/kWh)
1976	12·5	18·2	43·7	6·4	1·49
1977	13·6	21·5	53·3	9·1	1·75
1978	14·7	24·4	59·2	10·8	1·98
1979	15·4	27·1	65·4	12·2	2·15
1980	16·0	28·9	69·0	13·0	2·33
1981	17·1	31·3	75·9	14·1	2·55
1982	19·1	34·8	88·0	16·0	3·88
1982–1987	28·1–38·4	7·5% pa.	8·5% pa.	9·0% pa.	8·0% pa.

† White (1977).
‡ (1 therm = 105·5 MJ, 1 kWh = 3·6 MJ)

In the case of coal, the NCB introduced a new simplified price structure in 1970 which has been described by Locke (1980), This may be summarized by the relation:

$$\text{Pit head price} = (CV/100)(APV/100 - SA + GA + SS) \ \text{£/ton}$$

where CV is the calorific value (kJ kg^{-1})

APV is the area points values

SA is the secondary ash scale

GA is the grade adjustment

and   SS is the sulphur scale for which data are given in Table 41.

TABLE 40. *Comparison of energy costs, July 1980*†

Energy form	Unit of supply	Calorific Value	Average price		
		(kJ/unit)	(p/unit)	(£/MWh)	(p/therm)
Electricity	kWh	3600/kWh	2·84	28·4	83·2
Natural gas	ft^3	1092/ft^3	0·27	8·90	26·1
Fuel oil					
35 seconds	litre	38000/l	15·24	14·44	42·3
200 seconds	litre	40570/l	13·41	11·90	34·9
950 seconds	litre	40800/l	11·93	10·53	30·8
3500 seconds	litre	41000/l	11·08	9·73	28·5
Propane	tonne	50400/kg	£174/tonne	12·43	36·4
Butane	tonne	49600/kg	£158/tonne	11·47	33·7
Coal	tonne	28180/kg	£44·50/tonne	5·68	16·7
Industrial coke	tonne	27900/kg	£84·30/tonne	10·88	31·8
High–quality blast					
furnace coke	tonne	27900/kg	£85·80/tonne	11·07	32·5
Large foundry coke					
(S. Wales origin)	tonne	27000/kg	£93·80/tonne	12·50	36·6

† NIFES (1980).

Such data are changing with time as, indeed, are the costs of other fuels. Significant variations in cost occur depending on locality and the annual demand for a given fuel and there are situations in which a particular fuel is just not available—gas is a prime example of this. Tariffs

TABLE 41. *UK coal price structure*†

Revised area points values, industrial formula	Pence per point (APV)
Area	Industrial coals
Scotland	11·30
North East	10·29
North Yorkshire	10·10
Doncaster	10·10
Barnsley	10·10
South Yorkshire	10·00
Western:	
Lancashire	10·37
Cumbria, North Wales and Staffordshire	10·10
North Derbyshire	10·10
North Nottinghamshire	10·10
South Nottinghamshire	10·10
South Midlands: Leicestershire, S. Derbyshire and Warwickshire	10·10
Kent	10·88
South Wales	10·88

Secondary Ash Scale (SA)					
Ash content (%)	£	Ash content (%)	£	Ash content (%)	£
2	0·09	13	1·06	24	2·56
3	0·13	14	1·20	25	2·70
4	0·17	15	1·34	26	2·84
5	0·22	16	1·47	27	2·97
6	0·31	17	1·61	28	3·11
7	0·39	18	1·75	29	3·25
8	0·48	19	1·88	30	3·38
9	0·57	20	2·02	31	3·52
10	0·65	21	2·16	32	3·66
11	0·79	22	2·29	33	3·79
12	0·93	23	2·43	34	3·93
Adjustments for 0·1% are interpolation				35	4·07

† Locke (1980).

TABLE 41. *continued*

Grade adjustment £ per ton (GA)

	Washed £	Blended £	Untreated £
Graded coals	+ 1·65	+ 1·15	+ 1·00
Smalls 25 mm and over	+ 0·85	+ 0·35	+ 0·20
Smalls less than 25 mm	+ 0·65	+ 0·15	Nil

Sulphur scale £ per ton (SS)

Sulphur Range (%)	£	Sulphur Range (%)	£
0·80 and below	+ 0·22	2·41–2·60	− 0·44
0·81–1·00	+ 0·11	2·61–2·80	− 0·55
1·01–1·80	Datum	2·81–3·00	− 0·66
1·81–2·00	− 0·11	3·01–3·20	− 0·77
2·01–2·20	− 0·22	3·21–2·40	− 0·88
2·21–2·40	− 0·33	3·41 and above	− 0·99

are an important consideration which will not be discussed here. Suffice to note that important savings can often be made by selecting the correct tariff. Fuel prices then are highly variable functions and in assessing a particular energy scheme, it is preferable to use up to date information obtained directly from the suppliers if at all possible.

C. Costs of Equipment

Data on the investment required for various energy conversion projects are sparse and those that are available must be treated with caution, since costs vary not only with inflation but also with the size of the project and, in the case of new developments, the technology of the operation. Problems are also different when considering major projects such as a nuclear power station compared with a more modest installation such as a diesel generator. In the latter case the best data are usually obtained direct from the supplier. Some information on the investment required for the generation of thermal and electrical energy is given in Table 42 which has been recalculated as £(1980). Similar data comparing oil- and coal-fired plant with a light water reactor which are in $(1976) are given in Fig. 100. Some information on the cost of steam boilers, provided by John Thomson Cochran is shown in Fig. 101, which is in £(1979). These values are for water-tube boilers and a useful cost comparison presented by Field (1975),

TABLE 42. *Capital investment in energy projects*†

Option	Date of commercial service	Capital investment £(1980)/kW
Coal-fired boiler		
(1000 MWe)		450
Nuclear LWR		
(1000 MWe)		530
Oil:		
boiler (1000 MWe)		280
turbine (100 MWe)		110
Gas boiler	1990	500
	2000	450
Air-cooled turbine	1990	110
Atmospheric fluidized bed	1990	450
	2000	400
Fuel-cell	1990	140
MHD	2005	450
	2010	385
Geothermal		330
Solar		900
Wind		1350
Fusion		1750
Ocean thermal		3000

† World Energy Conference (1978).

shown in Fig. 102, enables a rapid estimation of shell boiler costs. Some data on the costs of diesel generating sets supplied by British Engines are given in Fig. 103. These vary a great deal depending on the degree of automation involved. For smaller plant items, use is usually made of cost correlations which take the form:

$$C = C_b(Q/Q_b)^m$$

where C is the cost, C_b a base cost and Q and Q_b, the capacity and base capacity respectively and m is an index which varies from 0 at minimum capacity to 1 when multiple units are installed. Over a given size range, a plot of C and Q on logarithmic axes shows that m is constant and this provides a useful cost correlation. Values of Q_b, C_b and m for various items of equipment associated with boiler plant are given in Table 43.

Mention has already been made in Chapter 8 of the investment required on projects depending on renewable energy sources. Here the data are very variable with promised decreases in costs as the various technologies develop. As a first-order estimate, the following values may be noted all of which relate to £(1979). The cost of windmills ranges from

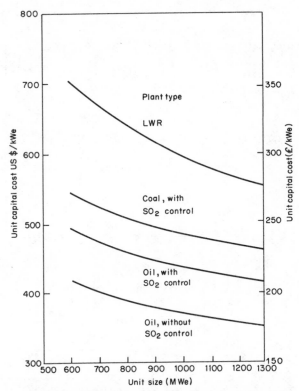

Fig. 100. *Unit capital costs of power plants as a function of unit size. Cost basis: Dec. 1981 start up; costs include natural draught cooling towers; plants have two identical units.* (World Energy Conference 1978.)

TABLE 43. *Typical equipment cost correlations*†

Item	Base size, Q_b	Base cost, C_b £(1979)	Size range	m
Blower (150 kN m⁻²)	0·7 m³ s⁻¹	8750	0·7 – 3 m³ s⁻¹	0·35
Air compressor	180 kW	170 000	180 – 1500 kW	0·29
Heat exchanger:				
shell and tube	5 m²	2750	5 – 30 m²	0·48
finned tube	65 m²	11 500	65 – 300 m²	0·58
reboiler	37 m²	8750	37 – 56 m²	0·25
Centrifugal pumps	7·5 kW	2775	7·5 – 18·6 kW	0·68
	18·6 kW	7600	18·6 – 75·0 kW	0·86
Storage tanks	1·5 m³	550	1·5 – 6·5 m³	0·66

† Backhurst and Harker (1973).

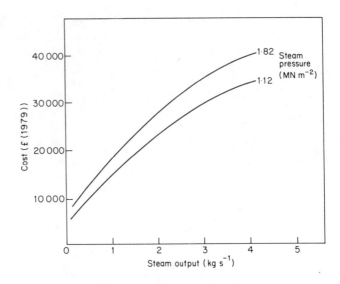

Fig. 101. *Costs of steam boilers* (John Thomson Cochran 1979).

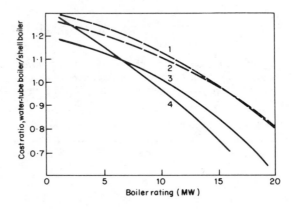

Fig. 102. *Cost comparison between shell and water-tube boilers* (Field 1975).

Curve	Medium generated	Working pressure (MN m⁻²)
1	Steam	1
2	HTW	1·6
3	Steam	1
4	HTW	1·6

HTW = high-temperature water

£200 to £1000/kW depending on the size and a solar cell costs $30/W, although a huge effort is devoted in the US to reaching $1–2/W by 1983. Data on heat pumps vary according to the particular installation, though £1000 to provide the energy demands of a four-bedroomed house is not

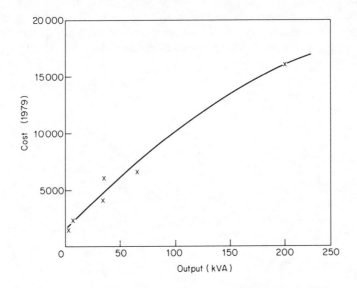

Fig. 103. *Costs of diesel-powered generating sets* (British Engines 1979).

unreasonable. Energy storage is considered later in this chapter, but the investment in batteries may be noted here. The most optimistic values range from £40 to £50/kW year for lead–acid and nickel–iron designs, and a hydrogen–oxygen fuel cell lies in the same range. The most promising battery at around £25/kW year is the sodium–sulphur type, though this has still to be made to work commercially.

D. Costs of Energy

The cost of energy within a fuel is a relatively straightforward calculation and some values are given in Table 40. Where energy, particularly thermal and electrical, is produced, the costing is more complex since, in addition to capital charges, insurance, depreciation, and interest, the running costs have to be included together with maintenance. The important parameter is the cost of the energy and this is particularly so with electrical power.

In the UK, 1979 costs range from around 1 p/kWh for a Magnox reactor to 1·31 p/kWh for oil-fired power stations, 6–12 p/kWh for wind-generated power and 30–50 p/kWh for wave-generated power where the main cost is that of concrete structures. A coal-fired station produces power at 1·29 p/kWh (CEGB 1979), of which around 75% is the cost of fuel. In the UK, modernization of existing plant with a growth in the capacity of a station, coupled with increased efficiency and the effects of the nuclear programme, have kept electricity costs low compared with those of fossil fuels. Some comparisons along these lines are made in Fig. 104 (CEGB 1979),

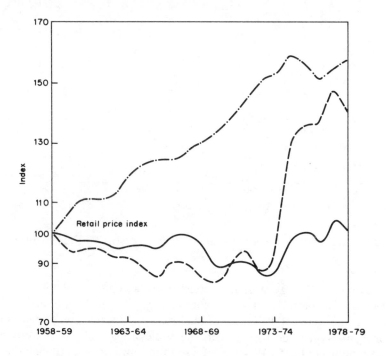

Fig. 104. *CEGB costs adjusted for changes in the Retail Price Index* (1958–9 = 100). *(—·—·) Index of average earnings of employees in the UK. (–––) Average price of fossil fuel per GJ. (—) Total cost per* kWh. *(CEGB 1979.)*

and the standard and night price costs are given in Fig. 105. At the present time, nuclear stations are proving the cheapest in terms of cost per unit energy produced, in spite of the very high investment involved, and some 1975 data are shown in Fig. 106 which is taken from Field (1975). These relate to thermal energy and the cost of electricity generation must be added.

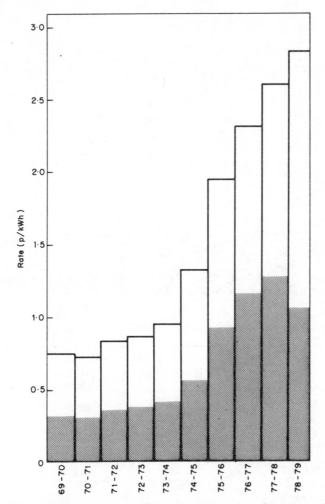

Fig. 105. *Comparison of standard domestic and night prices. Open histogram; standard domestic rate (winter price levels); shaded histogram, domestic night rate (winter price levels).* (Electricity Council 1979.)

Some recent data for other routes to electrical energy published by the World Energy Conference (1978) are given in Table 44. It should be noted that 1 mil is equivalent to $0·001 and the costs relate to 1977.

So far the cost of energy produced on a relatively large scale has been considered. Probably of more immediate interest to the small manufacturer is the value of energy in its various forms and such considerations as the

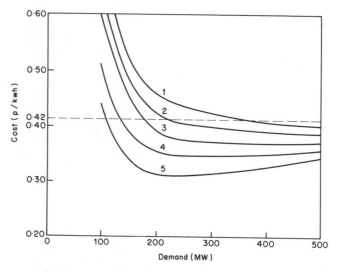

Fig. 106. *Cost of heat delivery by a* 100 MW *swimming pool reactor.*
Reactor cost (£M): 1, 11.5; 2, 10.0; 3, 8.5; 4, 7.0; 5, 5.5. (Field
1975.)

TABLE 44. *Cost of electricity and efficiency for various power systems* (1977)

	Cost of electricity (mils/kWh)†	Overall energy efficiency (%)	Minimum total capital cost ($/kW)
Advanced steam	30–38	34–40	610
Open-cycle gas turbine			
no bottoming	31–37	16–19	190
organic bottoming	33–39	20–22	330
Combined cycle	23–33	21–37	350
Closed-cycle gas turbine:			
no bottoming	33–49	15–34	670
organic bottoming	38–43	35–38	860
steam bottoming	36–45	30–34	810
Supercritical CO_2	50–79	35–41	1200
Liquid-metal Rankine	40–61	34–41	920
Open-cycle MHD	41–48	40–53	1050
Closed-cycle	46–73	26–46	1100
Liquid-metal MHD	58–110	17–39	1500
Fuel cells:			
high-temperature	43–45	24–34	860
low-temperature	31–60	13–31	240

† 1 mil = $0·001

cost of electricity generation on site. An operator must know the value of the thermal energy in, say, a waste effluent stream in order to assess whether or not heat recovery is economically feasible. Such calculations may be made using the data in this and previous sections and two simple examples are offered as an indication of the approach.

Example 10.1

What is the cost of steam produced at $2 \, \text{kg s}^{-1}$ at a pressure of $1 \cdot 12 \, \text{MN m}^{-2}$?

From Fig. 101, the cost of a package boiler to achieve this output is £24 000. To this must be added factors as follows:

buildings	say 15%	
insulation	15%	
installation	15%	
piping	10%	
foundations	10%	
structures	6%	
electrical	10%	
fuel storage	15%	

A total of 96%, giving a total cost of £$(24\,000 \times 1 \cdot 96) = £47\,050$. Thus the capital charges will include:

depreciation over, say, 10 years	= £4705/year
interest at, say, 15%	= £7058/year
insurance, rates, etc., at 15%	= £7058/year

A total of £18 820/year.

Considering the running costs, the most important is the fuel, which will be taken as 3500 s fuel oil. The enthalpy of the steam is $2780 \, \text{kJ kg}^{-1}$ and the enthalpy of the feed water at, say, $320 \, \text{K} = 4 \cdot 18(320 - 273) = 197 \, \text{kJ kg}^{-1}$. Hence energy transferred to the steam $= 2583 \, \text{kJ kg}^{-1}$. Assuming an efficiency of 80%, the energy to be supplied by the oil $= (2583/0 \cdot 8) = 3229 \, \text{kJ/kg}$ steam and for a calorific value of $41\,000 \, \text{kJ l}^{-1}$ (Table 40), the oil required is $3229/41\,0000 = 0 \cdot 0788 \, \text{l/kg}$ steam costing $(0 \cdot 0788 \times 9 \cdot 66/100) = £0 \cdot 0076/\text{kg}$ steam. The annual output of steam based on 8000 hr/year operation $= (2 \times 3600 \times 8000) = 5 \cdot 76 \times 10^7$ kg and the cost of oil is $(5 \cdot 76 \times 10^7 \times 0 \cdot 0076) = £437\,760/\text{year}$. For maintenance, labour and spares, a value of £5000/year may be taken which gives a total cost of £461 580/year. Thus the cost of steam $= (461\,580/5 \cdot 76 \times 10^4) = \underline{£8 \cdot 0/\text{tonne}}$. This is somewhat higher than the 1979 figures for lower pressure steam of £5·70/tonne (Locke 1980) but of the same order, and obviously a greater accuracy can be obtained with a closer assessment of the various factors involved.

Example 10.2

What is the cost of generating power using a diesel generator with an output of 50 kVA?

From Fig. 103, the cost of a generator is £6000, which allowing for buildings, installation, foundations, structures and electrical switch-gear, comes to a total of ca. £10 000. With depreciation over 10 years, interest at 15% and those items proportional to investment such as insurance, at 15%, the annual capital charges are £4000/year.

   Assuming an efficiency of 40%, the energy required from the oil fuel is 125 kW, which for an operating period of 8000 hr/year, is equivalent to $3·6 \times 10^6$ MJ/year. Assuming a calorific value of 40·57 MJ l^{-1}, the oil required is $8·87 \times 10^4$ l/year, which at £0·108/l costs £9600/year. Including £1000/year for maintenance and labour, the total costs are £14 600/year or 182·5 p/hr. The cost of the electricity is thus 182·5/50 = 3·6 p/kWh which may be compared with 2·84 p/kWh for power from the grid as shown in Table 40.

It is often helpful to express energy costs in equivalent terms to afford a direct comparison of alternatives. From Example 10.1, a cost of £8/1000 kg is equivalent to 0·314 p/MJ if, say, 2550 kJ/kg of latent heat can be recovered from the steam. The electrical cost is then 3·6/3·6 = 1 p/MJ and in a similar way the value of energy in waste water at 310 K can be shown to be around 0·3 p/MJ. This is important in assessing whether or not the energy is worth recovering and this sort of consideration, together with a comparison of alternatives, forms the basis of later sections.

III. ENERGY SCHEMES

A. Introduction

The main aim in any energy conversion process, given the limitations of availability of resources, convenience and environmental considerations, is operation under minimum cost conditions which usually means maximum efficiency of conversion. In other words, the economics of the operation dominate all other considerations. In achieving these ends many schemes have been proposed for a variety of applications, including total energy, combined heat and power and so on and since these all have an important bearing on the economics, it is convenient to consider them under this general heading of energy schemes.

It is important to consider traditional processes, however, and particularly the comparison of alternatives. To some extent this has been dealt with in the previous section where, for example, the cost of power generated with a diesel generator was compared with power from the grid. It will be shown in later sections how given, say, a waste stream the various means of heat recovery may be compared on a cost basis. As a typical example of costing such proposals the following scheme proposed by Sansom (1979) may be considered, which is in essence a form of combined heat and power.

In many process industries, steam is generated at 1150 kN m^{-2} and then reduced by valves to say 205 kN m^{-2} for distribution in quantities of 6–20 kg s^{-1}. At the same time, electric motors, consume say, 1·5–2·5 MW of electrical power. The proposal would be to reduce the steam pressure using turbines which could be used to either generate electricity or to drive the machinery directly. Using some typical 1974/1975 data taken from a paper mill, it was found that the average running load on the turbine was 261 kW. The steam flow at this load was 1·6 kg s^{-1} and the enthalpy change in the steam as it passed through the turbine was 176 kJ/kg steam. The cost of fuel was 13·65 p/therm (0·129 p/MJ) and for a boiler efficiency of 80% with operation for 8000 hr/year, the steam costs become:

$$(1\cdot6 \times 176 \times 0\cdot129 \times 3600 \times 8000 \times 100)/(1000 \times 100 \times 80) = £13\,078/\text{year}$$

Taking the cost of electricity as 2 p/kWh and an efficiency of 95% for an electric motor, then the cost of power from the grid is:

$$(261 \times 8000 \times 2 \times 100)/(100 \times 95) = £43\,958/\text{year}$$

which gives a saving of £30 880/year. The total capital expenditure was around £200 000, which gives a pay-back time of some 6 years, and probably much less at today's prices.

The use of steam to generate power and also for use as heating medium is essentially the basis of total energy, discussed in the next section.

B. Total Energy

A total energy system is one in which a fuel provides all the energy requirements of a site by on-site generation of electricity, waste-heat recovery from prime movers and the provision of supplementary heat as

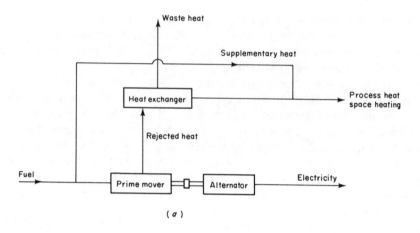

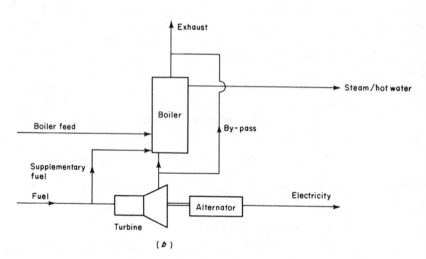

Fig. 107. *Total energy schemes. (a) Typical total energy scheme. (b) Scheme incorporating gas turbines.*

required. Perhaps the most familiar example of a total energy system is the car, in which the gasoline not only provides motive power, but heat and electrical energy and in which provision is made for storing the latter. Total energy, however, is more usually applied to a production site and outlines of two typical schemes are shown in Fig. 107. The term is also applied more generally to combined heat and power systems though in this section the discussion is confined to on-site utilization of the heat. There is nothing new about a total energy system and there are over 500 installations in the

USA (Total Energy Publishing 1970) with a potential market of some 72 000 systems (Nelson 1967). In the UK only some 8% of electricity generated has been outside the public sector, though total energy is attracting much attention mainly due to the oil crisis and also the availability of new equipment, particularly in the field of automatic control (Voysey 1967). Obviously gas and oil prices dominate the economics of total energy and the crucial factor is the balance between the costs of central generation, particularly nuclear-based and the high cost of transmission and distribution.

The economics of a total energy scheme have been discussed by Diamant (1970) and Shearer (1970) and may be simplified as follows. Assuming the fuel is natural gas at 24 p/therm (say 22·8 p/100 MJ), the cost of the electricity generated at, say, 33% efficiency would be 68·9 p/100 MJ. This may be compared with the grid cost of 2·84 p/kWh (67·7 p/100 MJ) which is almost the same value, but the heat recovered for process use is a bonus and providing the depreciated value of the capital equipment is less than the value of the steam or hot water produced, then the scheme is viable. Obviously the higher the conversion efficiency in the total energy scheme, the more attractive it becomes. One such example is at Players in Nottingham (Tearle 1969), which uses $8 \times 1 \cdot 1$ MW gas turbine sets. Steam raised from the $4 \times 1 \cdot 11$ kg s^{-1} heat recovery boilers at $1 \cdot 27$ MN m^{-2} is used to power a steam turbine which drives a centrifugal water chiller in addition to use at a lower pressure for process, space and water heating. The overall efficiency of this scheme is 65–75% and it is obviously an extremely attractive commercial venture. Stocks (1969) has described an installation in the USA in which a natural gas turbine drives a 1000 kVA generator. The exhaust was fed directly to drier-furnaces supplying 5 MW of the 5·8 MW peak demand and savings of $38 000 were achieved for an investment of $150 000. In the UK, a scheme was installed in 1963 at Aldershot (Young 1967). This consisted of four heavy fuel oil engines with an output of 8·56 MW. Heat was recovered from the exhaust gases by cooling water which was then flash-evaporated to steam producing around 7·5 MW while direct fired boilers produced a further 21·5 MW. Over a period of some nine months 31 685 MWh was generated at an efficiency of 38·5% and the overall efficiency of the scheme was 63·53%. In 1970 figures, the net generating cost was 0·31 p/kWh compared with 0·62 p/kWh from the grid.

In selecting the equipment suitable for a particular total energy scheme, the ratio of thermal to electrical energy required is of prime importance. The thermal efficiency of any prime-mover can be expressed as the ratio of heat to power production and for a diesel or spark-ignition engine this is about 1, making it most suitable for schemes with a limited demand for heat such as commercial buildings. Where the heat/power demand is greater than 4, then gas turbines may be considered; steam turbines are suitable for ratios in excess of 10. Obviously, a given demand ratio can be matched more exactly by combinations of prime-movers and data on various prime-mover–heat-recovery systems are given in Table 45 prepared by Daglish (1971).

TABLE 45. *Characteristics of prime-movers and heat recovery system*

Prime mover	Fuels	Efficiency of generation (%)	Heat recovery system	Overall thermal efficiency (%)	Heat recovered (MJ/kWh)
Steam turbine (black pressure)					
	Coal, oil, natural gas	10–15	Back pressure steam	85	20
Gas turbine		15–20	Exhaust only	70	10
	Light oil LPG, natural gas		with after firing	85	65
			Direct heat for drying	90	15
Reciprocating engines					
(i) diesel	oils, nat. gas	35–40	Exhaust only	55	2
			Jacket and exhaust	75	4
(ii) spark ignition	LPG, nat. gas	25–30	Exhaust only	55	2
			Jacket and exhaust	75	4

The savings which total energy and on-site generation can produce are particularly important when power and heat demands are a significant part of an organization's overheads. Shearer (1970) has suggested that at least part of the power should be generated on site where the peak load is in excess of 3 MW. The disadvantages of private generation are, of course, extra capital investment, space and manpower, and also competing demands for available funds coupled with the reluctance to enter what may be a subsidiary field of activity. These factors may partly explain why many schemes which show a good return on the capital do not always go ahead.

C. Combined Heat and Power

In simple terms, a combined heat and power system may be thought of as a total energy scheme applied to a power station. The general principles are illustrated in Fig. 108(*a*) where a CHP scheme is compared with a conventional station. In the latter, 55% of the energy in the fuel is lost in luke-warm water which is not useful for most heating purposes. By modifying the turbine into the so-called "pass out" or "back pressure" mode, however, the electricity produced falls to 25 MJ but a further 65 MJ is available as useful heat in the form of water at 360 K which is ideal for district heating schemes. In this way the overall efficiency of the operation is increased from 35% to 90%. This very significant saving must be off-set

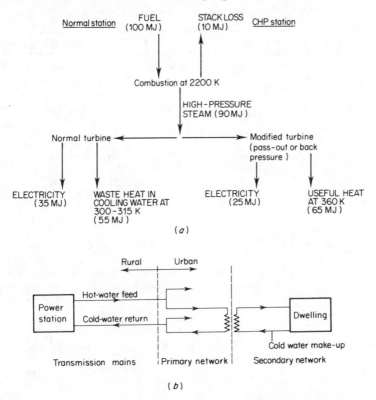

Fig. 108. *(a) Comparison of conventional and CHP power stations. (b) Heat delivery system from a CHP station.*

against the extra capital cost of the power station and that of the district heating scheme and the economic viability of such a scheme depends on factors such as the distance from the power station to the dwellings, the population density and the scale of the operation. Although the ex-works costs of heat from a large power station are low, the main problem is that of delivering this heat to a consumer, typically a householder in a large city. A typical delivery scheme is shown in Fig. 108(*b*). Large transmission mains are required between the power station and the city (a distance of say 15 km) and within the city there must be primary and secondary networks for the supply of heat and hot water to individual dwellings. Some recent figures have been reported by Marshall (1977) for the cost of heat delivery by such a system based on a depreciation rate of 10%. These are shown in Table 46(a).

TABLE 46(a). *Cost of heat delivery of CHP system†*

Housing Density (dwellings/acre)	Cost of Heat Delivery (£/dwelling year)			
	Transmission	Primary network	Secondary network	Total
Small city (pop. 100 000)				
10	30	40	130	200
20	30	25	70	125
50	30	15	55	100
Large city (pop. 1 000 000)				
10	10	40	150	180
20	10	25	75	110
50	10	15	55	80

† Marshall (1977).

TABLE 46(b). *Comparison of UK and European CHP schemes*

	% Space heating by CHP	Total CHP/space heating load (10⁹ kWh/year)	% District heating by CHP plant
UK	1	5	10
Germany	8	46	70
Denmark	40	28	26
Sweden	20	18	17

The viability of CHP/district heating depends very much on future fuel prices and also on depreciation rates. A comparison of CHP schemes with the present "fuel-mix" and also complete conversion to gas-fired central heating is shown in Fig. 109. This would suggest that with present discount rates and increasing fuel costs the use of CHP/district heating is not attractive and unlikely to be so except in special cases. Studies of the long-term situation, however, show that CHP could play an important role by the year 2000 and beyond, at a time when indigenous natural gas and oil supplies are becoming scarce. The important point here is that with a long time-scale in order to build up a network, say 15 years, then some sort of decision must be taken at this stage. As plentiful natural gas remains available, there is an economic barrier to CHP/district heating and severe restrictions on public capital expenditure present further limitations to its installation. In some European countries, it has been possible to develop district heating schemes with relatively low interest rates and these have proved fairly economic in operation. Some data on these installations are given in Table 46(b).

In making such comparisons, factors such as the differences in the type and density of dwellings are important, together with climatic differences

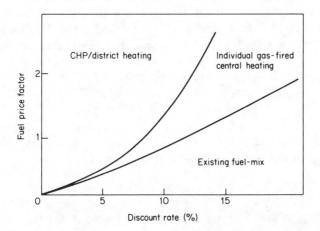

Fig. 109. *Diagram illustrating the area in which CHP is economic. Basis: 20 dwellings per acre* (Marshall 1977).

and the wide availability of town (and later natural) gas in the UK. A final point is the saving of energy with CHP schemes in the absence of natural gas and oil supplies. It has been calculated that if 25% of the space and water heating load is met by the conversion of ten large cities, the savings in million tonnes of coal equivalent would be:

heat only boilers 11, electric heat pumps 12, synthetic natural gas boiler 17 and direct electrical heating 30.

In essence then, the technology of CHP is well known and even if there are economic limitations at the present time to its exploitation, it will become more viable especially as gas prices rise and the time is opportune for mounting development programmes in this area.

D. Transmission of Energy

It was shown in the previous section how the key factor to economically viable operation of a CHP/district heating scheme is the cost of transporting hot water from the power station. Morgan (1974) has given some detailed costing based on experience in Sweden and compared CHP with a local boiler and electrical energy generated in a nuclear station. It was found that even at the 100 km distance the overall cost of a 650 MW heat supply lay well below the cost of local generation from oil based on 1974 prices. Some recent work by Mitchell (1977) has compared the costs of transporting hot water from a power station by rail tankers and a pipeline with the cost of a local boiler. For a load of 200 MW, the local boiler provided heat at around 170 p/GJ compared with $(100 + 1·7L)$ p/GJ for rail and $(60 + 4L)$ p/GJ in a pipeline, where L km is the distance involved. These values are based on fuel costs of 120 p/GJ and doubling this gives:

local boiler   320 p/GJ
rail $143 + 1·87$ p/GJ
pipeline $103 + 4·8L$ p/GJ

Pipeline costs of course vary widely with the terrain, though an approximate value for the annual cost is given by:

$$(130D - 4·4 + 3·1 \times 10^{-7}P^3/D^5)L \quad £(1977)/\text{year}$$

where D and L are the pipe diameter and length in metres and P is the peak mean daily power in MW.

It can be shown that the optimum pipe diameter is approximately $0·05P^{0·5}$ and hence the annual costs become:

$$(7·9P^{0·5} - 4·4) \quad £(1977)/\text{km year}$$

It is convenient at this stage to broaden the discussion to the general transportation of energy and some data on this are given in Fig. 110. In general, the cost of large-scale transportation of fossil fuels over long distances is low compared with the value of the fuel. A more important issue for developing countries is the local distribution of energy. For fixed systems such as electrical systems or gas pipelines, the capital cost is largely independent of the quantity of energy delivered. It rather depends on the density of energy consumers. Electrical grids and gas pipelines are economic in areas of high population density; road transportation is used in rural and remote areas. The following costs have been given to road and rail transport by Locke (1980):

Cost (p/tonne mile)

	road	rail
short hauls	3–15	5–11
long hauls	2–4	1½–7

In areas of low energy density, the energy transportation costs are of course lowest for the renewable energy sources, wind, solar and farm wastes with oils, kerosene, propane and diesel electric at a medium level and electric power and pipeline gases the most expensive.

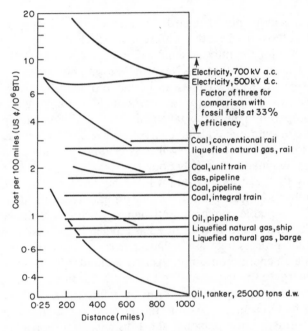

Fig. 110. *Energy transportation costs (World Energy Conference 1978).*

E. Energy for Transport

The discussion of the transport of energy leads fairly conveniently to a comment on the energy required for transport itself. At the present time, the pattern is one of petrol driven vehicles for short and medium distances, diesel and electrically driven rail for long journeys with air for the longest journeys. As oil fuels become less available this pattern must change and certainly much more attention will be given to the efficiency of conversion. Some data on this are quoted in Table 47 taken from Goss (1972).

TABLE 47. *Overall propulsion efficiencies†*

Conversion system	Propulsion energy/chemical energy in fuel (%)
Diesel/internal combustion	25–35
Gasoline/internal combustion	20–30
Fossil fuelled power plant/electric motor	10–25
Fuel cell/electric motor	40–55
Kerosene/jet engine	20–35
Fossil fuel/Rankine external combustion	15–35

† Goss (1972).

The figures may only be regarded as an indication of system efficiency since other authors quote rather different values. For example Pole (1973) quotes 10–18% for the internal combustion engine and 18–23% for power station/electric motor systems. Nevertheless on this basis, the fuel cell holds great promise provided it can be made practically available in the next 10–15 years. In considering synthetic fuels, the energy requirements for their preparation must be taken into account. For example, in the manufacture of synthetic oil from coal some 67% of the chemical energy in the coal is lost and hence the overall conversion to mechanical engine in a conventional engine is extremely poor.

Probably the most likely trend will be the development of electrically powered transport which can use various primary fuels, including nuclear, and has an acceptable conversion efficiency which can be improved. It is vital that the energy consumed is used as efficiently as possible not only in the conversion process but in selecting a particular mode of transportation. Various data on energy consumption are presented in Table 48 which show the high energy cost of the motor car and air transport and hence the desirability of promoting surface forms of public transport as a means of conserving fuel resources. Again, the electric car and the bicycle are extremely attractive for personal short-distance transport. Similarly for freight, there should be a movement from the roads to railways and shipping including the developing of inland waterways. The electricity for both public and personal transport can be generated in coal and nuclear power stations and oil should be reserved for applications where there is no practicable alternative. The programme of rail electrification will again promote energy conservation and more freight should be transferred to the railways coupled with the development of inter-city and urban rail services. A great many of the short journeys within a few miles of base can be carried out with electric cars powered in the first instance by lead–acid batteries and later by improved types. The first models are now reaching the production stage (Richardson 1973) and these have importance not only in the conservation of energy but in the protection of the environment.

TABLE 48. *Energy consumption in transport*†

Mode of transport	Energy consumption	
	Passenger (passenger miles/gal)	Freight (ton miles/gal)
Double-deck bus (25 passengers)	175	
Double-deck bus (70 passengers)	490	
Train (100 passengers)	250	
Train (250 passengers)	625	400
Aircraft (80 passengers)	24	40
Car (4 persons)	120	
Electric car (2 persons)	454	
Cycling	1600 (equivalent)	
Walking	400 (equivalent)	
Shipping		6000
Diesel truck		200
Pipeline		3000

† Hendry (1974).

F. Energy Storage

1. Introduction

The ability to store energy is vital to the successful operation of the electric car discussed in the previous section and hence a brief discussion is perhaps apt at this stage. In simple terms, there are three important aspects of energy storage. Firstly, that of economic operation. The variation of the load of a fossil-fired and particularly that of a nuclear-fired power station is not only difficult to attain but leads to inefficiencies in energy utilization. It is far more economic to work at a constant base-load and to store the excess energy, which is then used to meet peak demands. The second feature concerns renewable energy sources, particularly solar and wind. Energy is not always required when the sun is shining and an energy storage system is vital to the economic and successful operation of such an installation. The third consideration is that of convenience particularly in, say, an electric car or powering some remote facility such as a lighthouse or navigational aid. The form in which energy is stored depends very much on the amount involved, the form of the supply and the demand and the rate at which the energy is required. Thermal energy is stored in various materials, such as packed and fluidized beds (Harker 1979)—as in a pebble bed heater, for example—and is an important facet of energy recovery discussed later in this chapter. Other materials used for thermal storage include hot water as in solar panel circuits and concrete as in storage radiators. More recent developments make use of the latent heat of fusion of solids, the heat of dilution of acids and various gas–solid chemical reactions. The storage of energy to perform work is usually accomplished in two ways—by mechanical or electrical energy storage. The first includes pumped water storage with return through a turbine, the storage of kinetic energy in a fly-wheel and energy storage in compressed air in tanks or underground caverns.

The economics of storage are fairly easy. For Atlanta in Georgia the mean demand for power was 1800 MW in 1970 with a peak of 3500 MW. To install generating capacity to meet this peak at, say, $400/kW would cost some $680 million. Provided the energy storage schemes cost less than this, storage is a better solution, even ignoring for the moment the savings achieved by avoiding having idle generating plant.

In the past, peak electricity has been generated using stand-by gas turbines or older steam-generating equipment though this has become less economic as the costs of coal and oil have soared and storage systems, together with an increased nuclear capacity, are becoming increasingly attractive.

2. The storage of mechanical energy

The pumped storage of water is perhaps the most widely used method of energy storage on the large scale. In essence, excess electrical power is used to pump water from a river or lake to a reservoir at a higher level. In order to cope with peak power demands, water is drawn from the reservoir and passed through turbines which drive generators. These are housed in a power station, located usually at the point of water discharge though underground in certain cases. As in other storage methods the capital investment, which is very high, and the efficiency of the operation must be such as to make the operation commercially attractive compared with the provision of additional generating facilities. The overall efficiency for power generation is the product of the efficiency of the pump-motor (say 88%) and that during drawdown through the turbine (say 85%). A typical

TABLE 49. *Pumped water storage costs†*

Storage capacity (kWh)	Volume (m³)	Total cost ($(1976))	Cost over 40 year depreciation period ($(1976)/kWh)
200	2 380	63 800	0·0218
2 000	23 800	510 000	0·0175
20 000	238 000	4 250 000	0·0146
60 000	714 000	11 500 000	0·0131

† Shepherd (1976).

value for the overall performance is thus 75%. A quoted value for the Seneca installation in Pennsylvania is 71–79% (Fitzgerald 1973). The storage area for a given generating capacity depends on the height of the water storage. For a pumped height of 30 m, the generating capacity is 0·08 kWh m^{-3} and some size and cost figures based on this value are given in Table 49 which incorporates the 75% efficiency value.

An important environmental consideration with pumped storage is the depletion of the upper reservoir during times of peak demand. This results in an unsightly exposure and prohibits recreational use.

Helium is in theory the ideal gas for gas compression systems, though the cost of a low-pressure tank for helium recovery is generally prohibitive and air is most commonly used. A simplified diagram of an air storage gas turbine power plant is shown in Fig. 111. A conventional gas turbine is modified so that the turbine and the compressor may be uncoupled and operated separately. During off-peak periods, the turbine is uncoupled and the compressor is driven by the generator which takes power from the grid. During peak periods, the compressor is uncoupled and the stored air is returned through the recuperator to the burner and the turbine which is now coupled to the generator thus delivering power to the grid. The cheapest underground storage areas are salt caverns, depleted gas and oil wells and abandoned mines, though a purpose-built cavity can be produced with nuclear explosives which appear particularly suited in the case of large gas volumes. A detailed cost study of a 220 MW air storage gas turbine plant has been reported by Olsson (1970) in which the efficiency was 71%. The equivalent efficiency of a conventional turbine is 27%. Costs were said to be around 70% of those of a conventional gas turbine plant and generally below those of pumped water storage.

A comparison of air-storage devices has been made by Fryer (1973) and this is summarized in Table 50.

Fly-wheels, which have been used for centuries for regulating the speed of machines and giving uniformity of motion, are particularly suited to

TABLE 50. *Comparison of various systems*†

System	Size (MW)	Capital cost ($(1973)/kW)	Total cost ($(1973)/kWh)
Pumped hydro.	7–600	75–125	0·09 –0·138
Gas turbines	58	77·6	0·112–0·127
	250	66·5	0·101–0·107
Steam peaking	135–400	105	0·146
Air storage	175	65·7	0·094
	542	42·2	0·076

† Fryer (1973).

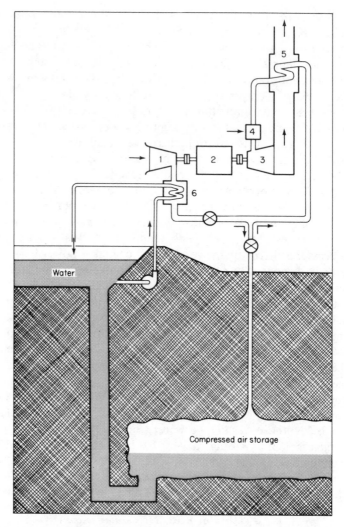

Fig. 111. *Air storage gas turbine plant.* 1 *Compressor;* 2 *motor/generator;*
3, *gas turbine;* 4, *combustor;* 5, *recuperator;* 6, *after-cooler.*
(Harboe 1973.)

energy storage because of their high energy and power densities. In power
plants the fly-wheel would be charged up at times of low power demand
and serve the same purpose as pumped water or air storage. In vehicle
applications, it has been estimated that a fly-wheel–internal combustion
engine combination could reduce the size of the equivalent engine by 50%
(Lawson 1971) and additional advantages are the use of regenerative

braking—storing energy normally lost as heat in the brakes. Lawson (1971) discusses the theory of energy storage in fly-wheels and surveys likely materials of construction and concludes that specific energies approaching those of lead–acid batteries (20–30 Wh kg^{-1}) can be achieved provided they are operated at a sufficiently high material working stress/density ratio. A further proposal in relation to vehicles is the recharging of fly-wheels at various points en route; this may find application in services operated on a shuttle-schedule.

3. The storage of electrical energy

The storage of electrical energy is best achieved in convenient, reliable and portable form in batteries which are either primary batteries which are not rechargeable or secondary batteries which are perhaps of the greater significance. The familiar dry cell consisting of a carbon electrode, a zinc can and a depolarizer which is mainly manganese dioxide, falls into the first category and is used where energy is needed in small amounts, particularly in portable applications. Developments in the 1960s resulted in the alkaline manganese cell which gave 4–18 times the capacity though at a greater cost and the magnesium–seawater cell which is particularly suited to marine applications such as emergency radios and torpedoes. Other very high performance and costly primary cells under development include the silver or zinc/air battery which are intended primarily for military use.

The most widely used secondary cell is the lead–acid storage battery which can supply both high and low currents over a wide temperature range, is capable of relatively long-term storage particularly in the dry charged condition, can undergo many hundreds of charge–discharge cycles and is relatively cheap. By comparison, a nickel–cadmium battery has a longer life, coupled with longer storage times and can provide a high current density on discharge with little decrease in voltage. It is expensive, however, and use is limited to small-size applications. The extended use of high-capacity nickel–cadmium batteries is not envisaged because of the limited supply of raw materials available for their manufacture. Costs of batteries have been given in Section II of this chapter though it is perhaps worth noting that the nickel–cadmium battery costs about ten times as much as a lead–acid battery and twenty times as much as a dry cell.

The development of a battery based on sodium and sulphur was started in the early 1960s. This is of particular interest for vehicles because of its high specific power–specific energy characteristics which, while not quite as high as the internal combustion engine, are vastly superior to the lead–acid cell, as shown in Fig. 112.

It has been suggested that a sodium–sulphur battery could give a driving range of 400–800 km, which would make electric vehicles truly practical. The battery consists of liquid sodium and liquid sulphur electrodes separated by a solid ceramic electrolyte containing beta-alumina, which is one of a general class of material with the formula $A_2O_nB_2O_3$ where n is 5–11, A is sodium, lithium, potassium or silver and B is aluminium, gallium or iron. The existence of these new electrolytic materials has opened up a very wide field of battery research and in spite of problems such as the need for high-temperature operation and short

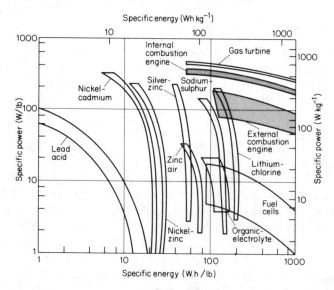

Fig. 112. *A comparison of performance of batteries and internal combustion engines.* (National Air Pollution Control Administration 1970.)

circuits due to diffusion of metallic sodium along beta-alumina crystal boundaries, the sodium–sulphur battery is perhaps the most promising area for the successful development of a practical electric car.

IV. ENERGY CONSERVATION AND RECOVERY

A. Introduction

The potential for energy saving has been quantified by Beijdorff (1979) for Western Europe and the data are replotted as Fig. 113 where the 1975 European energy consumption has been compared with what could be achieved with conservation; the total is broken down into iron and steel,

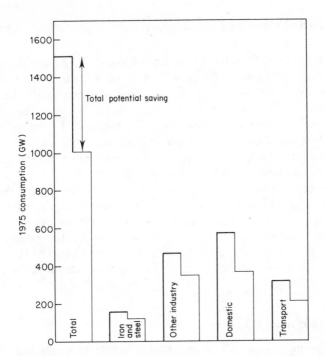

Fig. 113. *Primary energy consumption in W. Europe, 1975, showing potential savings.*

industry, domestic and transport sectors. The difference of 476 GW is the equivalent of about eleven Brent oil fields or five Gröningen gas fields, which is a very real saving of resources. The questions of whether such savings are possible, how they might be achieved and of the economics involved, are the subjects of this section.

1. *Ways of conserving energy*

There are three ways of conserving energy:

(a) Not using energy, for example, not heating a building, not running a process or not making a journey by car.

(b) By reducing the energy consumption. A building may be heated to a temperature which is lower and less comfortable than at present; a large car may be exchanged for a more economical one or the larger car run at reduced speeds.

(c) By enhancing the efficiency of the energy conversion and utilization. This could be achieved, for example, by insulating a house so that comfortable conditions can be maintained at a lower energy cost. A process might be modified for additional capital expenditure to realize fuel savings.

The first two options have very limited long-term possibilities for while hardship can be tolerated for short periods, any fall in living standards is not likely to be suffered for a prolonged time. It is only by the third option that permanent reductions in energy demand can be made, though capital investment, however small, will always be required. Extensive publicity, invariably from Government level, is required to induce the attitudes required by the public and it is apparent that the greatest incentive to conserve comes not from exhortations but from the stimulus of energy price increases. Once an individual or a company recognizes the advantages of conservation to himself or to his organization, the scope is there for savings which are often substantial and easily attained. Figure 113 indicates average savings of about 30% with the greatest potential in the domestic field and about 25% possible in general industry. The means of achieving these savings will be considered in more detail in the following sections.

B. The Economics of Conservation

The economic evaluation of any energy saving proposal will consist of three steps. The rate of present energy consumption must be calculated and compared with the reduction in demand which will occur when the means of conservation has been installed. The cost of the measure can be used to determine a rate of return on the capital investment. This last figure may be expressed as a percentage or alternatively as a cost divided by the reduction in energy consumption ($£/kW$ for example).

1. Investment

The investment required for energy conservation measures can vary considerably and has been discussed by Gyftopoulos (1978). For example, taking the domestic situation as a familiar case, draught-proofing a house could cost less than £10, while double-glazing the same house could exceed £1000. It is possible that the energy saved by each measure could be the same so that it is immediately apparent that draught proofing is the more attractive investment.

One way of considering investment costs is to compare them with production costs of prime energy sources. This is often done by relating the cost of energy saving measures to the saving realized in terms of barrels or tonnes of oil equivalent, where:

1 barrel of oil equivalent (boe) $= 0 \cdot 135$ tonnes of oil equivalent (toe)
$\qquad\qquad\qquad\qquad\quad = 0 \cdot 212$ tonnes of coal equivalent
$\qquad\qquad\qquad\qquad\quad = 6 \cdot 12 \times 10^9$ J
$\qquad\qquad\qquad\qquad\quad \approx 1700$ kWh

For energy production or consumption, the barrel per day of oil equivalent (bdoe) or tonnes of oil equivalent per annum (toepa) are terms which are used, where:

$\qquad$ 1 bdoe $= 50$ tonnes of oil equivalent/annum (toepa)
$\qquad\qquad\quad = 2 \cdot 2 \times 10^{12}$ J/year
$\qquad\qquad\quad \approx 70$ kW

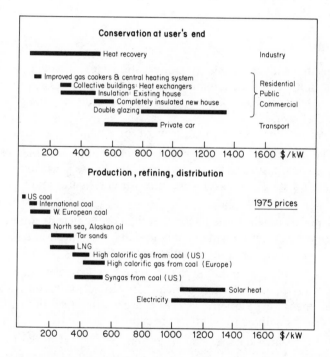

Fig. 114. *Comparison of investment in energy conservation with that in energy production from new sources.*

To take a simple example, consider an average car costing £4000 covering 10 000 miles per year at an average consumption of 25 miles/gallon. The 400 gal/year used is equivalent to approximately 9 barrels of crude oil. If it were possible to improve the engine, transmission and aerodynamic design to achieve a 25% petrol saving at an additional capital cost of £400, each car could save the equivalent 2·25 barrels of crude. Thus, 160 cars would save 1 barrel per day of crude at a cost of £64 000 or, from the above figures, at £914/kW.

Figure 114 shows investment in other forms of energy conservation equipment calculated in a similar way and compares these costs with those of production, refining and distribution. Although the costs cover a wide range and are calculated in $(1975) in Fig. 114, it is apparent that the capital investment for the measures is comparable to the production cost of the prime fuels. On this basis alone, the conclusion could be drawn, quite wrongly, that conservation expenditure is uneconomic. What has been omitted is the effect of time over which the measure will save energy in the future, i.e. the unit cost.

2. *Unit costs*

The investment made in energy conservation measures will last for the economic lifetime of the equipment involved and it is necessary to calculate the capital cost of the option divided by the units of energy saved to produce unit cost.

This calculation is not straightforward for a number of reasons.

(a) The life of the measure is not always clear. For example, insulation in a house could last for 80 years, whereas the house is usually purchased over a period of 25 years. To use the former figure could produce a misleadingly attractive figure.

(b) The way in which the measure is financed affects its total cost. For example, whether it is bought outright initially or financed by a loan over a period of years can affect the calculations significantly.

(c) The problem of inflation makes both total cost determination and estimation of resulting savings difficult. In general, inflation makes conservation measures attractive since energy costs rise throughout the lifetime of the equipment, whereas the capital cost are fixed at the outset.

Figure 115 shows data recalculated from the original work of Beijdorff (1979) which shows how the effect of time has altered the view of the investment costs presented earlier. It is apparent that conservation is an attractive proposition, not only to the individual consumer, but also to the nation with regard to its reserves.

3. *Rates of return*

From the examples already given, it is clear that rates of return, however they may be calculated, can vary considerably. The simple pay-back time is often used as an instant criterion for decision making. In times of uncertainty, industry requires a rapid pay-back time of typically 2 years, i.e. the investment should be repaid by the cash value of the savings in less than two years. Whilst this might appear unrealistic, there are many instances where such returns are possible. When the payback time expected by the consumer for various measures is examined, it is seen from Table 51 that human behaviour is sometimes quite illogical.

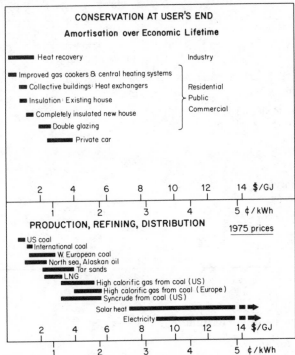

Fig. 115. *Comparison of unit costs of energy conservation with those of energy production from new sources.*

For example, simple control additions to a central heating system will pay for themselves more quickly that the consumer expects whereas double glazing, which is relatively poor investment is frequently installed before making the more cost effective steps to reduce heating bills. With increasing energy costs, it is likely in the future that the payback times will decrease. It remains to be seen whether the domestic sector will respond to the increased costs with further conservation measures as the householder may only notice the effect of his action reflected in a real reduction of his energy bills for a short period after his capital expenditure and before increased costs mask the effect.

328 FUEL AND ENERGY

Industrial measures will be considered carefully by accountants who will have their own financial targets for any investment. Government subsidies for various energy saving schemes certainly do encourage their installation and the future savings will be monitored to allow for inflation effects so that realistic appraisal of cost effectiveness can be made.

TABLE 51. *Comparison of economic lifetime, payback time and consumer payback requirement*†

Form of investment	Time (years)		
	Economic Lifetime	Subjective time horizon	Actual payback time
Industrial heat recovery	15	2	1–10
Improvements to domestic central heating equipment	10	3	1–2
Insulation	25	3	2–5
Double glazing	25	3	10–20
Compulsory insulation of a new house	25	10	5–7
Heat exchangers for recovery	15	2	2–4
(Cars	8	3	2–4)

† Beijdorff (1979).

C. Energy Conservation in Buildings

1. *Domestic buildings*

In the UK according to Leach (1976) buildings account for 40–50% of the total primary energy consumption with the domestic sector taking 29% of the total. In 1972, the breakdown of annual energy consumption per household was as follows:

Use	Net energy	
	GJ	%
Space heating	52	64
Water heating	18	22
Cooking	8	10
T.V., lighting etc.	3	4
	81	100%

There is thus considerable scope for energy saving in buildings and the obvious aspect on which to concentrate is space heating. In 1972, the UK energy consumption was $8\cdot83 \times 10^9$ GJ and from the above data $1\cdot64 \times 10^9$ GJ was used for domestic space heating. A saving of 10% of this figure, which could be achieved at relatively low cost, could save the nation nearly 2% of its energy use.

Heat losses in buildings are readily calculated from:

$$Q = UA\,\Delta t$$

where U is the overall heat transfer coefficient across the material of the construction, A its surface area and Δt the difference between inside and outside temperature. The coefficients, or U-values as they are termed in the building industry, are specified in Building Standards and some examples are included in Table 52. In order to size the heating plant for a

TABLE 52. *Calculated design day heat losses*

(a) 1975 Building regulations standard

Component	Area (m^2)	U-value $(W\,m^{-2}K^{-1})$	Δt (K)	Q (W)	Q (%)
Window and walls	85·5	1·8	18	2770	53·8
Floor	42·5	1·0	18	765	14·9
Roof	42·5	0·6	18	460	8·9
Ventilation at 1 air change/hr				1150	22·4
				5154	100·0

(b) Suggested new insulation standard

Component	Area (m^2)	U-value $(W\,m^{-2}K^{-1})$	Δt (K)	Q (W)	Q (%)
Windows (double glazed)	17·0	2·5	18	765	27·0
Walls	68·5	0·3	18	370	13·4
Floor	42·5	0·3	18	230	8·4
Roof	42·5	0·3	18	230	8·4
Ventilation at 1 air change/hr				1150	42·0
				2745	100·0

building, a knowledge of the U-values, areas and design temperatures (often 272 K and 294 K, outside and inside respectively) are required. Allowances are made for exposed locations, the ventilation required, hot water, appliance efficiency and usually a 10% overload factor in addition to the next highest standard boiler. This procedure usually results in oversized installations which run below their peak efficiency and are themselves wasteful.

Siviour (1976) presented data for an average house with a floor area of 85 m^2 and a volume of 200 m^3 using Building Regulation standards and taking one air change per hour for ventilation. By assuming higher standards of insulation, the data presented in Table 52 show that the space heating requirement can be substantially reduced by 47%. The effect of ventilation is important and one air change per hour represents effective draught stripping around doors and windows to a standard not always encountered in practice.

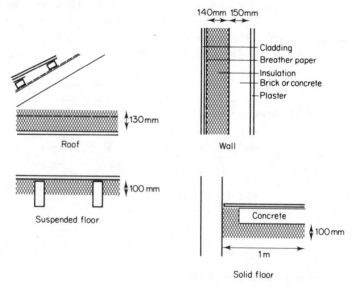

Fig. 116. *Insulation   thicknesses   required   to   achieve   U-values   of* 0·3 W m^{-2} K^{-1}.

The proposed *U*-values for floors, walls and roof are readily obtainable by the insulation requirements shown in Fig. 116 and only a change in statutory regulations is required to implement the saving.

Cornish (1976) has presented data on annual energy usage in houses and the results are included in Fig. 117 where the variable is the degree of insulation expressed as Σ AU. The wide range of total energy use is affected by variable factors such as income and thermal comfort sought by the occupants but the attraction of a high degree of insulation, i.e. low Σ AU is apparent. Figure 118 translates the calculations of Table 52 to an annual basis assuming an average temperature in the house of 291 K. The effect of improved insulation is quite obvious.

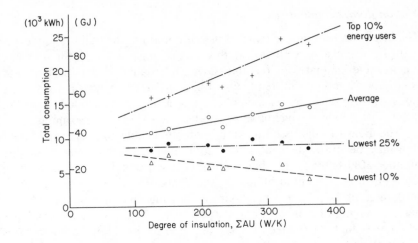

Fig. 117. *Distribution of total annual energy consumption against "degree of insulation", Σ AU.*

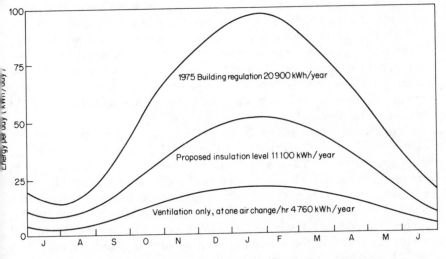

Fig. 118. *Calculated gross space heating requirements over a year. Internal temperature, 291 K. External temperature, monthly average for Capenhurst, UK.*

The use of heat pumps for domestic space heating is included with a description of their construction and operation in a later section. Specific suggestions for refitting existing houses have been presented by Petersen (1974) and further evidence for the needs for higher insulation standards in new housing has been discussed by Mottershead (1978).

2. Non-domestic buildings

The large variation in the types of use of non-domestic buildings together with an absence of statistics in this sector, makes it difficult to make quantitative estimates of possible savings. Broadly, a classification into continuously and intermittently used buildings may be made. In the former category hospitals, prisons and police stations might be included and in the latter, office blocks, civic buildings and schools form good examples.

The measures discussed previously are applicable and particular attention may be drawn to ventilation requirements. As has been seen, the number of air changes per hour contributes substantially to space heating loads. In non-residential buildings, the ventilation rate is often unnecessarily high at 2–3 changes per hour and halving this rate could produce a national saving of some 1–1·5% (Leach 1976). There are some examples where very high air change rates are required such as in operating theatres where hygiene and safety considerations are of overriding importance.

New office buildings use very large areas of glass and while domestic double glazing has only limited cost effectiveness, it becomes a more attractive proposition for glazing on a large scale. Offices and other intermittently used buildings can take advantage of a simple control system which uses data on inside and outside temperatures, the thermal response of the building and the heating system itself to provide the optimum start required to raise the inside temperature to its required level at the beginning of the occupancy period. Large savings are possible in this way and the same technique may be employed to shut the heating plant down at the end of the day.

Scope exists in large non-domestic buildings as well as on housing estates for the use of district heating systems where the heat is supplied from one source, such as hot water from a power station. Limited schemes are in use in the UK, but it is Sweden where most experience lies. Muir (1976) has described the situation in Sweden where there were fifty district heating schemes in use in 1976. Twelve generated both heat and electricity; fourteen provide electricity and heat from incineration of 600 000 tons of refuse per year and the remainder burn mainly oil. The town of Malmö provides interesting data for 1974/5 as follows:

Electricity generated   585·6 GWh (electricity)
Heat supplied from power stations 1664·2 GWh (heat)
Oil consumption   2 578 000 m³

If'the same quantity of heat were to be produced from individual boiler plants, 237 000 m³ of equivalent heavy oil would be required. Thus, Malmö, for an extra 20 000 m³ of oil can heat 60% of the town and generate 585·6 GWh of electricity. That quantity of electricity generated in the most efficient power station would consume 135 600 m³ of oil so that the combined heat and power district heating scheme saves over 115 000 m³ of oil annually—a very substantial example of conservation.

Other examples of conservation devices, notably the heat pump and the thermal wheel are included in the next section.

D. Energy Conservation and Recovery in Industry

1. *Introduction*

In the UK, industry accounts for more than 40% of the national energy consumption, using nearly 3×10^9 GJ annually. The efficiency of use of fuel varies considerably with the type of industry and processes involved and may range from less than 10% of the input energy being transferred to the product in some types of furnace to 100% efficiency with some forms of electrical heating.

Any industrial process requiring energy may be examined to determine:

(1) the useful heat required by the process or the product;
(2) the heat losses which are unavoidable or irrecoverable;
(3) the heat losses which can be avoided or reduced;
(4) the heat losses which can be economically recovered.

These losses can be quantified by a detailed examination of the process with measurement of relevant flows and temperatures; methods presented in Chapter 9 may be used in the subsequent calculations. As an example, consider the following energy balance in Table 53 carried out over a glass tank and its regenerator.

TABLE 53. *Energy balance over a glass tank*

	Stream	Temperature (K)	Enthalpy (kW)	(%)
In	Air	297	154·8	1·5
	Oil, sensible	297	11·1	0·1
	Oil, CV	–	9688·0	94·6
	Sand	297	21·3	0·2
	Electricity	–	370	3·6
			10 245 kW	100%
Out	Molten glass	1493	1241·0	12·1
	Flue gas	806	3848·1	37·6
	Losses from furnace	–	5156·0	50·3
			10 245 kW	100%

In the absence of these data, it might have appeared logical to attempt to recover heat from the flue gas as the first step towards energy recovery. With the detailed figures, it is seen that the losses are substantially greater from the outside surfaces of the furnace and provide greater scope for savings.

A further example taken from a plant operating three processes is shown in Fig. 119 in which the data are represented in the form of a Sankey diagram. Although a detailed study of the processes is not included, it is

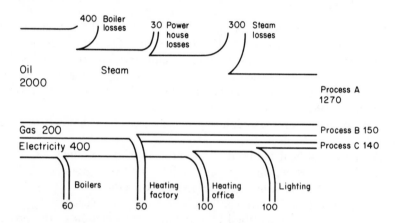

Fig. 119. *Sankey diagram of energy input and end uses (all values are in kW).*

clear that, as a priority, the losses from the steam and boiler should be examined first of all since it is in those areas that maximum benefit is to be gained.

Having quantified the problem, the choice of suitable equipment for energy recovery will now be considered in the following section.

2. *Equipment for heat recovery*

The approach which will be adopted here is to describe the main types of recovery equipment which are commonly available and illustrate their application by reference to suitable examples. The descriptions which follow cannot be comprehensive owing to the very wide range of industries which could make use of the many variations of the basic devices.

(a) Shell and tube heat exchangers. The shell and tube heat exchanger is a versatile and economic piece of equipment which finds wide use in an

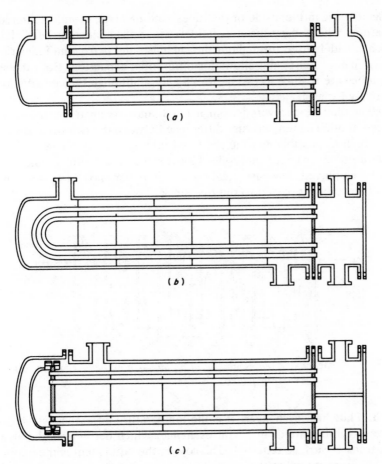

Fig. 120. *Main types of shell and tube heat exchangers. (a) Fixed tube plate exchanger. (b) U-tube exchanger. (c) Floating-head type exchanger.*

extensive range of industries. Three important examples of the many varied types of shell and tube exchangers, are shown in Fig. 120, which is based on BS 1500 (1958). In (*a*) the unit has fixed tube plates, which is a cheap and relatively simple form of construction. It is virtually impossible, however, to clean the outside of the tubes and this type of unit is limited to applications where the shell-side fluid is relatively clean. Figure 120(*b*) shows the U-tube form of construction. This again is relatively simple and the design allows for differential thermal expansion between the shell and the tubes. The entire tube bundle is easily removed so that cleaning the outside of the tubes is quite straightforward. Because of the bend, it is difficult to clean the inside of the tubes, and this type of unit is limited to situations where the tube-side fluid is clean. The floating head design which is widely used throughout the chemical and petroleum industries is shown in Fig. 120(c) and allows for differential expansion. Both the shell and tubes are readily accessible for cleaning, although the construction is relatively expensive.

Heat may be recovered from a hot liquid stream to preheat a cold process fluid. The temperature difference between the two streams should be as high as possible and the shell and tube type of exchanger is ideally suited to recover heat from boiler blowdown and hot effluent streams. It may be employed as a waste heat boiler where very hot flue gases may be used before being passed to the flue stack.

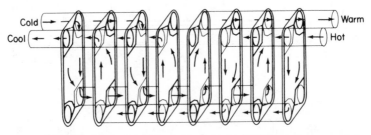

Fig. 121. *Schematic representation of a plate heat exchanger expanded to show the flow pattern.*

(b) **Plate heat exchanger.** It is the temperature difference which exists between the two fluids in a heat exchanger which determines the area of heat transfer surface required. The cost of the equipment is then approximately proportional to that area. There are many applications in the field of heat recovery where only small temperature differences exist even though the heat available for recovery is high. In these cases, the size of conventional equipment would be very large and the cost high and it would be better to make use of the plate type heat exchanger which is designed specifically for these applications.

A plate heat exchanger, illustrated schematically in Fig. 121, consists of a series of parallel plates, separated by gaskets and arranged in such a way that the hot stream passes between alternate plates whilst the stream to be heated passes in parallel between the hot plates. The plates are corrugated and the flow path width is small, so that high turbulence exists in the fluid streams, resulting in high heat transfer coefficients. Very large heat transfer areas are contained within a small volume stack of plates and the system is easily extended by the addition of further plates to the stack.

An example of the use of a plate heat exchanger is shown in Fig. 122 (Department of Energy 1979). Exhaust vapour from two evaporators enters a condenser into which condenser recycle water at 307 K is sprayed. The vapours are cooled and the latent heat recovered in the hot condensate at 347 K. This stream enters a plate heat exchanger where boiler feed water is preheated from 281 K to 338 K. The condensate stream is cooled from 347 K to 307 K and is returned to the condenser and any excess is

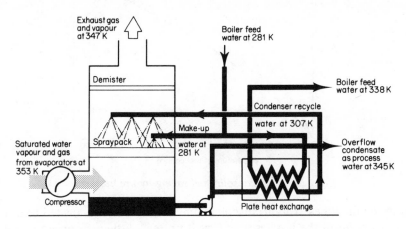

Fig. 122. *Heat recovery from evaporator exhaust vapour.*

used as process water. The plate exchanger used had a total heat transfer area of 55 m² and recovered approximately 2 MW.

(c) Recuperators. A recuperator is a heat exchanger which recovers heat from flue gases, usually preheating the incoming combustion air. The economic attraction of this operation is apparent from Fig. 123 which shows the saving which can be made in fuel consumption as a function of flue gas temperature and the temperature of the preheated air. Figure 123 applies to coal and is for illustration only; comparable data may be constructed for other fuels.

At its simplest, a recuperator may take the form illustrated in Fig. 124, in which the essential feature of keeping the two streams separated by means of a heat exchanger surface is shown. The flue gas temperature will determine the materials of construction; mild steel, cast iron and refractory materials are often used. The flue gas and the preheat air may flow either co- or counter-currently with the latter allowing the highest pre-heat temperature to be attained. For large systems, a bank of tubes may be installed with the flue gas passing over the outside of the tube surfaces and

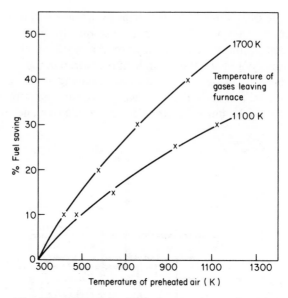

Fig. 123. *Potential solid fuel saving by pre-heating.*

air inside the tubes. This arrangement may conveniently be located near to the exit point of the hot gases and, as it presents little resistance to flow, the resulting pressure drop is low, which is often an important consideration. Where the gases are dusty, the recuperator tubes may be fitted with a continuous scraper mechanism to allow maximum rates of heat transfer to be maintained.

A recent development quoted by the Department of Energy (1979) is the integration of a recuperator with a burner system such that the waste gases are drawn back through the combined unit to preheat the incoming combustion air (see in Fig. 125). The device is claimed to reduce gas consumption by 50% and is being used in furnaces operating at temperatures in excess of 1720 K.

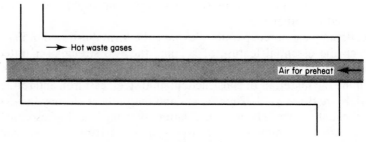

Fig. 124. *Single-tube recuperator.*

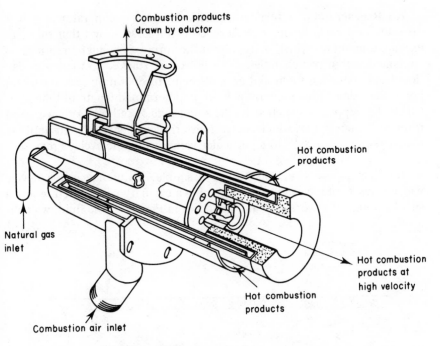

Fig. 125. *Self recuperative burner system.*

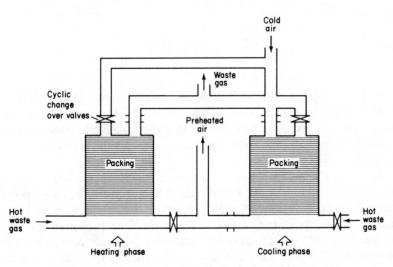

Fig. 126. *Countercurrent regenerative heat exchange system.*

(d) Regenerators. A regenerator differs from a recuperator in that it operates in a cyclic manner. Reference to Fig. 126 shows that the heat exchange medium, which is usually in the form of chequer firebricks, is contained within two chambers. The bricks are stacked so that gases can flow freely between them and around them. In operation, hot waste gas heats one side of the regenerator for a predetermined length of time after which the supply is switched to the other side. Cold air is then passed through the hot matrix which cools, transferring its heat to the air until the matrix temperature falls to a particular value, when the cycle is reversed.

(e) Heat pipes. The heat pipe is a simple, maintenance-free device which consists of a closed tube containing a capillary wick structure and a small amount of a working fluid, as shown in Fig. 127. The fluid, which is

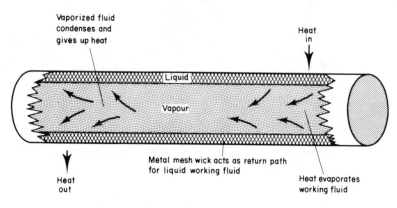

Fig. 127. *A heat pipe.*

selected for the particular application, is evaporated by a source of heat at one end of the tube. The vapour flows along the tube to the other end, where it gives up its latent heat and condenses to the liquid state, returning to restart the cycle by a combination of gravity and the capillary action in the mesh.

Heat pipes usually operate in the range 230–620 K and vary in length from 100 mm to 3 m. As the overall rate of heat transfer depends upon the external conditions outside the pipe, enchanced rates are achieved by the use of banks of tubes which are often fitted with fins. They may be used for both heating and cooling applications and for heat recovery in situations where thermal wheels (see the next section) also offer the potential of saving.

(f) Thermal wheels. A thermal or heat wheel consists of a matrix of heat exchanger material, typically knitted corrugated wire mesh, formed into a series of segments, the whole assuming the appearance of a wheel whose diameter can range from 0·5 m to 5 m and have a depth of 0·3 to 0·5 m. The medium is such that very large heat exchange areas are available although 97% of the device is free space, providing very low pressure drops through the wheel. The idea is not new, it was patented by Ljungstrom more than 60 years ago as a device for recovering heat from flue gases in power stations.

The principle of the operation is shown in Fig. 128. The regenerator is installed with one half in the exhaust warm air stream from which heat is to be recovered and the other in the fresh air intake duct, such that the exhaust and intake streams are counter-current. Large volumes of air may

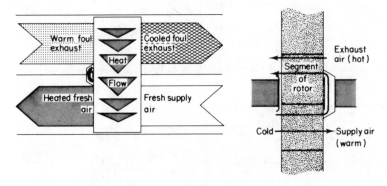

Fig. 128. *The principle of the thermal wheel.*

be handled ranging from 0·15 to 40 m³ s⁻¹ at temperatures up to 1200 K. Providing the air streams are balanced, up to 80% of the heat may be recovered.

Applications are often associated with large volumes of air where fairly small temperature differences exist between outgoing and incoming streams. As contaminated air can be handled by thermal wheels, air from foundries and hot, dusty environments can be used to provide clean warm air for other parts of the same factories.

A typical industrial installation is shown in Fig. 129, in which eight stacks remove hot dusty air from above small furnaces and deliver the air to a single duct which exhausts to atmosphere via a heat wheel at a rate of 0·7 m³ s⁻¹ at 440 K. Incoming air at 280 K is heated to 410 K and distributed, after dilution, to an adjacent workshop. The heat recovered is

70 kW and although only used for the 30-week heating season, the installation recovered its capital cost in under two years.

To illustrate the use of a thermal wheel operating at a low temperature difference, reference may be made to Fig. 130, which shows an installation

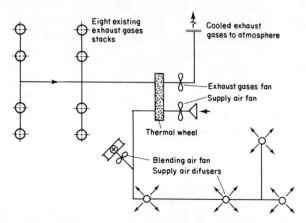

Fig. 129. *A thermal wheel installation in industry.*

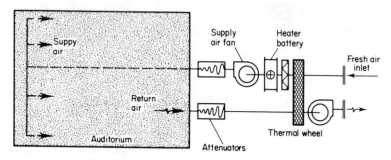

Fig. 130. *A thermal wheel for heating and ventilation.*

ventilating a large civic hall designed to seat up to 500 people. Removing air at 8·25 m³ s⁻¹ at 294 K, incoming air may be preheated from an outside temperature of 272 K to 290 K at the same volumetric rate. The small temperature boost required before admitting warm fresh air to the auditorium may be supplied from a substantially smaller boiler installation.

(g) **The heat pump.** The heat pump is a device which extracts low-grade heat from a suitable source and upgrades this heat to a higher temperature using external higher grade energy. In essence it acts as the reverse of a refrigerator, in which heat is released from the cooling unit to the surrounding room. Thus cold air outside a house can be regarded as the inside of a refrigerator and a heat pump acting between the outside and inside of a house can be used to warm the inside area.

The principle of operation is simple and is illustrated in Fig. 131. The compressor A, which is usually powered by an electric motor, raises the temperature and pressure of the working refrigerant fluid. The now hot

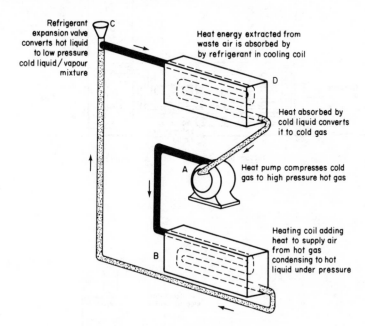

Fig. 131. *The principle of the heat pump.*

refrigerant gas enters a heat exchanger B where it is condensed by giving up its latent heat to the stream which is to be heated, usually air or water. The refrigerant, as a liquid under pressure, passes to an expansion valve C where it is converted to a low pressure, cold liquid/vapour mixture. The final part of the cycle is completed by heat exchanger D where heat is absorbed by the cold fluid from a low temperature source converting it to cold gas when it re-enters the compressor. The compression-type heat pump uses a mechanical compressor, but the process may be carried out by chemical absorption in a liquid and subsequent expulsion of the hot gas by heating in an absorption-type heat pump.

The coefficient of performance (COP) of a heat pump is defined as the ratio of the heat supplied to the work done and is maximized by keeping

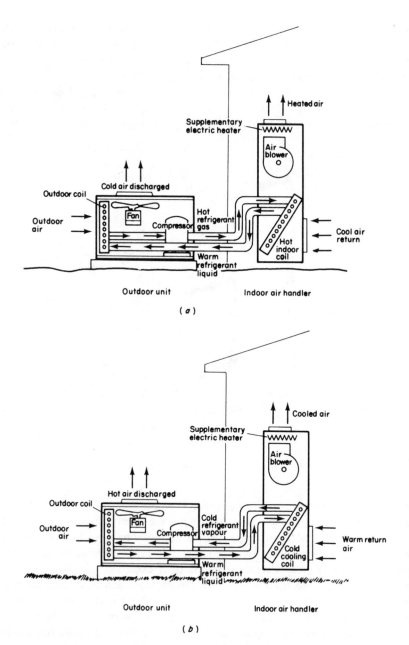

Fig. 132. *The heat pump used for space heating and cooling.*

the difference between source and sink as small as is practicable. Typical COP values fall in the 2–5 and 1·2–1·5 for the compression and absorption type heat pumps respectively. The potential for energy saving by means of the heat pump is therefore considerable and two applications are considered below.

Space heating. The effect of a heat pump by absorbing heat—even from cold outside air in winter—and transferring it to inside air heating to domestic or industrial premises, is usually achieved by having the system divided into two units as shown in Fig. 132(*a*). As the coefficient of

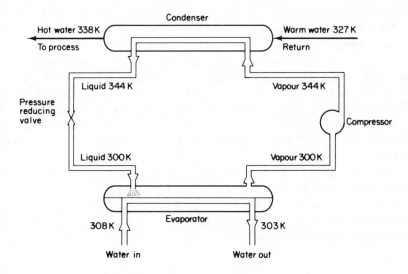

Fig. 133. *A heat pump for water heating.*

performance falls with decreasing outside temperature, a supplementary electric heater is often included to avoid over-large installations. Figure 132(*b*) shows how the flow of working fluid may be reversed to provide internal cooling in summer. The whole-year average COP of 2·35 which can be realized from commercial units now available means that 2·35 kW of space heating can be attained for the expenditure of 1 kW of input electrical energy.

Water heating. Industrial heat pumps are available with power inputs of up to 600 kW capable of providing a water heating capacity of up to 3000 kW. Figure 133 shows a typical application with water returning from a process at 327 K being upgraded to 338 K using a heat pump operating from an available source at 308 K, a temperature too low to be normall useful. The COP in this case is 4·4 and for a delivery of 1 MW, only 227 kV of electrical power is required for the compressor. A conventional boile plant with an average efficiency of 75% would require a fuel input o 1330 kW for the same output. Thus the running costs of the alternativ systems are readily calculated and the economics of the heat pump for particular application may be easily determined.

E. Conclusion

This book has attempted to cover many aspects of fuel and energ technology. Rapidly changing world economics and the political implica tions of the distribution of future energy resources make the years aheac uncertain. There is no doubt that new energy sources will have to b developed and each increase in the cost of a barrel of oil will tend to mak the development both more economically attractive and even more vital The role that conservation and recovery has in the future has yet to be full realized. Some of the major possibilities have been included in thi chapter, others of lesser significance at the present time have beer omitted.

Until the cost and scarcity of energy really acts as a brake on the rate o consumption and nations are compelled to conserve, it is reasonable t assume that measures will not be adopted at the rate necessary for futur generations to enjoy the full benefit that energy sources and conversion ar capable of bestowing on society.

V. FURTHER READING

Backhurst, J. R. and Harker, J. H. (1973). "Process Plant Design" Heinemann, London.

Beijdorff, A. F. (1979). "Energy Efficiency". Shell International Petro leum Co., London.

Department of the Environment (1971). "Thermal Insulation of Build ings". HMSO, London.

Department of Energy (1978). "Fuel Efficiency Booklets". HMSO London.

Diamant, R. M. E. (1970). "Total Energy". Pergamon Press, Oxford.

Dryden, I. G. (Ed.) (1975). "The Efficient use of Energy".

Goodall, P. M. (1980). "The Efficient use of Steam". IPC Science and Technology Press, London.

Holland, F. A., Moores, R. M. and Watson, F. (1974). "Introduction to Process Economics". Wiley, New York.
Institute of Fuel (1961). "Waste Heat Recovery". Chapman and Hall, London.
Jensen, J. (1980). "Energy Storage". Newnes-Butterworths, London.
Lyle, O. (1975). "The Efficient use of Steam". HMSO, London.
NATO (1976). "Thermal Energy Storage". Pergamon Press, Oxford.
Payne, G. (1977). "The Energy Manager's Handbook". IPC Science and Technology Press, London.

References

ABBOTT *et al.* (1955). *Oil Gas J.* (7), 92.
AKITA, K. (1971). *Ind. Eng. Chem.* **11**(4), 739–751.
ALLEN, J. D. (1973). *J. Inst. Fuel* **46**, 123–133.
ANDERMANN, R. E. and HALDIPUR, G. B. (1978). *ACS Fuel Chem. Prep.* **23**, 3–11.
ANDERSON, G. A. (1971). *Steam Heatg. Eng.* **41**(11), 20–25.
ANDERTON, P. and BIGG, P. H. (1965). "Changing to the Metric System". HMSO, London.
ANON. (1956). *Pet. Processing* **3**, 135.
ANON. (1970a). *Gas J.* **344**, 156.
ANON. (1970b). *Coal Age* **75**(11), 120.
ANON. (1971a). *Oil Gas J.* **69**, 86.
ANON. (1971b). *Pet. Press Serv.* **38**(11) 419–421.
ANON. (1971c). *Chem. Eng. News* **49**(33), 42.
ANON. (1972a). *Chem. Eng.* **79**, 54.
ANON. (1972b). *Steam Heatg. Eng.* V1343.
ANON. (1972c). *Gas World* **175**(4582), 515–530.
ANON. (1972d). *Oil Gas J.* **70**, 25.
ANON. (1972e). *Gas World* **175**(4578), 386.
ANON. (1976). *Oil Gas J.* **83**, 12.
ANON. (1977). *Heat. Air Cond. J.* **54**(547), 31.
ANON. (1978). *Power* **122**(9), 37–52.
ANON. (1978a). *Elec. Power* **202**(17), 38–39.
ANON. (1978b). *Nuc. Eng. Int.* **23**(279), 37–39.
ATTAR, A. and CORCORAN, W. H. (1977). *Ind. Eng. Chem. Prod. Res. Dev.* **16**(2), 168.
BAADE, P. K. (1978). *ASHRAE Trans.*, 84–101.
BABKIN, R. L. and PAPOU, A. G. (1972). *Thermal Engineering* **19**, 34.
BACKHURST, J. R. and HARKER, J. H. (1973). "Process Plant Design". Heinemann, London.
BAGZIS, L. D. and MADDOX, R. N. (1970). *Proc. Nat. Gas Proc. Assoc.* **49**, 41–45.

BARRON, R. F. (1970). *Hydrocarb. Proc.* **49**(11), 192–194.
BAUN, M. M. and STREET, P. J. (1971). *Comb. Sci. Tech.* **3**, 231–243.
BAUMGARTH, B. J. (1978). *Kerntechnik* **20**(8/9), 379–383.
BEAUJEAN, J. M. and CHARPENTER, J. P. (1979). "A Review of Energy Models". Institute of Applied Systems Analysis.
BEESTING, M. *et al.* (1977). *Fuel* **56**(3), 319–324.
BEIJDORFF, A. F. (1979). "Energy Efficiency". Shell International, London.
BELGIAN STANDARDS (1972). BS NBN411 M22282, Brussels.
BELL, H. S. (1930). "American Petroleum Refining", 2nd Edn. Van Nostrand, Princeton.
BENNINGTON, G. (1978). "Solar Energy—A Comparative Analysis to The Year 2020". Mitre Corporation.
BERG, G. J. van der and SUPP, E. (1970). *Chem. Proc. Eng.* **51**, 53–57.
BETZ, A. (1927). *Die Naturwissenschaften* **XV**, N46, 10th Nov.
BIGG, P. H. (1964). *Brit. J. App. Phys.* **15**, 1243.
BOYS, C. V. (1906). *Proc. Roy. Soc.* **A77**, 122.
BRIDGER, G. W. (1972). *Chem. Proc. Eng.* **53**, 38.
BRITISH CARBONIZATION RESEARCH ASSOCIATION (1978). *BCRA Rev.* **5**(1), 1–90.
BRITISH ENGINES (1979). British Engines, Wallsend on Tyne. Private communication.
BRITISH STANDARDS (1942). BS1016, British Standards Institution, London.
BRITISH STANDARDS (1956). BS1016, British Standards Institution, London.
BRITISH STANDARDS (1960). BS1017, British Standards Institution, London.
BRITISH STANDARDS (1961). BS526, British Standards Institution, London.
BRITISH STANDARDS (1967). "The Use of SI Units". Publication PD5686, British Standards Institution, London.
BRITISH STANDARDS (1970). BS4587, British Standards Institution, London.
BRITISH STANDARDS (1971). BS4591, British Standards Institution, London.
BRUCE, J, (1977). *Brit. Steel* **35**, 23–27.
BRYANT, MANLEY and McCARTY (1935). *Oil Gas J.* (5), 50.
BURDICK, G. (1931). *Oil Gas J.* (4), 26.
CAMPBELL, K. and STERN, J. (1970). *J. Inst. Pet.* **56**, 243–253.
CARR, R. L. (1970). *Brit. Chem. Eng.* **15**, 1541–149.
CARRUTHERS, R. (1978). *Nature* **273**(5664), 592.
CEGB (1979). Annual Report. HMSO, London.
CHAMBERLAIN, E. A. C. (1970). *Min. Engr.* **121**, 1–15.
CHAPMAN, R. E. (1972). *Amer. Assoc. Pet. Geol. Bull.* **56**, 2185–2191.
CHIU, C-H. (1978). *Hydrocarb. Proc.* **57**(9), 7.
CLAYTON, W. H. (1971). *Amer. Power Conf.* Chicago.
COAL AND COKE INDUSTRY, USSR. (1961). **12**, 31–12.
COCKERHAM, R. G., PERAIRAL, G. and YARWOOD, T. A. (1965). *J. Inst. Gas Engrs.* **5**, 73.
CONWAY, H. L. *et al.* (1973). *Chem. Eng. Prog.* **69**(6), 110–112.
COREY, R. C. (1969). "The Principles and Practices of Incineration". Wiley, Interscience, New York.
CORNISH, J. P. (1976). *Proc Symp., Int. Council Bdlg. Res. Studies.* The Construction Press, Rochdale.
COTTRELL, O. P. (1933). *Oil Gas J.* (11), 64.
CORER, A. E. *et al.* (1971). *Nat. Mtg. Amer. Chem. Soc.* Paper 14, 162.

CRAGOE, J. (1929). US Bureau of Mines, Pub. 97.
CSIRO (1971). *Coal Res.* **44**, 2–6.
CUSUMO, J. A. *et al.* (1978). "Catalysis in Coal Conversion". Academic Press, London and New York.
DAGLISH, A. G. (1971). In "Industrial Fuels" (ed. P. C. Bell). Macmillan Press, London.
DAVIDSON, R. C. (1943). *Oil Gas J.* (3), 116.
DAVIES, C. (1970). "Calculations in Furnace Technology". Pergamon Press, Oxford.
DAVIES, H. S., LACEY, J. A. and THOMPSON, B. H. (1969). *Combustion and Flame* **9**, 38.
DAVIES, H. (1977). *Coal Age* **82**(5), 97–82.
DAVIS, L. L. (1928). *Ref. Nat. Gaso. Mfr.* (3), 90.
DAWSON, W. M. (1981). Engelhard Industries (France), 92120 Montrouge, Paris. Private communication.
DENTON *et al.* (1975). *CEGB Research* **2**, 28.
DIAMANT, R. M. E. (1970). "Total Energy". Pergamon Press, Oxford.
DIAMANT, R. M. E. (1972). *Heat Vent. Engr.* **46**(545), 273–277.
DIDIER WERKE, A. G. (1961). UK Patent 879117.
DONARTH, E. E. and HOERING, M. (1977). *Fuel Proc. Tech.* **1**(1), 3–20.
DARLING, I. (1978). *World Coal* **4**(10), 21–23.
DRAPER, L. and SQUIRE, E. M. (1967). *Trans. Roy. Inst. Nav. Arch.* **109**, 85.
DUNNINGHAM, A. C. and GRUMELL, E. S. (1927). *J. Inst. Fuel* **10**, 170–177.
DUVAL and KALICHEVSKY (1959). *Oil Gas J.* (4), 122.
EDE, A. J. (1966). *Int. J. Heat Mass Transfer* **9**, 837.
EGLOFF, SCHAAD and LOWRY (1931). *Chem. Rev.* **8**, 1.
ELECTRICITY COUNCIL (1979). *Annual Report* 1978–179.
ELLIS, SIR CHARLES (1953–1954). *Trans. Inst. Gas Engrs.* **103**, 28.
ERDA (1977). *Tech. Inf. Cent. Oak Ridge, Tenn.* NTIS TID 3359.
ESPACH, R. H. (1950). *Ind. Eng. Chem.* **42**, 2235.
EWING, R, C, (1970). *Oil Gas J.* **68**(4), 91–93.
FARRER, G. L. (1970). *Oil Gas Int.* **10**(6), 70.
FICKETT, A. P. (1978). *Sci. Amer.* **239**(6), 54–67.
FIELD, A. A. (1975). *Energy World* (8/9). 7–15.
FITZGERALD, J. F., COOPER, E. A. and SOLOMAN, F. P. (1973). *IEEE Trans.* **PAS-92**(5), 1510.
FRANKLIN, N. L. (1979). *Chem. Eng.* (340), 53–46.
FRYER, B. C. (1973). Report BNWL-1748. Battelle Pacific North West Labs, Richland.
GAINS, D. L. and O'BRIEN, T. B. (1970). *World Oil* **170**, 83–87.
GARDNER, J. W. (1973). "'New Frontiers in Electricity". Foulis, London.
GARNER, L. L. and MILLAR, D. J. (1977). *World Oil* **184**, 52–56.
GHOSH, T. K. (1971). *Fuel* **50**, 218–221.
GLENDENNING, I. and COUNT, B. M. (1976). *Chem. Engr.* (313), Sept. 595.
GLUSKATER, H. J. (1977). *Energy Sources* **3**(2), 125–131.
GOLDING (1955). "The Generation of Electricity by Wind Power". E. and F. N. Spon Ltd., London.
GOODALL, P. M. (1980). "The Efficient Use of Steam". IPC Science and Technology Press, Guildford.
GOODGER, E. M. (1953). "Petroleum and Performance". Butterworth, London.

GOODGER, E. M. (1979). *App. Energy* **5**, 81–84.
GOOT, B. G. (1978). *Oil Gas J.* **76**(16), 76–84.
GOSS, W. P. and MCGOWAN, J. G. (1972). *Transportation* **11**, 265–289.
GOUTHAL (1902). *C.R. Acad. Sci. Paris* **135**, 477.
GRIFFITHS, R. F. (1978). *Atom* (266), 314–325.
GRIGSBY, E. K. (1973). *Hydrocarb. Proc.* **52**(5), 133–135.
GRUMMELL, E. S. and DAVIES, I. A. *Fuel* **12**, 199.
GUNN, D. (1972–1973). *Works Eng.* (11), 29–32; (1)17–20.
GYTTOPOULOS, E. D. (1978). *Harvard Business Review* (3/4).
HAENSEL, V. (1950). *Oil Gas J.* (3), 82.
HAENSEL, V. and DONALDSON (1953). *Pet. Processing* **2**, 236.
HANDLEY, D. (1970). *Bull Ass. Pet. Acts. Adm.* **9**(2), 30–32.
HANSEN, W. (1977). *Proc. Fluid Bed. Comb. Tech.* 213–215. Mitre Corp.
HANSFORD, R. C. (1947). *Ind. Eng. Chem.* **39**, 849.
HARBOE, H. (1973). *ASEA J.* **44**(2), 43–47.
HARKER, J. H. (1967). *J. Inst. Fuel* **40**, 206–213.
HARKER, J. H. and ALLEN, D. A. (1969) *J. Inst. Fuel* **42**, 183–187.
HARKER, J. H. and HINDMARSH, C. E. (1979). *J. Inst. Energy* **L11**(410), 45–48.
HARRIS, J. A. and SOUTH, R. (1978). *Gas. Eng. Man.* **18**, 153–174.
HATTMANN, E. A. and ORTUGLIO, C. (1971). *Analyt. Chem.* **43**, 345–356.
HENDRY, A. W. (1974). *Energy World* (4), 4–9.
HICKMAN, R. G. *et al.* (1978). *Watson House Bull* **42**(299), 57–59.
HILL, Sir J. (1978). *Atom* **266**, 340–341.
HIMUS, G. W. (1946). "Fuel Testing", 2nd Edn. Leonard Hill, London.
HODGKINSON, N. and THURLOW, G. G. (1971). *A. I. Ch. E. Symp. Series* **73**(161), 108–114.
HOLLAND, M. B. (1978). *Chart. Mech. Engr.* (11), 40–46.
HOLMES, J. M. *et al.* (1977). *Coal Proc. Tech.* **3**, 40–46.
HORTON, L. (1955). *Fuel Sci. Pract.* **34**, 14.
HOWE, A. *et al.* (1979). *Energy World* (8), 11.
HUNT, H. C. *et al.* (1978). *Atom* (226), 326–333.
HUNTINGTON, F. R. (1971). *Coal Min. Pract.* **10**, 35–49.
HURD and SPENCE (1929). *J. Amer. Chem. Soc.* **51**, 3353.
INSTITUTE OF FUEL (1975). "*Fluidised Combustion*". Symp. Series 1. London.
INSTITUTE OF PETROLEUM (1964). "Standard Methods for Testing Petroleum and its Products". London.
INSTITUTE OF PETROLEUM (1978). "Methods for Analysis and Testing", 37th Edn. Heyden, London.
INSTITUTION OF MECHANICAL ENGINEERS (1978). *23rd. Int. Gas Turbine Conf.* London.
IRVING, J. B. and BARLOW. A. J. (1971). *J. Phys. E.* **4**, 232–236.
IYER, V. (1948). *Scientific Notes* **VI**, No. 63. India Meteorological Department.
JACKS, J. P. G. and MCMILLAN, J. C. (1977). *Hydrocarb. Proc.* **56**, 133–136.
JACOB, R. R. (1971). *Hydrocarb. Proc.* **50**, 132.
JAGGARD and JOHNSON (1956). *Pet. Reform.* **8**, 157.
JOHNSON, M. E. *et al.* (1978). *Los Alamos Sci. Lab. Rep.* LA7088 OC–92.
JOHN THOMSON COCHRAN (1979). John Thompson Cochran Ltd., Glasgow. Private communication.
KARIM, G. A. and D'SOUZA, M. V. (1972). *J. Inst. Fuel* **45**, 335–339.

KARTSOV, A. A. (1972). *Proc. 8th. World Pet. Cong.*
KATELL, S. *et al.* (1973). *165th. Nat. Meeting Amer. Chem. Soc. Dallas,* Paper 42.
KEEPIN, G. R. (1978). *Nuc. Mater. Man.* **VII**(3), 44–58.
KING HUBBERT, M. (1962). "Energy Resources". Nat. Acad. Sci., Nat. Res. Council Pub. 1000–D, Washington.
KING HUBBERT, M. (1969). *"Resources and Man"*. Freeman, San Francisco.
KING, P. J. and MORTON, F. (1971). *Mutech Chem. Eng. J.* (17), 9–18.
KOCH. G. (1978). *Kerntechnik* **20**(8/9), 363–169.
KOENIG, J. B. (1973). "Worldwide Status and Geothermal Energy" (Eds. Kruger, P. and Otte, C.). Stanford University Press, California.
KORDESCH, K. V. (1971). *J. Electrochem. Soc.* (5), 812–817.
KVASNITSKAYA, S. N. and TABALA, V. A. (1970). *Coke Chem. USSR* **12**, 10–11.
LAMB, G. H. (1977). "Underground Coal Gasification". Noyes Data.
LAMBRIX, J. R. *et al.* (1969). *Chem. Eng. Prog.* **65**(11), 65.
LANGLAIS and WALKEY (1952). *Pet. Refr.* **8**, 79.
LAVACHEV, L. A. *et al.* (1973). *Combustion and Flame* **20**, 259–289.
LAVOISIER and LAPLACE (1784). "Memoire sur la Chaleur". Memoires Acad. Royale des Sciences, Paris.
LAWSON, L. J. (1971). *Int. Energy Conv. Eng. Conf. Boston, Mass.* 1142–1150.
LEACH, S. T. and DESSON, R. A. (1976). *Proc. Symp. Int. Council Bldg. Res. Studies.* The Construction Press.
LEE, C. K. (1978). *Combustion and Flame* **32**, 271–276.
LEWIS, G. (1978). *Elec. Power* **24**(9), 665–672.
LINDEN, H. R. (1969). *Amer. Gas J.* **1**, 81.
LINDEN, H. R. (1971). *Coal Age* **76**, 73.
LITTLEWOOD, K. (1977). *Prog. Energy Comb. Sci.* **3**(1) 35–71.
LOCHMANN, W. J. and HAWELL, R. D. (1977). *Hydrocarb. Proc.* **56**(5), 197–199.
LOCK, A. E. (1972). *Ind. Proc. Heating* **12**(1), 22.
LOCKE, H. B. (1980). "Fuel Efficiency 1980". National Industrial Fuel Efficiency Service Ltd., London.
LOMBARDI. P. J. (1972). *Oil Gas J.* **70**, 83–86.
LUND, H. A. (1952). *Pet. Processing*, 326.
LUNTZ, D. M. (1977). *Chem. Eng. Prog.* **73**(6), 49–54.
MAALOUF, B. (1979). *OAPEC Bull.* (3), 24–29.
MACCORMAC, M. and WROBEL, J. (1965) *J. Inst. Gas E.* **5** 424.
MACKENZIE, K. G. (1939). *Ref. Nat. Gaso. Mfr.* **11**, 494.
MACKUSICK and ALVES (1944). *Oil Gas J.* (4), 126.
MACRAE, J. C. (1964). "An Introduction to the Study of Fuel". Elsevier, Amsterdam.
MARGEN, P. H. (1974). *Energy World* (7), 11–14.
MARIANOWSKI, L. G. *et al.* (1978). US Patent 4079171.
MARINOV, V. N. (1977). *Fuel* **56**(2) 153–170.
MARSHALL, W. (1977). *Energy World* **39**, 3–9.
MATTHEWS, R. T. (1970). *Assoc. Pet. Geol. Bull.* **54**, 428.
MCCARTNEY, J. T. (1971). *Fuel* **50**, 226–235.
MCDONALD, C. F. (1978). *Energy Int.* **15**(6), 33–35.
MCKINNEY, J. D. and STIPANOVITCH, J. (1971). *Proc. Amer. Petrol Inst. Div. Refn.*, 692–712.

MCMULLAN, J. T., MORGAN, R. and MURRAY, R. B. (1976). "Energy Resources and Supply". Wiley, London.

MEKLER *et al.* (1953). *Oil Gas J.* (11), 200.

MEYER, R. F. (1978). *Oil Gas J.* **76**, 334–346.

MILLER and KOHL (1953). *Oil Gas J.* (4), 175.

MITCHELL, I. H. (1977). British Rail Engineering, Derby; Personal communication.

MIX, W. T. (1978). *Oil Gas J.* **76**(16), 84–92.

MONROE, E. S. (1971). *Combustion* **43**, 35–38.

MOORE, B. J. (1977). "Analysis of Natural Gases". US Bureau of Mines, Washington DC.

MOORE, B. R. (1978). *Engineering* **218**(7), 681–683.

MORBECK, R. C. (1955). *Oil Gas J.* (1), 94.

MORTIMER, J. (1972). *Engineer* **234**, 42–43.

MOTT, R. A. (1948). *J. Inst. Fuel* **21**, 139.

MOTTERSHEAD, F. R. M. *et al.* (1978). *Technical Publication.* Eurisol-UK., London.

MUIR, N. (1976). *Proc. Symp. Int. Council Bldg. Res. Studies.* The Construction Press, London.

MURTY, P. S. and EDGE, R. F. (1963). *J. Inst. Gas Eng.* **3**, 21.

NAILEN, R. L. (1970). *Power Eng.* **74**, 46–48.

NASH and HAWES (1938). "Principles of Motor Fuel Preparation and Application", 2nd. Edn, Vol. 1. Wiley, New York.

NATIONAL AIR POLLUTION CONTROL ADMINISTRATION (1970). "Control Techniques for CO, NO_2 and Hydrocarbon Emissions from Mobile Sources". US Government Print Office, Washington DC.

NELSON, W. L. (1947). *Oil Gas J.* (12), 118

NELSON, W. L. (1952). *Oil Gas J.* (6), 113

NELSON, W. L. (1952a). *Oil Gas J.* (1), 369

NELSON, H. W., GOLDSTONE, S. E. and HALE, R. W. (1967). "The Commercial Market for Total Energy". Battelle Memorial Institute, Columbus, Ohio.

NICKLIN, T., FARRINGTON, F. and WHITTAKER, R. J. (1970). *J. Inst. Gas Engr.* **10**, 123.

NIFES (1979). *Energy Management* 6th Nov.

ODEN *et al.* (1950). *Pet. Refinr.* **4**, 103.

OLDS, F. C. (1978). *Power Eng.* **82**(11), 46–56.

OLENIN, A. S. (1963). *Trans. 2nd. Int. Peat Symp. Leningrad.*

OLIVER, G. F. and OLDEN, M. J. F. (1964). *J. Inst. Gas Engr.* **4**, 106.

OLSSON, E. K. A. (1970). *ASME Paper* 70–GT–34.

OPEN UNIVERSITY (1974). "Energy Conservation, Power and Society". OU Press, Milton Keynes.

PARR, S. W. (1928). *Univ. Illinois Bull.* No. 180.

PENCHENKOV. G. M. (1972). *Russ. J. Phys. Chem.* **46**(2), 217.

PETERSON, S. R. (1974). National Bureau of Standards, Washington D.C.

PHILIPPI, G. T. (1969). *Int. Ser. Mons. Earth Sci.* **31**, 25–46.

PLEE, S. L. and MELLOR, A. M. (1978). *Combustion and Flame* (6), 32–43.

POHLENZ, J. B. (1970). *Oil Gas J.* **68**, 158.

POOLE, H. (1918). "The Calorific Power of Fuels", 3rd Ed. Chapman and Hall, London.

POLE, N. (1973). "Oil and the Future of Personal Mobility". Eco Publications, Cambridge.
PORCHER, G. (1973). *Promoclim.* **4**, 3–43.
PORTER, H. C. and OVITZ, F. K. (1917). *US Bureau Mines Bulletin 136.*
PUTNAM, P. C. (1948). "Power from the Wind". Van Nostrand, New York.
RALSTON, O. C. (1915). *US Bureau of Mines Paper 93.*
RAO, C. S. R. (1977). *Comb. Sci. Tech.* **16**(3–6), 215–227.
REID, W. T. (1971). "External Corrosion and Deposits in Boilers and Gas Turbines". Elsevier, New York.
RICHARDSON, K. (1973). *Sunday Times* 3rd June.
RIJEN, W. M. L. and EL SAIGH, I. D. S. (1970). *World Petrol.* **41**, 34–39.
ROBSON, B. (1977). *Int. J. Energy Res.* **1**(2), 157–177.
ROPER, F. G. (1978). *Combustion and Flame* **31**, 251–258.
ROSA, R de. (1973). *Energy Int.* **10**(1), 7–9.
ROWE, D. M. (1978). *Proc. I E E Rev.* **125**(11R), 1113–1136.
RUDAKOV, G. W. (1970). *Erdöl Kohle Erdgas Petrochem.* **23**, 404–410.
RYDER, C. (1976). *Energy World* (11), 2–6.
SALTER, S. H. (1974). *Nature* **249**, 70.
SANSOM, T. B. (1979). *Energy Management* (11), 11.
SCHARBOROUGH, J. A. (1971). *Iron Steel Engr.* **48**(11), 60–65.
SHEARER, A. (1970). *Works Eng. Fact. Services* **65**, (3/5).
SHULTZ, KING and THOMPSON (1930). *J. Amer. Chem. Soc.* **52**, 1239.
SCHUMANN, H. (1970). *Min. Petrol.* **25**, 66–76.
SCHWARTZ, A. (1971). *Anal. Chem.* **43**, 389–393.
SELLSCHAPP, F. (1971). *Erdöl Kohle Erdgas Petrochem.* **24**(1), 8–13.
SEYLER, C. A. (1900). *Proc. S. Wales Inst. Engrs.* **16**, 21.
SEYLER, C. A. (1937). *Proc. S. Wales Inst. Engrs.* **53**, 274.
SEYLER, C. A. (1950). *J. Inst. Fuel* **23**, 91.
SHAW, T. L. *et al.* (1974) *Nature* **249**, 730.
SHAW, T. L. (1975). *J. Eng.* **116**(4), 87.
SHAW, T. L. (1976). *The Chem. Engr.* **313**, (Sept.), 593.
SHEPARD, M. L., CHADDOCK. J. B. COCKS, F. H. and HARMAN, C. M. (1976). "Introduction to Energy Technology". Ann Arbor Science Publishers Inc., Michigan.
SHINNAR, R. (1978). *Chem. Tech.* **8**(11), 686–693.
SILLIMAN (1871). *J. Amer. Chem. Soc.* **2**, 18.
SIVIOUR, J. B. (1976). *Proc. Symp. Int. Council Bldg. Res. Stud. Doc.* The Construction Press, London.
SOUTHWOOD, J. R. M. (1978). *Proc. Inst. Mech. Engs.* **192**(34), 311–323.
SPIERS, H. M. (1945). "Technical Data on Fuel", 4th Edn. World Power Conf., London.
STANLEY and EGLOFF (1939). *Ref. Nat. Gaso. Mfr.* **6**, 227.
STEENSTRUP, N. V. (1958–1959). *Trans. Inst Gas. Engrs.* **108**, 45.
STOCKMAN, L. P. (1940). *Oil Gas J.* (7), 36.
STOCKS, W. J. R. (1969). *Comb. Eng. Prog.* **43**, 7.
STOCKWELL, P. B. and SAWYER, R. (1970). *Lab. Pract.* **19**, 279–283.
STOPES, M. C. (1919). *Proc. Roy. Soc.* **B90**, 480–487.
STOPES, M. C. (1935). *Fuel Sci. Pract.* **14**, 4–13.
STREICH, M. (1970). *Nat. Gas Proc. Assoc.*, Denver.
SUMAN, G. O. and ELLIS, R. C. (1977). *World Oil* **185**, 43–51.

SWEET, C. (1978). *Energy Policy* **6**, 107–118.
TALES, G. E. (1973). *Chem. Proc.* **17**(2).
TAYLOR, A. A. and PATTERSON, W. S. (1929). *J. Soc. Chem. Ind.* **48**, 105.
TAYLOR, F. M. E. and Hughes, L. V. (1978). *Heat. Vent. Engr.* **52**(607), 19–21.
TEARLE, K. A. (1969). *Ind. Proc. Heating* **9**, 30.
TEARLE, K. A. (1972). *Ind. Proc. Heating* **12**, 30.
TEMPLE, R. W. and NAPLOI, R. N. (1970). *Hydrocarb. Proc.* **49**, 89–92.
THACKUK, A. R. and WALLENBARGER, R. A. (1970). *Can. Petrol.* **11**, 86–89.
THORNTON, D. E. J. and BRINDLEY, K. W. (1978). *Brit. Nuc. Energy Soc. Proc.*, 55–62.
THORNTON, D. P. (1970). *Chem. Eng.* **77**, 108.
THRING, M. W. (1962). "The Science of Flames and Furnaces". Chapman and Hall, London.
TOTAL ENERGY PUBLISHING CO. (1970). *Total Energy Directory and Data Book*. Illinois.
TOWNSEND, L. G. (1971). *Petrol. Rev.* **25**, 317–321.
TSAROS, C. L., KNABEL, S. J. and SHERIDAN, L. A. (1967). Office of Coal Research, Washington D.C.
TSAROS, C. L. *et al.* (1968). *R & D Report 22*. Office of Coal Research, Washington D.C.
TWIDELL. J. (1978). Paper to I. E. E. 4th Dec. London.
UHL, W. C. (1970). *World Petrol.* **41**(6), 40–46.
UNITED NATIONS ORGANISATION (1972). *Statistical Year Book.*
URAM, R. and CRULL. M. (1972). *Control Eng.* **19**(2), 31–34.
US BUREAU OF MINES (1972). *Bulletin 659.*
US OFFICE OF SCIENCE AND TECHNOLOGY (1961). Washington DC.
VEILLAT, H. and CONG, H. R. (1968). *Ind. Gaz* **85**, 83.
VOYSEY, R. G. (1967). *J. Inst. Fuel.* **40**, 311.
VUISTAVKINA, T. (1930). *Neftyanoe Khoz.* **18**, 1000.
WARD, J. (1971). *Chem. Proc. Eng.* **52**(9), 79–88.
WEINERT and EGLOFF (1948). *Pet. Processing* **6**, 585.
WHEELER, R. V. (1922). *Gas Journal* **157**, 702.
WHITE, N. A. (1977). *Energy World* (11), 2–9.
WHITWELL. J. C. and TONER, R. K. (1969). "Conservation of Mass and Energy". Blaisdell, USA.
WILLIAMS, A. (1976). "Combustion of Sprays of Liquid Fuels". Elek Science, London.
WILSON, D. G. (1978). *Sci. Amer.* **239**(1), 27–37.
WINKLER, M. (1977). *Gas Turb. Int.* **18**(2), 90–97.
WOOLEY, M. and PLATTS, J. (1975). *New Scientist* (May) p. 241.
WORLD ENERGY CONFERENCE (1978). "World Energy—Looking ahead to 2020" IPC Science and Technology Press, Guildford.
YOUNG, C. (1967). Diesel Engineers and Users Association, Publication 314. London.
ZIENTARA, D. E. (1972). *Chem. Eng.* **79**(20), 19–29.

Index